the source

3

the source 3

kevin
mayhew

First published in Great Britain in 2005 by:
KEVIN MAYHEW LTD, Buxhall, Stowmarket, Suffolk IP14 3BW
Tel: 01449 737978 E-mail: www@kevinmayhewltd.com

Acknowledgements

The publishers wish to express their gratitude to the copyright holders who have granted permission to include their material in this book.

Every effort has been made to trace the copyright holders of all the songs in this collection and we hope that no copyright has been infringed. Apology is made and pardon sought if the contrary be the case, and a correction will be made in any reprint of this book.

The following editions are available:

Combined Words Edition	ISBN	1 84417 331 3
(includes source 1, 2 and 3)	ISMN	M 57024 396 9
	Catalogue No.	1470103
Full Music Edition Volume 1	ISBN	1 84003 120 4
	ISMN	M 57004 204 3
	Catalogue No.	1470104
Full Music Edition Volume 2	ISBN	1 84003 724 5
	ISMN	M 57004 859 5
	Catalogue No.	1470105
Full Music Edition Volume 3	ISBN	1 84417 332 1
	ISMN	M 57024 397 6
	Catalogue No.	1470107

Printed and bound in Great Britain by William Clowes Ltd, Beccles, Suffolk

Foreword

Ascribe to the Lord the glory due to his name;
worship the Lord in the splendour of his holiness.
Psalm 29:2

The psalmist's call to worship reverberates throughout Scripture. Here, and in many other passages, it is clear that God created us to glorify him, and this desire to worship is hard-wired into the essence of our beings and runs through the very fabric of our lives. We seek to build a lifestyle of worship that glorifies Jesus and, as we 'sing and make music in our hearts to the Lord', we express our loving response to the one who 'first loved us'.

Working on a project that seeks to resource worshippers is always a privilege, and being part of the compilation team on **the source 3** has been a huge blessing. There has been a tangible sense of excitement listening to the dynamic outpouring of new praise and worship material from around the world. Yet, as our spirits were lifted by the inclusion of the very latest songs, there was a humbling realisation that, in another sense, **the source 3** is simply a further refrain in that unending song of praise that has risen from worshipping hearts across the centuries; this juxtaposition of old and new is central to the vision for **the source 3**.

Alongside modern praise and worship songs, the old hymns are enjoying something of a revival. Worship leaders are keen to honour this glorious heritage that has so enriched the Church's worship over many years. **the source 3** faithfully reflects this desire to put the very best of old and new together: alongside cutting-edge new material by the world's leading worship songwriters are fine old hymns full of great doctrinal truth. In a few examples, this blend of traditional and modern has been further underlined by new musical settings of old words. **the source 3** reflects the huge diversity of music used by the worshipping Church today and, together with volumes 1 and 2, **the source** is exactly what it says: a truly comprehensive musical resource that will have a wide appeal across churches of many denominations. This new volume stands alongside the first two titles and we are pleased to acknowledge the foundational work undertaken by Graham Kendrick in the compilation of books 1 and 2. The latest addition to **the source** series brings the total number of songs in the three volumes to 1700, making **the source** one of the largest collections of praise and worship material and hymns currently available. Included are the very best songs from the generation of writers who have had a powerful impact on our worship over recent years. However, new writers have not been forgotten and Kevin Mayhew Publishers have gathered some excellent worship songs from exciting new writers whose songs appear in print for the first time.

We looked for songs with a clear Godward focus and the collection was carefully chosen with congregational singing in mind. The songs in **the source 3** will find a place wherever groups, large and small, gather to worship together; from groups meeting in the home to huge congregational celebrations, **the source 3** will give a voice to worshippers everywhere. This collection will have a broad appeal; indeed, **the source 3** perfectly complements the whole extensive range of praise and worship resources available from Kevin Mayhew. However worshippers seek to express their love for the Lord; whatever their musical, liturgical and denominational preferences; be they sitting in the organ loft or ready to plug in the latest guitar effects pedal, they can do so with the confidence that they will find the songs in the Kevin Mayhew collection to facilitate their worship. **the source 3** certainly reflects this well-rounded and inclusive approach.

In A. W. Tozer's book, *Worship – the Missing Jewel*, the author reminds us that God's Spirit restores and ignites the spirit of worship within us and that worship is the primary function of the believer. It is out of 'enraptured, admiring, adoring and worshipping souls, then, God does his work. The work done by a worshipper will have eternity in it.' It is our heartfelt prayer that in the hands of the worshipping worker for Christ, **the source 3** may be an effective and powerful resource.

BARRY HART

BARRY HART
JONATHAN BUGDEN
Compiling Team

COLLEEN HART
Project Co-ordinator

DONALD THOMSON
TRACY COOK
Music Setters

ANGELA SELFE
Cover Design

● the source

1100 A Father to the fatherless *Father to the fatherless*

Words and Music: Paul Oakley

2. A lover to the loveless,
defender of the weak;
the healer of all brokenness,
restorer of my dreams.
High King of love, God of all grace,
perfect in power, and strong to save;
you have become my all in all,
my comfort and my peace.

3. My substitute, my sacrifice,
my perfect, spotless Lamb;
my risen Lord, my gift of life,
my Saviour and my Friend.
High King of love, God of all grace,
perfect in power, and strong to save;
you have become my righteousness,
my glory and my song.

1101 All around your throne

Words and Music: Sue Rinaldi

2.
D
D.C.
CODA
Em9
A
turn - ing. From a
G
D/F♯
G
A
whis - per to a loud shout, the sound of free-dom will ring out.
D
G
D
And we say yes, Lord, we are rea - dy to be a
G
A
1.
D
2.
D
liv - ing sa - cri - fice. From a

1102 Alleluia, alleluia, Jesus, risen Lord of life!

Words and Music: Bernadette Farrell

2. Light of the nations: Jesus Christ!
   Way, truth and life: Jesus Christ!
   Bearing our sorrows: Jesus Christ!
   With us through time: Jesus Christ!

3. Living among us: Jesus Christ!
   Word in our flesh: Jesus Christ!
   Servant of others: Jesus Christ!
   Friend of the poor: Jesus Christ!

1103 All I am, Lord

All of me

Words and Music: Tré Sheppard

2. All I want, Lord, all I'll ever need
is all of you, Lord, in all of me.
All I know, Lord, all that I can see
is all your mercy over all of me.

1104 All I can bring

Words and Music: John de Jong

Moderato
Capo 1
1. All I can bring, all that I have you gave to me, even my life and all these gifts I call my own. Amazing grace, that rescued a sinner such as me;
and try my heart, O Lord, my God. Let nothing within, no secret sin drive us apart. In these last days, when the love of so many will grow cold,

A♭/C B♭m7 Fm7 D♭ E♭
G/B Am7 Em7 C D
what else can I do, but take my place be - fore your throne.
may I be found list-'ning to you, close to your heart.
D♭/F E♭/G Chorus A♭ E♭/A♭ D♭2
C/E D/F♯ G D/F♯ C2
All that I have I give
A♭ A♭2/C A♭/C E♭sus4 E♭
G G2/B G/B Dsus4 D
to you, my Je - sus. I
A♭ E♭/A♭ D♭2 D♭ E♭ E♭2 E♭
G D/G C2 C D D2 D
will-ing - ly give my life for you, my Lord.
D♭2/F E♭/G A♭ E♭/A♭ D♭2
C2/E D/F♯ G D/G C2
Let me walk in your ways, serv - ing you, my Sa -

A♭ A♭2/C A♭/C E♭sus4 E♭ D♭2 E♭ D♭2/F
G G2/B G/B Dsus4 D C2 D C2/E
- viour. All that I have is yours,
Fm7 E♭/G Fm7 E♭ D♭2
Em7 D/F♯ Em7 D C2
all that I have is yours.
Fm7 E♭ D♭2 E♭ Fm7 E♭ D♭2
Em7 D C2 D Em7 D C2
E♭ Fm7 E♭ D♭2
D Em7 D C2
1.
2.
D.S.
2. Teach me your ways

To him who is able to keep you from falling
and to present you before his glorious presence
without fault and with great joy –
to the only God our Saviour
be glory, majesty, power and authority,
through Jesus Christ our Lord, before all ages,
now and for evermore! Amen.

Jude 24-25

1105 All my days

Beautiful Saviour

Words and Music: Stuart Townend

3. I long to be where the praise is never-ending,
yearn to dwell where the glory never fades,
where countless worshippers will share one song,
and cries of 'worthy' will honour the Lamb!

1106 All of heaven's treasure

Words and Music: Tim Lomax

D E D/A A
you our gra - cious Lamb, the King of Hea - ven.
D/E E A D
We'll feast with you and
A D A C♯ F♯m
live for you. You are our Je -
D E7sus4 E7 A
- sus, King of kings!

1107 All of me

Words and Music: Mike Busbee and Martyn Layzell

2. All of me,
Jesus, you have all of me;
ev'rything to you I bring,
now I am yours.
All of me,
Jesus, you have all of me;
I surrender as I sing,
now I am yours.

1108 All of my heart

All that I need

Words and Music: Wayne Huira and Eric Niu

F#sus4/C# F#aug Bm A E/G#
- tered in your arms, em-braced in your love.
Em7 G/A Bm A E/G#
Je - sus, you're all that I need,
Em7 G/A G/D D G/D D 1st time D.C.
Je - sus, you're all that I need.
A D A
Joy, peace, pre - sent help in times of
D A D A
need. Fa - ther, se - cu - ri - ty, Sa - viour, co - ver me.

D
F#sus4/C#
F#aug
I am shel - tered in your arms, em-braced
Bm A E/G#
Em7 G/A
Bm A E/G#
in your love. Je-sus, you're all that I need,
Em7 G/A
G/D D
Je - sus, you're all that I need.
G/D D
G/D D

Therefore God exalted him to the highest place
and gave him the name that is above every name,
that at the name of Jesus every knee should bow,
in heaven and on earth and under the earth,
and every tongue confess that Jesus Christ is Lord,
to the glory of God the Father.

Philippians 2:9-11

1109 All of you *Enough*

Words and Music: Louie Giglio and Chris Tomlin

Dsus4 C2 G C2/E Dsus4 C2
G C2 Dsus4 G/B
1. You're my sup - ply, my breath of life;
2. You're my sa - cri - fice of great - est price;
C2 Am7 Dsus4
still more awe - some than I know.
still more awe - some than I know.
G C2 Dsus4 G/B
You're my re - ward, worth liv - ing for;
You're my com - ing King, you are ev - 'ry - thing;
C2 Am7 Dsus4
still more awe - some than I know. And all of you

CODA
Dsus4 G C Dsus4 C
More than all I want, more than all I need,
G/B C Dsus4 G C
you are more than e-nough for me. More than all I know,
Dsus4 C G/B C
more than all I can, you are more
1. Dsus4
than e-nough.
2. Dsus4
D.S. al Fine
than e-nough. And all of you

1110 All shall be well!

Words: Timothy Dudley-Smith | Music: Orlando Gibbons

SONG 46 10 10

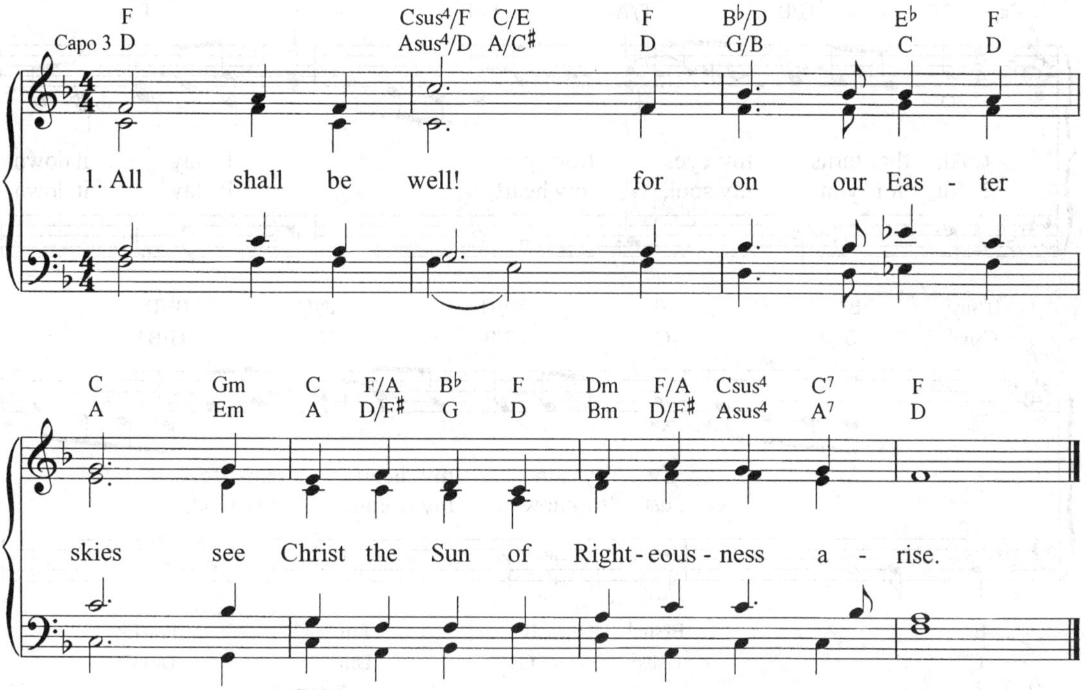

2. All shall be well!
   the sacrifice is made;
   the sinner freed,
   the price of pardon paid.

3. All shall be well!
   the cross and passion past;
   dark night is done,
   bright morning come at last.

4. All shall be well!
   within our Father's plan
   death has no more
   dominion over man.

5. Jesus alive!
   Rejoice and sing again,
   'All shall be well
   for evermore, Amen!'

1111 All that turns my eyes from you *I lay it down*

Words and Music: Don Harris and Gary Sadler

A♭ B♭sus4 B♭ Cm B♭ A♭ E♭/G
F Gsus4 G Am G F C/E
here at your feet I lay it down.
B♭sus4 B♭ E♭ Gm7
Gsus4 G C Em7
Here at your feet,
A♭ B♭sus4 B♭ E♭ Gm7 A♭ B♭sus4 B♭
F Gsus4 G C Em7 F Gsus4 G
here at your feet,
Cm B♭ A♭ B♭sus4 B♭ E♭ B♭/D
Am G F Gsus4 G C G/B
here at your feet I lay it down.
Last time
A♭/C B♭/D Cm A♭ B♭sus4 B♭ E♭
F/A G/B Am F Gsus4 G C
D.C.

1112 All the beauty I can see *All I need*

Words and Music: Brian Thiessen

1. All the beau - ty I can see, if it could be - long
2. A - ny great - ness I a - chieve, ev - 'ry praise I may
3. If I'm gi - ven com - fort here, of - fered what the world

to me
re - ceive I would give it all for you.
holds dear,

Chorus

All I need, you are all I need,

A C#m B/D# A
I have found it true, life comes
B E A
on - ly from you. All I need,
E E/G# A
you are all I need, no-thing else
C#m B/D# A B F#m E/G#
will do, no one else but you.
A Bsus4 B E
D.C.

1113 All the kings will bow

Words and Music: David Gate

All the kings will bow, fall down at your

feet, peo-ple of the earth will lay down their

crowns and lift up your name. We shall come and

praise, fall down at your feet,

Em7 D/F# G Asus4
in the pre-sence of the Ho - ly One we'll fall on - to our
C2 Am7 G/B C2 D
knees. With an-gels and arch - an-gels sing-ing, with the
Am7 G/B C2 D Am7 G/B
voice of hea - ven's choir bring-ing songs of love that
C2 D Am7 G/B C2 Chorus D
rise up to your throne. You are who
G D/F# Em7 C2
was, and is, and is to come: Je - sus, Son of God.

1114 All we, like sheep

Words and Music: Don Moen

B♭ B♭2/D E♭maj7 E♭/F B♭maj7 B♭2/D
G G2/B Cmaj7 C/D Gmaj7 G2/B
Lord, show us your mer - cy and grace,
E♭maj7 E♭/F F/G E♭maj7
Cmaj7 C/D D/E Cmaj7
take us to your ho-ly place; for-give our sin and heal our land,
B♭2/D Cm7
G2/B Am7
we long to live in your
1.
E♭/F F E♭/F F
C/D D C/D D
pre - sence once a-gain.
To verse 2
E♭maj7 B♭2/D Cm7 E♭/F F E♭/F F
Cmaj7 G2/B Am7 C/D D C/D D
2.
E♭/F F E♭/F F B♭ B♭2/D
C/D D C/D D G G2/B
D.S.
pre - sence once a-gain.
3.
E♭/F F E♭/F F B♭
C/D D C/D D G
Fine
pre - sence once a-gain.

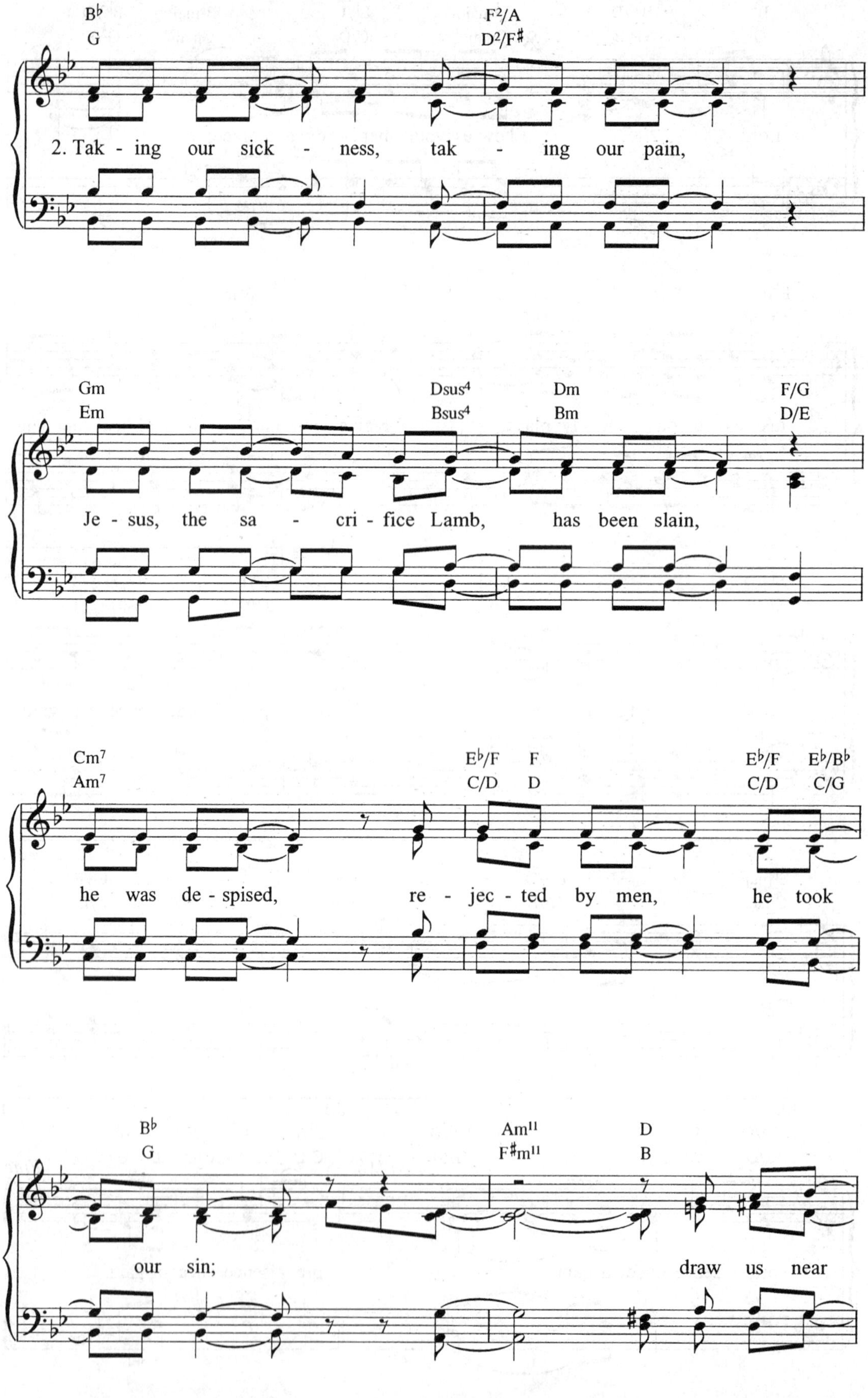
B♭ F2/A
G D2/F♯
2. Tak - ing our sick - ness, tak - ing our pain,
Gm Dsus4 Dm F/G
Em Bsus4 Bm D/E
Je - sus, the sa - cri - fice Lamb, has been slain,
Cm7 E♭/F F E♭/F E♭/B♭
Am7 C/D D C/D C/G
he was de - spised, re - jec - ted by men, he took
B♭ Am11 D
G F♯m11 B
our sin; draw us near

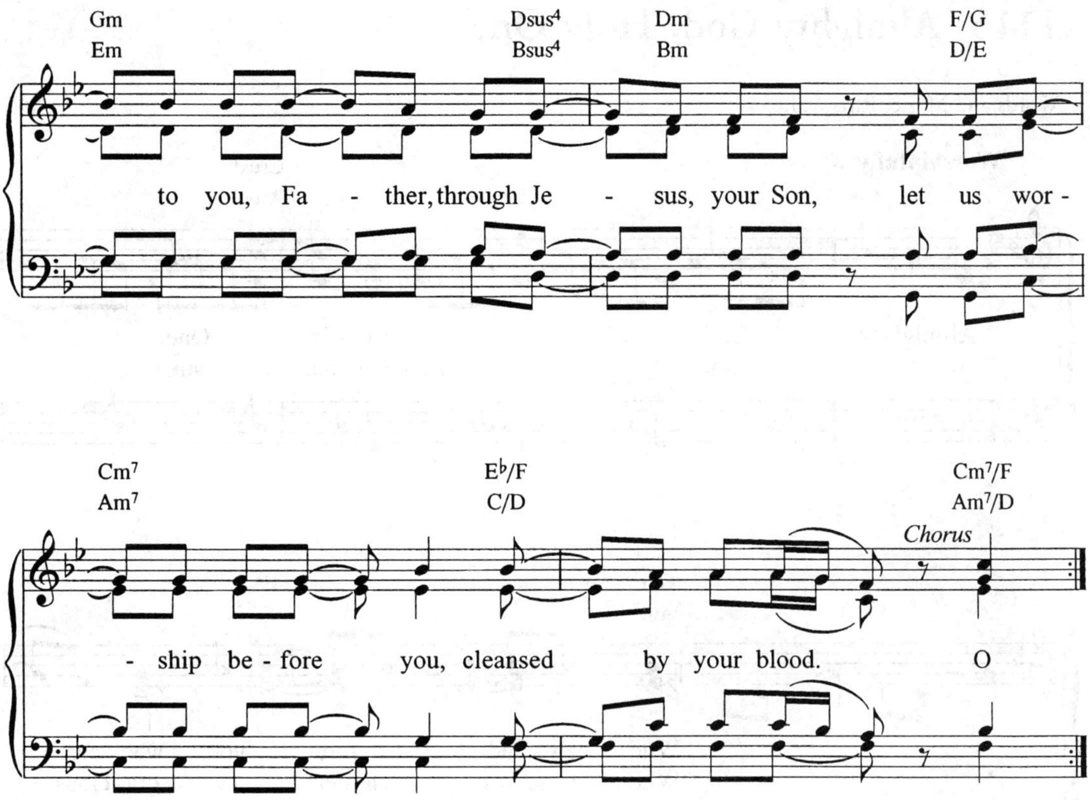
Gm Dsus4 Dm F/G
Em Bsus4 Bm D/E
to you, Fa - ther, through Je - sus, your Son, let us wor -
Cm7 E♭/F Cm7/F
Am7 C/D Am7/D
Chorus
- ship be - fore you, cleansed by your blood. O

1115 Almighty God, Holy One

Words and Music: Rhys Scott

Al-migh-ty God, Ho - ly One.
Lamb, who bore our sin.

Who can stand be - fore you, who can
Who de-serves such mer - cy, gra-cious

come? Per - fect I come
King?

to your throne of grace, I'm stand-ing in

F2 D2
Christ,
Gm7 Em7
I'm clothed in his right - eous -
Csus4 Asus4
ness. To
Dm2 Bm2
know your
B♭ G
pre-sence,
Csus4 Asus4
to seek your
Dm2 Bm2
face.
Gm7 Em7
Fa-ther, I de-light
Csus4 C7sus4/G Asus4 A7sus4/E
in your em-brace.
1.
F2 D2
And I
2.
F2 D2
Gm7 Em7
Csus4 Asus4
Al-migh-ty
D.S.
3.
F D

1116 A love so amazing

Love so amazing

Words and Music: Paul Oakley

1. A love so a-maz-ing has come to
2. Your ways are faith-ful, your works are

save me, and this love chan - ges ev - 'ry - thing.
beau - ti - ful, your word sets the cap - tives free.

Fa - ther, you
Your hand up -

found me, your good - ness sur - rounds me;
on me heals and re - stores me,

C
G
I'm yours for e - ter - ni - ty.
your grace fills my ev - 'ry need.
Chorus
G
And you will al - ways be the King on the
- ter love that's e - ver been
C
G
throne, now your praise will al - ways be on my
shown, and your song in me just has to be
C
Em7
C
tongue,
sung,
no one else could do the things that you've done in my life.
D
1, 5.
C
D.C.
Fine
2, 4.
C
D.S.
There's no grea-

3.
Am7 C G
You said, if I fol - low you,
Am7 C G
I'll know the truth and do the things you do.
D Am7 C
Yours is the king - dom and the
G Am
pow'r, for e - ver, Lord, you'll al -
F D
- ways be my God.
D.C. al Fine

Now to him who is able to do
immeasurably more than all we ask or imagine,
according to his power that is at work within us,
to him be glory in the church
and in Christ Jesus throughout all generations,
for ever and ever! Amen.

Ephesians 3:20-21

1117 A love so undeserved *Amazing*

Words and Music: Matt Redman

1. A love so un-de-served, a gift that's free, you
2. For-give - ness runs so deep with - in your heart of

la - vish on me. A peace I could not earn, and
lov - ing kind - ness; and, should a soul for-get, the

mer - cy for the free - dom of my soul.
cross of Christ re - minds us ev - 'ry day.

Chorus
That's what's so a-maz - ing a-bout your

C/G F/A C F
grace. That's what's so a-maz - ing a-bout your
C/G F/A C/E F
grace. Lord, ev - 'ry day you pour on me your
C/G F/A C
bles - sings of e - ter - ni - ty. And that's what's so a - maz -
F C/G F Fine C/E F Gsus4
- ing a-bout your grace.
C/E F Gsus4 1.

2.
C/E
F
Free-ly I've re-ceived, now free - ly to give.
C/G
F/A
Free - ly I've re-ceived, now free - ly to give.
C/E
F
Free - ly I've re-ceived, now free - ly to give,
C/G
3
F/A
2nd time D.S.
give my life to you. (And)

The Lord will roar from Zion
and thunder from Jerusalem;
the earth and the sky will tremble.
But the Lord will be a refuge for his people,
a stronghold for the people of Israel.

Joel 3:16

1118 And after all *Unashamed*

Words and Music: Paul Oakley

With energy

1. And af - ter all, everything
 To lose it all, and find a friend
2. Could it be that you should put
 Bruised for me, ma - jes - ty

I once held dear just proved to be so
who's al - ways near could on - ly be my
on hu - man flesh, your glo - ry laid a -
up - on the cross, for - sak - en and des -

vain.
gain.
- side?
pised.

And when I think
When I think

of what you've done for me,
of what it cost for you,

F#m D E
to bring me to the Fa - ther's side:
to bring me to the Fa - ther's side:
Chorus A E/G#
Un - a - shamed and un - a - fraid,
Un - a - shamed and un - a - fraid,
F#m D A
I will choose to wear your name, in a world so full
I will love you all my days, I don't care what peo -
1, 3.
E/G# F#m D F#m/C#
of hate, I will al - ways live your
- ple say, I'm un - a - shamed and un - a -

Bm
Bm7/A
E
2nd time to Bridge
way.
fraid.
Bm
Bm7/A
E
D.C.
2, 4.
F#m
D
D.S.
5.
F#m
D
I will al - ways live your way.
un - a-shamed and un - a -
A
E/G#
F#m
D
fraid.
shamed.)
(I'm un - a -
Bridge
A
Fine
Bm
Bm7/A
I know some will say it's

E
Bm
fool - ish - ness:
you can't make
Bm7/A
E
Bm
a blind man see.
But I know
Bm7/A
E
that there is pow - er in the cross
Bm
Bm7/A
E
D.S.
to save those who be - lieve.

1119 Angels bow

Words and Music: Keith Getty

F
D
B♭2
G2
Gm7
Em7
An - gels bow be - fore you, kings fall at your com-mand.

C
A
Dm
Bm
Am
F♯m
Gm
Em
And yet your love comes down to earth to fal - len man.

C
A
Dm
Bm
B♭
G
How can I know your work - ings, e -

Gm7
Em7
F/A
D/F♯
C
A
Dm
Bm
Am
F♯m
ter - nal my - ste-ry? I must bow down and give my life, must

Gm A Dm C2/E
Em F♯ Bm A2/C♯
fol-low you. And I love you,
F B♭ F2/A
D G D2/F♯
Lord, ev - 'ry-thing be-longs to you, is known by you, and
Gm7 C7 Dm C2/E
Em7 A7 Bm A2/C♯
made for your e - ter - nal glo - ry. You, my
F B♭ Csus4 C F
D G Asus4 A D
Lord, re-ceive the praise of my thank - ful heart.

1120 A purple robe

Words: Timothy Dudley-Smith

Music: David Wilson

A PURPLE ROBE 86 86 Triple

Dm Dm7 G C2 Dm Am7
stumb - ling fi - gure bowed and scarred I see my Sa - viour
all his love to sin - ners shown I sing my Sa - viour's
Dsus4 Dm
Fine
B♭ C7 F
go.
name.
3. Fast to the cross - 's spread - ing span,
Dm Am7 Dsus4 Dm B♭ F
high in the sun - lit air,
all the un - num - bered
Gm Dm9 Dm/F Gm7 E7/G♯ Asus4 A
D.C. al Fine
sins of man I see my Sa - viour bear.

1121 Arise and sing

Words and Music: Mel Ray

(♩ = 120)
A A/C♯ Bm7 D E D/F♯ E/G♯ A A/E A A/C♯ Bm7 D6
A - rise and sing, ye child - ren of Zi - on, for the Lord has de - li - vered

E7sus4 E9 A A/C♯ Bm7 D E D/F♯ E/G♯ A
thee; a - rise and sing, ye child - ren of Zi - on, for the

Bm7 E E7 A D Chorus A/C♯ F♯m7
Lord has de - li - vered thee. O - pen up your hearts and re -

Bm7 E7 A D A/C♯ F♯m7
joice be - fore him, o - pen up your hearts and re -

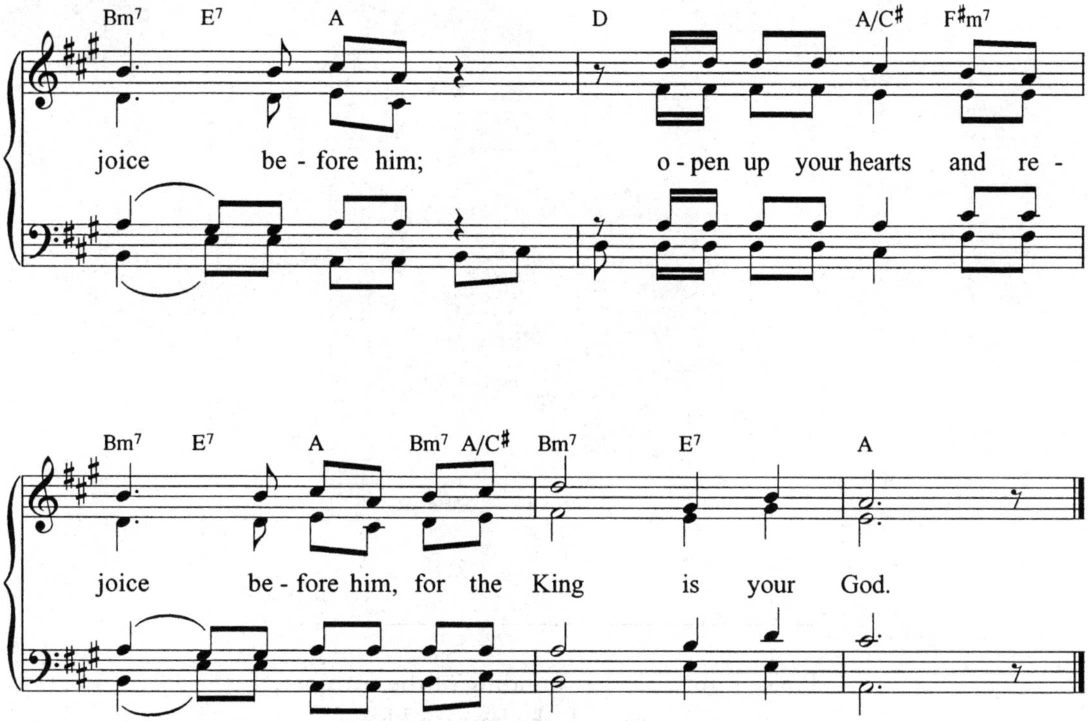
Bm7 E7 A D A/C# F#m7
joice be - fore him; o - pen up your hearts and re -
Bm7 E7 A Bm7 A/C# Bm7 E7 A
joice be - fore him, for the King is your God.

Praise him with the sounding of the trumpet,
praise him with the harp and lyre,
praise him with tambourine and dancing,
praise him with the strings and flute,
praise him with the clash of cymbals,
praise him with resounding cymbals.

Psalm 150:3-5

1122 Around you such beauty *I bow down*

Words and Music: Steve Cook and Vikki Cook

A/E E Amaj9 F#m
not con-tain your pre - sence: ho - ly are you, Lord.
won my heart for e - ver: how I love you, Lord.
E Esus4(2) A/E E B C#m
And as I
And as I
B C#m A2
be - hold your glo - ry I'm un-done.
be - hold this mer - cy I'm un-done.
E2 E2/G# Chorus A2
I bow down at your feet,
E2/G# A2 E2/G#
I bow down at your feet, I bow down

B/D♯
C♯m
at your feet
for you are my God,
B
1.
Asus2
D.S.
my God.
2. You
2.
A2/C♯
B Chorus
3.
Asus2
Esus2
I bow down

1123 As angels looked on

As angels

Words and Music: James Gregory

F G Am7 Chorus F C
To your ma - jes-ty I bow.
To your ma - jes-ty I bow.
You are the Al - migh - ty One.
F C/E Am7 G/B C G C/E F C
You will be a-dored in all the earth. No one is as won - der-ful,
1, 3. 2.
F Dm7 C (Fine) D.C. F Dm7
won-der-ful as you. won-der-ful as
G Am7 G/B F C F Am7 G
you. We bow down, we bow down,
1. 2.
F Am7 G G Chorus Am7 D.S. al Fine
we bow down be-fore you, Lord. You are the Al -

Praise God in his sanctuary;
praise him in his mighty heavens.
Praise him for his acts of power;
praise him for his surpassing greatness.

Psalm 150:1-2

1124 As for me and my house

Words and Music: Tom Brooks, Martin J. Nystrom and Don Harris

Am7 F#m7 Dm7 Bm7 B♭maj7 Gmaj7
-low our God and o-bey his voice; from this day
2nd time to Coda
F2/A D2/F# Gm7 Em7 B♭/C G/A F2 D2 Dm7 Bm7 B♭maj7 Gmaj7
and for the rest of our lives, we will serve the Lord.
F2/A D2/F# Gm7 Bm7 B♭/C G/A F2 D2 Dm7 Bm7 E♭maj7 Cmaj7 F2 D2
Verse
We will
B♭m7 Gm7 E♭ C B♭ G F2/A D2/F#
not bow to a-no-ther god, we will have
A♭2 F2 B♭2 G2 Fmaj7/C Dmaj7/A
no o-ther gods but you; we will

Dbmaj7 Bbmaj7 Eb C Bb2/D G2/B F/C D/A
not serve two mas - ters, we sur -
Db2 Bb2 Eb/F C/D
ren - der our lives to you, we sur -
Ab/Bb F/G Gm7 Em7 Bb/C G/A C/D A/B Am7 F#m7 Gm7 Em7 Bb/C G/A D.S.
ren - der our lives to you. As for
CODA
Gm7 Em7 Bb/C G/A F2 D2
we will serve the Lord.

1125 As high as the heavens

Words and Music: Greg Shepherd

2. How great your salvation
that once on the cross you died for me;
how I love your grace.
And, Lord, you have risen,
death has now lost its sting for me;
how I love your name.

3. You're Lord of all heaven
and you have prepared a place for me;
how I love your reign.
Returning in glory,
I'll be with you eternally;
how I love your love.

1126 As high as the heavens *The voice of hope*

Words and Music: Lara Martin/Abundant Life Ministries

C2 Dsus4 D Chorus
you re-main the same King of kings. You are the voice of
G D/F# Em7
hope, the an - chor of my soul.
D Csus2
Where there seems to be no way,
D2 C G G2
you make it pos - si-ble. You are the Prince of
C2 D2 C G
Peace, a-midst ad - ver - si-ty

D/F# Em7 C2 D7sus4
my lips will shout for joy to you the Most
C2 G2/B C2 Dsus4 D
Last time
Em9
Fine
High!
C2 G/B
2. You were the one be - fore time be- gan; there's
C2 Dsus4 D C2
no-thing be -yond your con-trol. My con - fi-dence, my as -
G/B C2 Dsus4 D
D.S. al Fine
sur - ance rest in your un - chang-ing word! And

1127 As if you were not there

Words and Music: John L. Bell and Graham Maule

Solemnly (♩ = 60)

ILICH 67 88 9

2. As if you were not there,
famine and flood together
usher death, disease and terror;
stricken mothers wonder whether
God heeds pray'r, as if you were not there.

3. As if you were not there,
we televise the dying,
watch the helpless victims crying,
salve our consciences by sighing,
'Life's unfair!' as if you were not there.

4. As if you were not there,
your Son, when faith defied him,
faced a crowd which crucified him,
leaving friends who had denied him
in despair, as if you were not there.

5. Because he rose again
and showed God's love is vaster
than the ultimate disaster,
we entreat you now to master strife
and pain, because he rose again.

1128 As I look at you

Words and Music: Andrew Grinnell

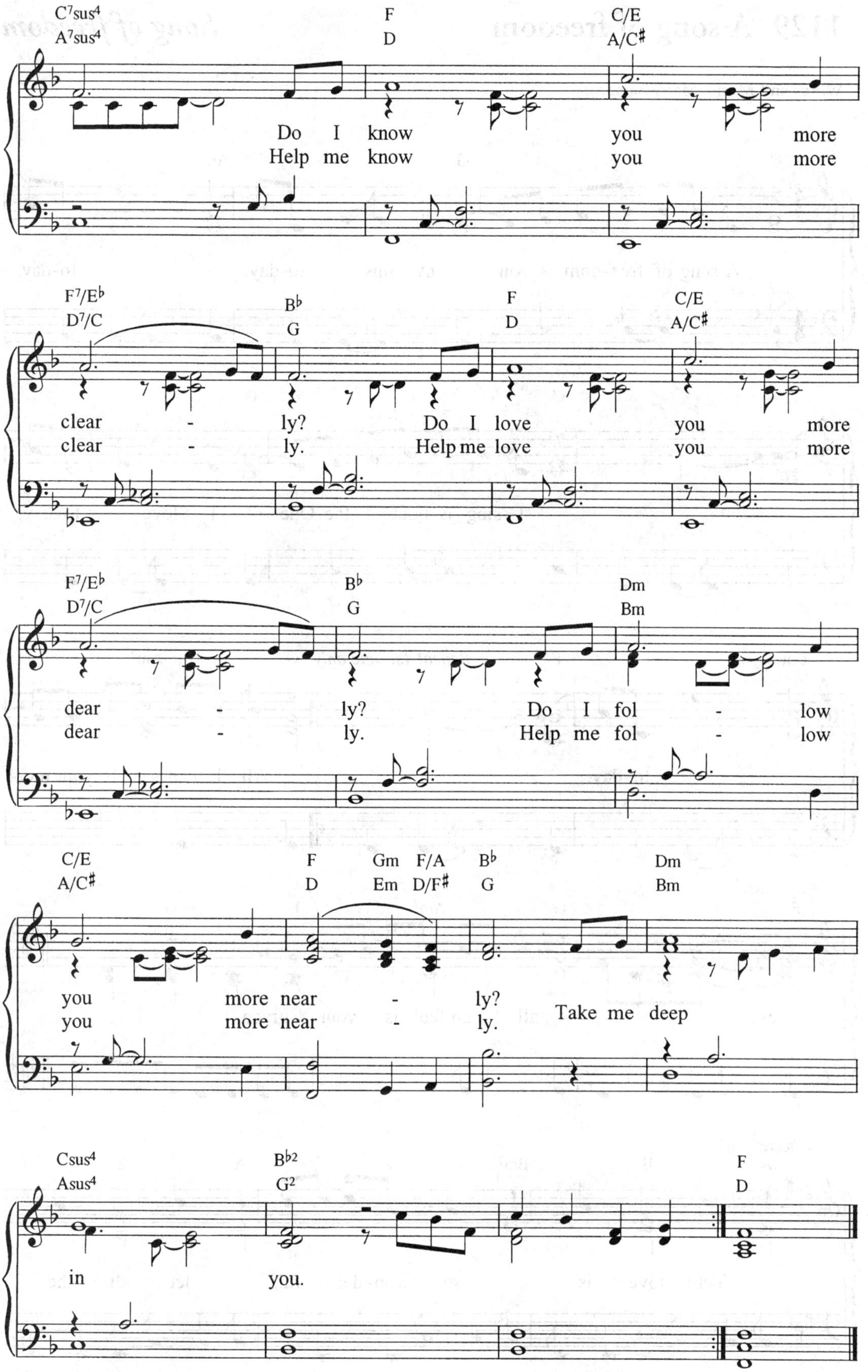
C7sus4 A7sus4 F D C/E A/C♯
Do I know you more
Help me know you more
F7/E♭ D7/C B♭ G F D C/E A/C♯
clear - ly? Do I love you more
clear - ly. Help me love you more
F7/E♭ D7/C B♭ G Dm Bm
dear - ly? Do I fol - low
dear - ly. Help me fol - low
C/E A/C♯ F D Gm Em F/A D/F♯ B♭ G Dm Bm
you more near - ly?
you more near - ly. Take me deep
Csus4 Asus4 B♭2 G2 F D
in you.

1129 A song of freedom

Song of freedom

Words and Music: Marty Sampson

Bm7 D Bm7 D
peo - ple sing that our God reigns a - bove all.
1. 2.
A E Bm7 D.C. A E
Bm7 D A Chorus E Bm7 D
Your love is so won-der - ful,
A E Bm7 D Bm7
let all the peo - ple sing that our God reigns
D A E Bm7 D
a - bove all.

Bm7
D
A
E
F#m7
D
All I can see is your mer - cy,
E
F#m7
D
all I can feel is your grace.
A
Chorus
E
Your love is
Bm7
D
A
E
Bm7
D
so won-der - ful, let all the peo - ple sing that
Bm7
D
A
E
our God reigns a - bove all. Your love is

Bm7 D A E Bm7 D
so won-der - ful, let all the peo - ple sing that
Bm7 D A E
our God reigns a - bove all,
Bm7 D A E Bm7 D
a - bove all, a - bove all,
A E Bm7 D A E Bm7 D
a-bove all.

1130 As the light of the sun *Lord of the harvest*

Words and Music: Chris Bowater and Andy Bromley

G D C
fame, hear the sound of your name.
Chorus
G C2
Lord of the har - vest, send out the work - ers,
G D C2
Lord of the har - vest, we pray, we pray.
G C2
Lord of the har - vest, send out the work - ers, we pray.
1.
Last time
D.S.
G C2 C2
As the

2.
C2
D
Fields are whit - er than they e - ver have been
C
G
but the work-ers are few.
So, Lord, I give
D
C
my - self to help the reap - ing, to ga-ther pre-cious souls
D
C
D.S.S. al Fine
to you.

1131 As we bring our songs *How long?*

Words and Music: Graham Kendrick

A A/G D/F# G A A/G
Lord, till you come? How long till the earth is filled
Lord, till you come? How long till the whole world hears
D/F# G D/F# G Em7
with your song? How long un - til your jus - tice shines
and the work is done, un - til at last we see
Repeat 2nd time only
G/A A D Dsus4 D G
like the sun? How long, Lord, till you come? How long
your re - turn?
A A/G D/F# G D/F# G
till the earth is filled with your song? How long?
1.
D Gmaj7/B
How long?

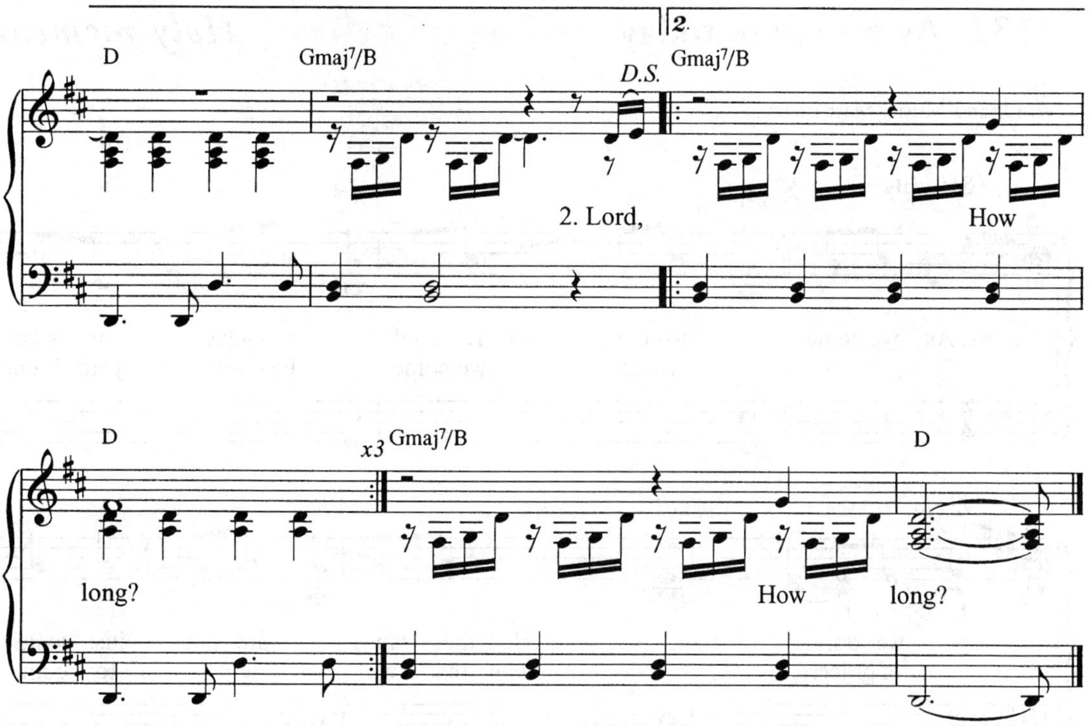

2.
D
Gmaj7/B
D.S.
Gmaj7/B
2. Lord,
How
D
x3
Gmaj7/B
D
long?
How
long?

1132 As we come today *Holy moment*

Words and Music: Matt Redman

Bsus4
Chorus
F#m7
E/G#
Come, come, come, let us
run, run, run through your
A2
Bsus4
1.
F#m7
wor - ship God with our hands held
gates, O God, with a
E/G#
D2
high, and our hearts bowed down. We will
2.
F#m7
E/G#
Last time to Coda
D2
shout of love, with a shout of love.
CODA
D.S.
D2
2. Lord, with con - shout of love. Let this be a
F#m7
E/G#
1.
A2
2.
A2
ho - ly mo - ment now. Let this be a

1133 As we come to your throne

You are worthy

Words and Music: Andrew Grinnell

1. As we come to your throne, ev-'ry tongue will
giv - ing you our praise, stand - ing here with one voice,
join us in this place draw - ing near, bow - ing low

call - ing out your name we're
hum - bled by your grace. For

join - ing with cre - a - tion in wor-ship of the Son who
he whom we a - dore came not to rule by force, but

on the cross of suff-'ring died for all! You are
as a suff-'ring ser - vant died for all!

F C/E Dm Am7
D A/C♯ Bm F♯m7
wor - thy, you are wor - thy, you are
Gm Am7 B♭ B♭/C F2 Csus4
Em F♯m7 G G/A D2 Asus4
wor - thy of all hon - our and all praise. You are
F C/E Dm Am7
D A/C♯ Bm F♯m7
wor - thy, you are wor - thy, you are
Gm Am7 B♭ F/C C7 F C/E
Em F♯m7 G D/A A7 D A/C♯
wor - thy of all hon - our and all praise.
1. 2.
Dm B♭ B♭ F
Bm G G D
2. Ev - 'ry tribe,

1134 As we gather

Words and Music: Graham Kendrick

1. As we gather, Father, seal us in the love that knows no fear. Draw us, heal us, reconcile us, may there be a place of refuge here.

Chorus

Who share one living bread, one Father's love, one Saviour's grace,

2. No more outcasts, no more strangers,
all dividing walls are down.
Here is love that redefines us,
dignifies the least and lowest one.

3. Source of joy, belonging, friendship,
form your family likeness here.
Father, Son and Holy Spirit,
that the world may know our God is near.

1135 At the foot of the cross *Ashes to beauty*

Words and Music: Kathryn Scott

F#m7 Em7 E/G# D/F# A2 G2 B2 A2
my heart, yes, you've won
F#m7 Em7 E/G# D/F# A2 G2 A2/B G2/A Chorus E D B A
my heart. Now I can trade these ash-es in for
F#m7 Em7 E D B A F#m9 Em9
beau-ty, and wear for-give-ness like a crown.
Last time to Coda
E D B A F#m7 Em7 C#m7 Bm7 B A
Com-ing to kiss the feet of mer-cy, I lay ev-'ry bur-den down,
F#m9 Em9 B A
1.
E D B A
at the foot of the cross. 2. At the foot of the cross

2, 4.
3.
E D
B A
D.S.
Instrumental Bridge
I trade these ash-es in for
C♯m7 Bm7
A G
Bsus4 Asus4
D.S.S.
Yes, you've won
CODA
F♯m9 Em9
I lay ev - 'ry bur - den down, I lay
ev - 'ry bur - den down at the foot of the cross.

1136 At this table we remember

Words: Martin E. Leckebusch Music: German melody

STUTTGART 87 87

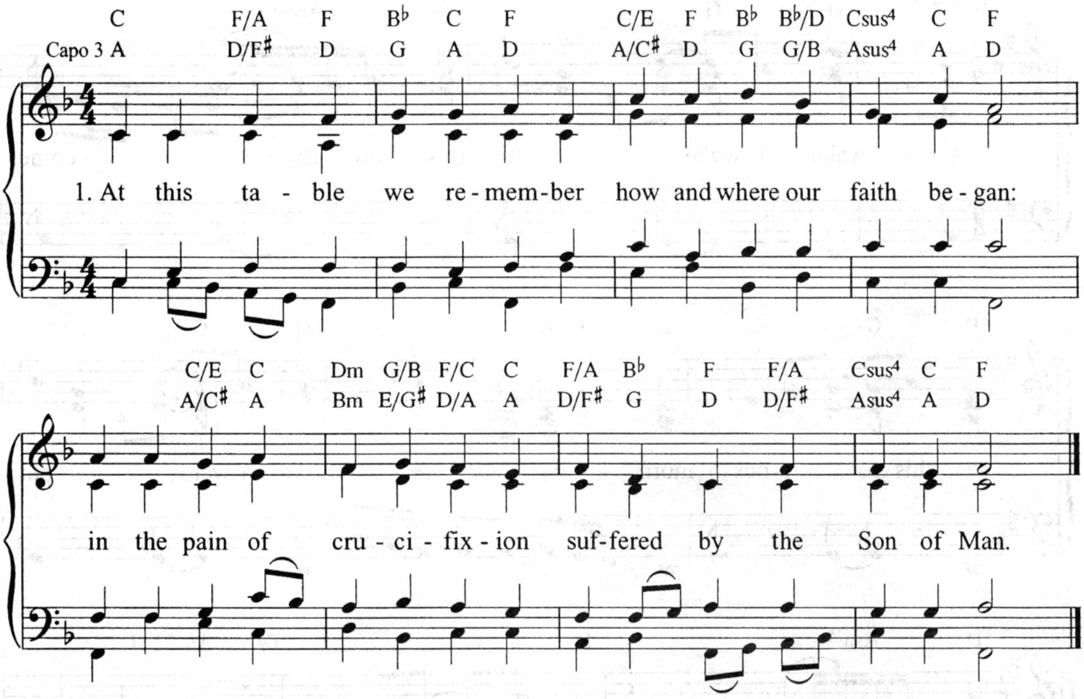

2. Looking up in adoration
faith is conscious – he is here!
Christ is present with his people,
his the call that draws us near.

3. Heart and mind we each examine:
if with honesty we face
all our doubt, our fear and failure,
then we can receive his grace.

4. Peace we share with one another:
as from face to face we turn
in our brothers and our sisters
Jesus' body we discern.

5. Bread and wine are set before us;
as we eat, we look ahead:
we shall dine with Christ in heaven
where the kingdom feast is spread.

6. Nourished by the bread of heaven,
faith and strength and courage grow –
so to witness, serve and suffer,
out into the world we go.

1137 Awake, awake

Words and Music: Godfrey Birtill

D
G
Shake your - self from the dust, a - rise.
D
G
Shake your - self from the dust, a - rise,
D
a - rise!

2. Awake, awake, awake new song,
come, join the beautiful rhythm.
Awake, awake, awake the dawn,
come, climb the beautiful mountain.
Stand up, stand up, stand up, stand up.
Break the chains off your neck, arise.
Break the chains off your neck, arise.
Break the chains off your neck, arise, arise!

1138 Awake, awake, O Zion

Our God reigns

Words and Music: Nathan Fellingham

With strength

1. A-wake, a-wake, O Zi-on, and clothe your-self with strength, shake
you have been re-deemed by the pre-cious blood of Je-sus, and

off your dust and fix your eyes on him. For
now you sit en-

throned with him. Our God reigns, he is
voice and

king of all the earth, our God reigns, and he's
sing a song of praise, our God reigns, the

2. How beautiful the feet are
of those who bring good news,
for they proclaim the peace that comes from God.
Rise up you holy nation,
proclaim the great salvation,
and say to Zion: 'Your God reigns.'

3. The watchmen lift their voices,
and raise a shout of joy,
for he will come again.
Then all eyes will see the
salvation of our God,
for he has redeemed Jerusalem.

1139 A wonderful Saviour *He hideth my soul*

Music: Frances Jane van Alstyne
(Fanny J. Crosby)

Words: William James Kirkpatrick

11 8 11 8 and Refrain

C F C G7/B C
1. A won-der-ful Sa-viour is Je-sus, my Lord, a won-der-ful Sa-viour to
G G7 C F
me: he hid-eth my soul in the cleft of the rock, where
C/G G G7 C Chorus G7
ri-vers of plea-sure I see. He hid-eth my soul in the
C F/C C G7 C
cleft of the rock, that sha-dows a dry, thirs-ty land; he

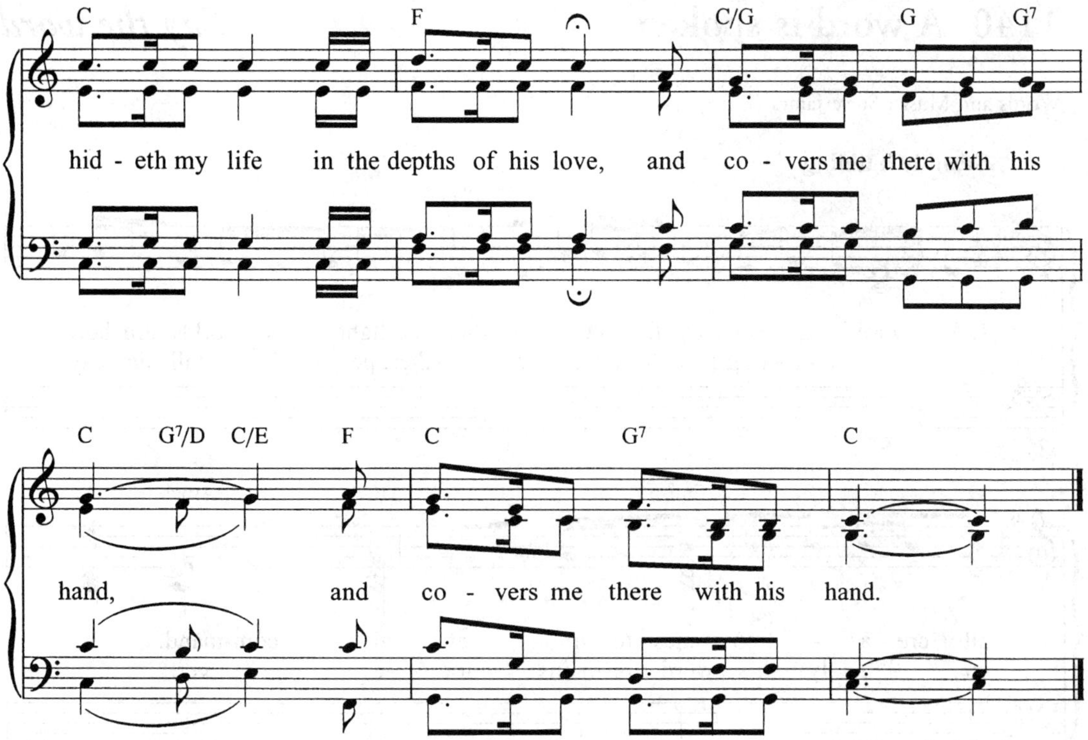

2. A wonderful Saviour is Jesus, my Lord,
he taketh my burden away;
he holdeth me up, and I shall not be moved,
he giveth me strength as my day.

3. With numberless blessings each moment he crowns,
and, filled with his goodness divine,
I sing in my rapture, oh, glory to God
for such a Redeemer as mine!

4. When clothed in his brightness transported I rise
to meet him in clouds of the sky,
his perfect salvation, his wonderful love,
I'll shout with the millions on high.

1140 A word is spoken *Say the word*

Words and Music: Steve James

Steadily building
D
F♯m
1. A word is spo-ken by the One, 'Let there be light' and worlds are born:
this cre - a - tion fades a - way, we wi - ther, per - ish, fall, de - cay,
G
Em7
D/A
Asus4
A
all cre - a - tion comes to life at his com-mand.
on - ly his word re-mains for e - ver.
D
F♯m
By your pro-mise we're sus-tained, the seed-time har-vest shall re-main,
Plant-ed in the hum-ble heart, a new cre - a - tion makes the start,
G
Em7
D/A
A
our Cre - a - tor's pro - mi-ses shall ne - ver fail. You're the
glo - rious-ly grow-ing to e - ter - ni - ty. You're the
Em7
Bm
A
migh - ty world-cre - a - ting God, whose glo - ry can - not
gra - cious, re - cre - a - ting God, whose peo - ple will not

Em7 Bm Asus4 A Chorus
fade, you're the pro - mise - keep - ing God. So say the
fade, you're the pro - mise - keep - ing God.
D/F# G Bm Asus4
word that brought the u - ni - verse to light. Say the
D G Bm Asus4
word that put the pow'rs of hell to flight. Say the
Am Em D/F# Em/G F#m7
word to make me whole that both wounds and heals my soul, say the
1.
Bm/G A/C# Bm/G A/C# Bm/G A/C# Bm/G A
word!
2. But

2.
G A/G Bm/G A/G G A/G
word! Let your Spi-rit cut deep in-to my soul, turn a re - bel heart
Bm/G Asus4 A Bm F#/A# Am Em
in - to your home. A new cre - a - tion, a ho - ly na-tion to your
A/C# D Bm/G A/G Bm/G Asus4 A D G
praise! Say the word, say the word,
Bm A D G Bm A D
say the word, say the word.

Let the name of the Lord be praised,
both now and for evermore.
From the rising of the sun to the place where it sets,
the name of the Lord is to be praised.

Psalm 113:2-3

1141 Beauty for ashes

Jesus won it all

Words and Music: Miriam Webster

Gm7 Em7 B♭/C G/A C A Chorus F D
God. He has won it, my sal - va -
D B D/F♯ B/D♯ Gm7 Em7 B♭/F G/D C/E A/C♯
- tion, my for - give - ness, at the cross. He is heal -
F/C D/A A7/C♯ F♯7/A♯ Dsus4 Bsus4 D B Last time to Coda
- ing, he's re - demp - tion for who - e -
Gm7 Em7 2nd time to B♭/C G/A C A
- ver would come he has won, that's the cross.
Fmaj7 Dmaj7 B♭maj7 Gmaj7 F D
2. All can take free - ly

B♭maj7 F B♭maj7 C
Gmaj7 D Gmaj7 A
water of life; let all who
F Dm Gm7
D Bm Em7
thirst, come worship Jesus Christ.
2nd time
B♭/C C D.S. B♭/C
G/A A G/A
He has won for in him
F Am
D F♯m
is the life that destroyed sin and death and he broke
Dm F/C D♭/E♭
Bm D/A B♭/C
ev'ry chain for the bound and oppressed. For in him

A♭ F
Cm Am
is the life that des-troyed sin and death and he broke
Fm Dm
Fm/E♭ Dm/C
B♭m7 Gm7
ev-'ry chain for the bound and op-pressed. He's a - live,
A♭/C F/A
Csus4add2 Asus4add2
C A
D.S. al Coda
he's a - live. He has won
CODA
Gm7 Em7
B♭/C G/A
C A
- ver would come he has won, that's the cross.
Fmaj7 Dmaj7
B♭maj7 Gmaj7
Fmaj7 Dmaj7
That's the cross.
B♭maj7 Gmaj7
Fmaj7 Dmaj7
Repeat ad lib.
B♭maj7 Gmaj7
F D
Je-sus won it all. Je-sus won it all.

1142 Because of you

Words and Music: Dave Bilbrough

Bm7
A
E
F#m7
E/G#
The way was o-pened up for me to know you as my God.
CODA
D.S. al Coda
Be-cause of
So I will sing for joy,
sing for joy, sing for joy to you. Yes, I will
sing for joy, sing for joy, sing for joy to
1.
2.
you. Yes, I will sing for joy to you.

1143 Befriended

Words and Music: Matt Redman

Em7
A7sus4
1. Be - friend - ed, be - friend - ed by the King a - bove all
vit - ed, in - vit - ed deep in - to this mys - te -
stound - ed, a - stound - ed that your gos - pel bec - koned
D
Em7
kings. Sur - ren - dered, sur -
ry. De - light - ed, de -
me. Sur - round - ed, sur -
A7sus4
1.
D
ren - dered to the Friend a - bove all friends. 2. In-
light - ed by the won - ders I have
round - ed, but I've ne - ver been so
2, 3.
D
Chorus
G
Em7
seen. This will be my sto - ry,
free.
A7sus4
D
this will be my song. You'll al - ways be my

1.
G
Em7
A7sus4
D
Sa - viour, Je - sus, you will al-ways have my heart.
Last time
2.
D
D
3. A- heart. heart. 4. De -
Bm7
A7sus4
ter - mined, de - ter - mined now to live this life for
D
Bm7
you. You're so wor - thy, my
A7sus4
D
D.S.
great - est gift would be the least you're due.

1144 Behold, I am the first and the last

Words and Music: Steve James

B♭ Dm B♭ F/A Gm Dm
G Bm G D/F♯ Em Bm
Glo - ry! Glo - ry! Glo - ry to
C/E Dm7 C F Dm
A/C♯ Bm7 A D Bm
you; be - hold I am the first and the
Last time
Am B♭maj9 B♭/C C F
F♯m Gmaj9 G/A A D
D.S.
last! (Be-)

1145 Behold the Lamb of God

Words: from John 1:29

Music: John L. Bell

1146 Behold the Son of God *Come, heal this land*

Words and Music: Robin Mark

(♩ = 63)
G D Em C
1. Be - hold the Son of God, who
hold the Son of God, who
G D Em C Am G
dies up-on the cross, suf-fer - ing my pu-nish-ment;
sits up-on the throne, o - ver death vic - to - ri - ous,
C G C G
sac - ri - fice of grace, though he dies yet shall he live for
hea - ven's Prince of Peace, though he died yet shall he live for
G/F D Dsus4 D Dsus4 D
e - ver. And
e - ver. And

G D Em C G D
here we stand, O God, as tro - phies of your
we shall stand, O Lord, be - fore that throne of
Em C Am G
grace, drawn from dark - ness in - to light,
grace, bought by your re - deem-ing love,
C G C G
of your Spi - rit poured; though we die yet shall we live for
pur-chased by the blood; though we die yet shall we live for
G/F D Dsus4 D Dsus4 D Chorus
e - ver. There is
e - ver.

C G D Em C
no con-dem-na - tion now for those who put their trust in you a-lone, we wor-
G Em7 D Dsus4 D
- ship you, O Son of God. There is
C G D Em C
no se-pa-ra - tion from his love, no pow'r on earth or heights a-bove can take
1.
G D G C/G G
us from you, Son of God. 2. Be-
2. 3.
G C/G G Chorus D.S. G C/G G
God, There is God.

1147 Be lifted up

Words and Music: Paul Oakley

Slow 4
E
B
Be lift - ed up,
be lift - ed up.

1.
A
B
E
As we bow down,
be lift - ed up.

2.
Last time
B
E
Fine
Be lift - ed
be lift - ed up.

A
E
Let the hea - vens re - joice,
let the na - tions be glad.

A
E
Let the whole earth trem - ble, for you are God.
A
C♯m7
Come and wor - ship the Lord in the beau - ty of ho -
B
A
- li-ness. As we bow down,
B
E
A
be lift - ed up. As we bow down,
B
E
D.S. al Fine
be lift - ed up, be lift - ed

1148 Belovèd and Blessèd

Words and Music: Stuart Townend

Steadily
C G C/E F G
1. Be - lov - ed and Bles - sed, the Fa - ther's pure de - light.
Bro - ther, my Com - for - ter, my Shep - herd and my Friend.
kind - ness, com - pas - sion for those who will draw near;
C F/G C G C/E
Re - deem - er, sus - tain - er, you're my
My Ran - som, my Right - eous-ness, you're the
ac - cep - tance, for - give - ness, and a
1. 2, 3.
F G C F/G C Chorus G/B
pas - sion and my prize. 2. My You're un -
Stream that ne - ver ends. You're the
love that con - quers fear.
Am D/F# G G/F C/E F Gsus4 G
chang - ing, you're mag - ni - fi - cent, you are all I could de - sire.
Word of life, you're the Bread of heav'n, you're the Li - on and the Lamb.

C G/B Am D/F♯ G G/F C/E
You're my Breath of life, Sun of Right-eous-ness, you're the
All with-in me cries, 'Lord, be glo-ri-fied by
1. 2.
F C/E Gsus4 G Gsus4 G Chorus 2 D.S.S.
D.S.
Love that sa-tis-fies. 3. There's You're the
ev-'ry-thing I am.'
3.
Gsus4 G Dm7 C/F G
Be-lov-ed. My Be-
1. 2.
Dm7 C/F G C
Repeat ad lib.
lov-ed. Be-

1149 Be my guide

Words and Music: Brian Thiessen

D
G
D
1. Be my guide, God of Ab - ra - ham, lead me
2. Be my guide in the dark of night, set all
3. Be my guide for the road a - head and should I

G
D
A
D
by your hand, you are strong and wise.
fear to flight, you are hope and truth. And I want to
feel mis - led, you are just and good.

G
D
G
D
A
trust in you and in all I do bring you hon - our and

D
Chorus
G
D
praise. How I love you, great and

G D A G D
migh - ty King. You are faith - ful,
G D A D
through the a - ges you ne-ver change.

1150 Better than the riches of this world *Better than life*

Words and Music: Marty Sampson

G D Em C
Bet-ter than the rich-es of this world, bet-ter than the sound of my friends' voi-ces.
G D Em C
Bet-ter than the big-gest dreams in my heart, that's just the start.
G Am7 Em C
Bet-ter than get-ting what I say I need, bet-ter than liv-ing the life that I want to,
G D Em C
bet-ter than the love a-ny-one could give, your love is. You
G Am7 G/B C Dsus4
hold me now in your arms and ne-ver let me go.

Em C G D
Chorus
You, O Lord, make the sun - shine, and the moon-
Em C G D
- light in the night sky; you give me breath and all your love, I
Em C G D
give my heart to you be - cause I can't stop fall-ing in love with you,
Em C Em C
I'll ne - ver stop fall - ing in love with you.
D Em C D G

1151 Bigger than the air I breathe

Words and Music: Tim Hughes, Rob Hill and Jon Mann-Smith

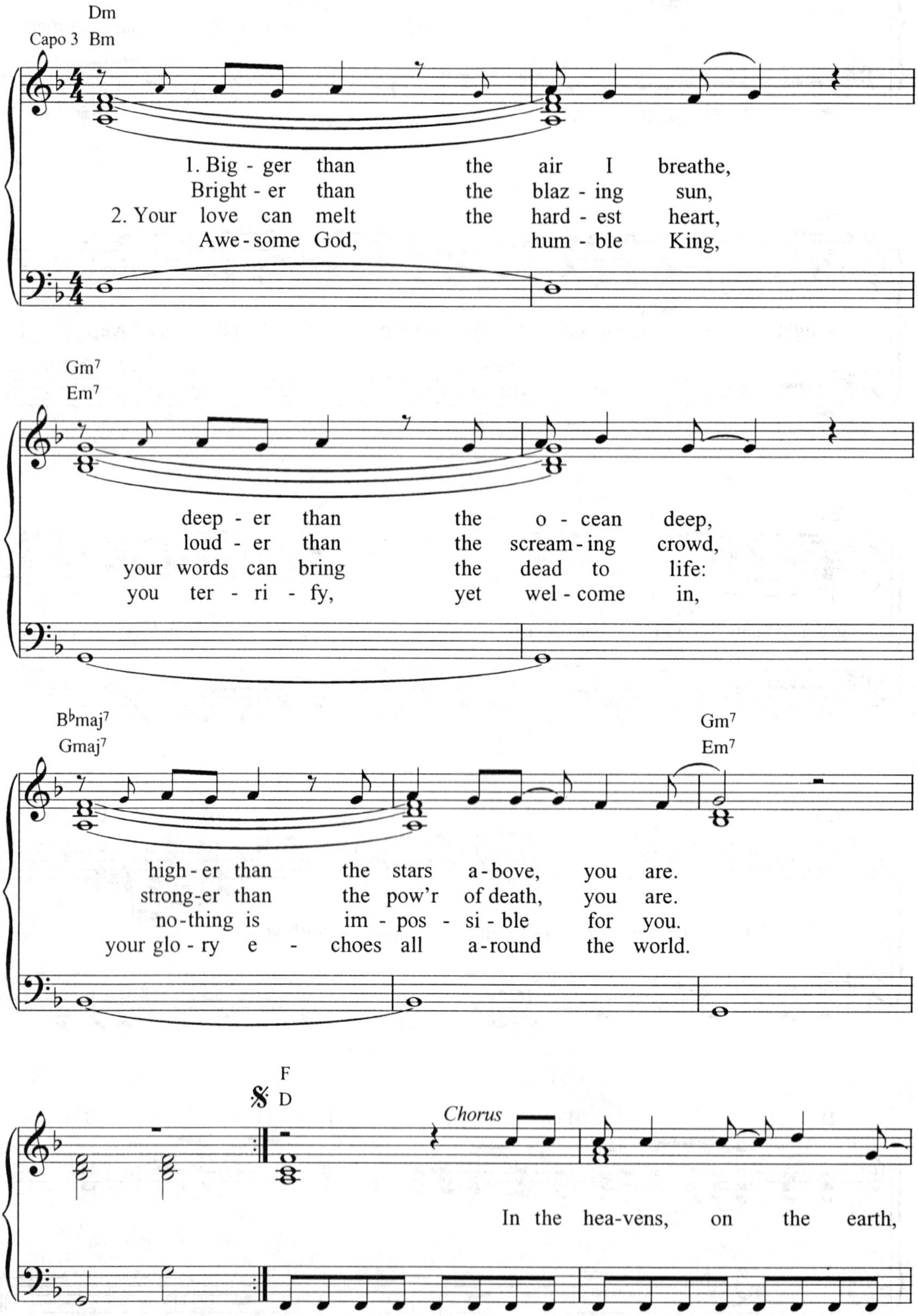
Dm
Capo 3 Bm
1. Big - ger than the air I breathe,
Bright - er than the blaz - ing sun,
2. Your love can melt the hard - est heart,
Awe - some God, hum - ble King,
Gm7
Em7
deep - er than the o - cean deep,
loud - er than the scream - ing crowd,
your words can bring the dead to life:
you ter - ri - fy, yet wel - come in,
B♭maj7
Gmaj7
Gm7
Em7
high - er than the stars a - bove, you are.
strong - er than the pow'r of death, you are.
no - thing is im - pos - si - ble for you.
your glo - ry e - choes all a - round the world.
F
D
Chorus
In the hea-vens, on the earth,

C/E
A/C♯
B♭maj7
Gmaj7
there is no one like you, God, and these
C
A
words are not e - nough to tell of who you are.
F
D
C/E
A/C♯
Who can know the mind of God? Who can
B♭maj7
Gmaj7
un-der - stand your ways? And these words are not e - nough
C
A
Dm
Bm
Fine
to tell of your great name.
G/B
E/G♯
Dm
Bm
G/B
E/G♯
D.C.
Bridge
Dm
Bm
G/B
E/G♯
You, you, you,

Dm
Bm
G/B
E/G♯
there's al - ways you, you, you, un-break - a - ble,
B♭maj7
Gmaj7
G/B
E/G♯
A/C♯
F♯/A♯
un-shak - a - ble, un-beat - a - ble.
Dm
Bm
G/B
E/G♯
You, you, you, there's al - ways you,
Dm
Bm
G/B
E/G♯
B♭maj7
Gmaj7
you, you. Take the world, but give me you,
G/B
E/G♯
A/C♯
F♯/A♯
D.S. al Fine
Lord Je - sus, you.

1152 Blessèd be your name

Words and Music: Beth Redman and Matt Redman

A
E
1. Bles - sed be your name in the
And bles - sed be your name when I'm
2. Bles - sed be your name when the
And bles - sed be your name on the
F♯m7
D
land that is plen - ti - ful, where your
found in the de - sert place, though I
sun's shin - ing down on me, when the
road marked with suf - fer - ing, though there's
A
E
streams of a - bun - dance flow, bles-sed
walk through the wil - der - ness, bles-sed
world's 'all as it should be,' bles-sed
pain in the of - fer - ing, bles-sed
D
be your name.
be your name.
be your name.
be your name.

A E F#m7
Ev-'ry bles - sing you pour out I'll turn back to
D A E
praise. And when the dark - ness clo - ses in, Lord,
F#m7 D Chorus A
still I will say: Bles-sed be the name of the Lord,
E F#m7 D
bles-sed be your name. Bles-sed be the
A E F#m7 E
name of the Lord, bles-sed be your glo - ri - ous name.

D
1.
D.C. (verse 2)
Last time
A
Fine
2.
A
E
You give and take a-way, you
F♯m7
D
A
E
give and take a-way. My heart will choose to say, 'Lord,
F♯m7
1.
D
2.
D
D.S. al Fine
bles-sed be your name.' You name.' Bles-sed be the

1153 Blessing, glory and honour

Words and Music: Sandi Sulander

(♩. = 42)
G G/B C C/D G
Bles - sing, glo - ry and hon - our,
Lift up the name of Je - sus,
G/B C C/D G D/F♯ Em E D/F♯ E/G♯
glo - ry and hon - our to your name, glo - ry and
lift up your hearts to him in praise for there is
Am Cmaj7
hon - our to your
pow - er in his
1, 3.
D C/D
name.
2.
D C/E D/F♯ Am/G G C/D
name. His name is Je - sus.

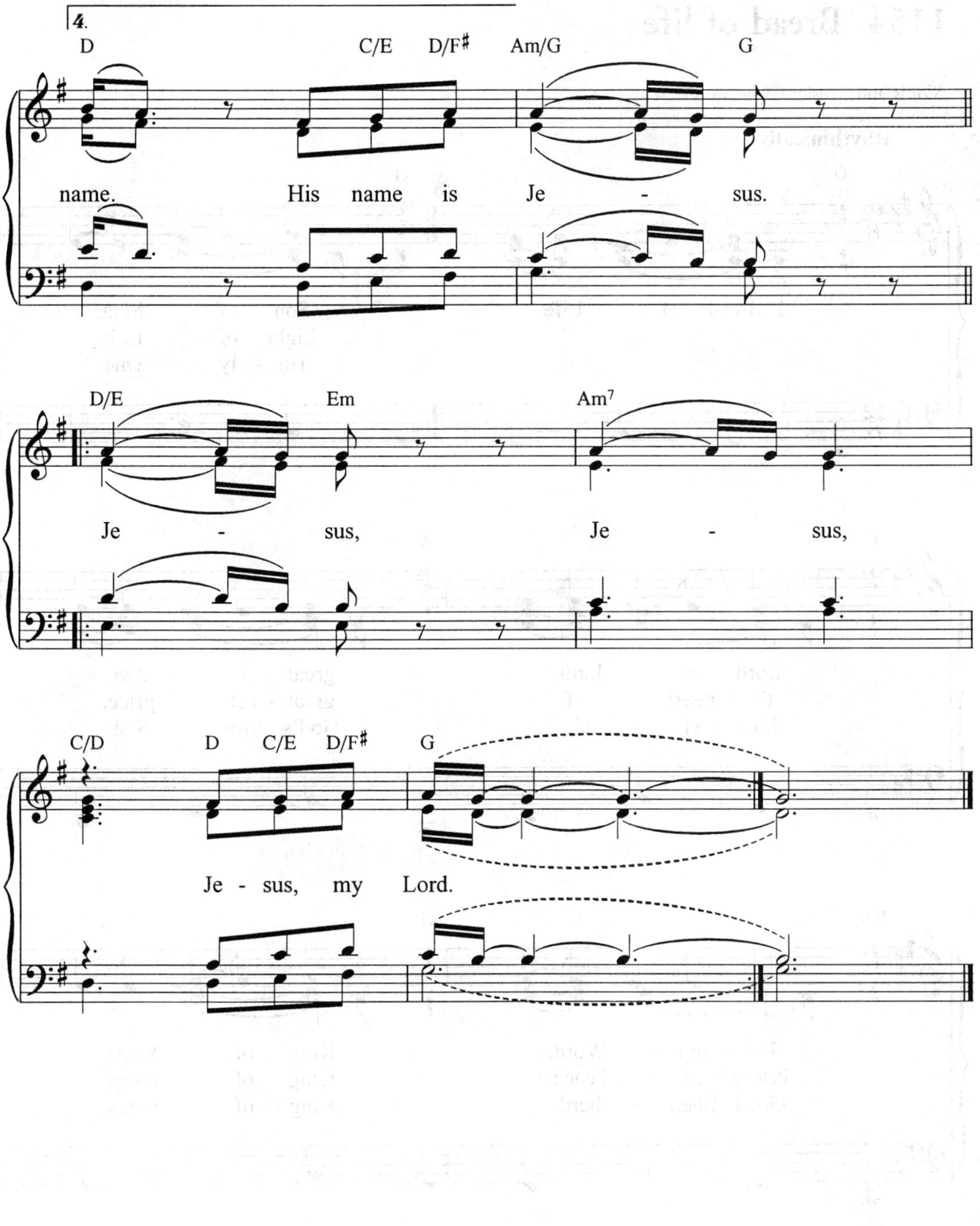
4.
D C/E D/F♯ Am/G G
name. His name is Je - sus.
D/E Em Am7
Je - sus, Je - sus,
C/D D C/E D/F♯ G
Je - sus, my Lord.

1154 Bread of life

Words and Music: Chris Storey

Rhythmically

D
G
1. Bread of Life,
Son of Man,
Light of Life,
Ho - ly One,
D
A
Lord of lords,
the Pearl of
Mes - si - ah,
great I Am,
great - est price,
God's own Son,
Bm
G
Liv - ing Word,
Prince of Peace,
Good Shep - herd,
King of kings,
King of kings,
King of kings,
D
A
1.
D
Lamb of God who takes a-way my sin. 2. God with us,

To restart song from the beginning
Last time
Fine
D.C.
D G D G D G D
sin.
sin.
2. D G D
sin. My Lord and my God,
A D G
Sa-viour of the world;
D A A7 Bm
you came down from hea-
G Bm G
-ven's glo - ry to die my death for me;
D A D
D.S.
Je - sus, you take a-way my sin. 3. Re-deem - er,

1155 Breathe on me

Words and Music: Andrea Lawrence and Noel Robinson

With intensity

Capo 1
E♭2 D2 Gm7 F♯m7 A♭2 G2 A♭/B♭ G/A
Breathe on me, O wind of change, a -
E♭ D Gm7 F♯m7 A♭2/C G2/B B♭9/D A9/C♯ E♭ D B♭m7 Am7
noint me with fresh oil from your throne. Lord, re - store
D♭/E♭ C/D A♭ G Gm7 F♯m7 Cm7 Bm7 B♭m7 Am7
me with new life, so I'm rea - dy to serve and I'm rea -
A♭ G Gm7 F♯m7 Cm7 Bm7 A♭2 G2
- dy to go, rea - dy to do your will.
Gm7 F♯m7 Cm7 Bm7 B♭m7 Am7
So I'm rea - dy to serve and I'm rea -

A♭ Fm7 A♭/B♭ B♭ E♭
G Em7 G/A A D
- dy to go, rea - dy to do your will.
C♭maj7 B♭m7 E♭2/G A♭m7
B♭maj7 Am7 D2/F♯ Gm7
Lord, help me to run this race and to live by your grace,
C♭maj7 D♭ E♭2
B♭maj7 C D2
all I want to do is your will.
C♭maj7 B♭m7 E♭2/G A♭m7
B♭maj7 Am7 D2/F♯ Gm7
Rea-dy to serve, rea-dy to go, rea-dy to do, rea-dy to be,
C♭maj7 D♭ E♭2
B♭maj7 C D2
rea - dy to do your will.

Praise the Lord, you his angels,
you mighty ones who do his bidding,
who obey his word.
Praise the Lord, all his heavenly hosts,
you his servants who do his will.
Praise the Lord, all his works
everywhere in his dominion.

Psalm 103:20-22

1156 Bring your best to their worst

Words and Music: John L. Bell

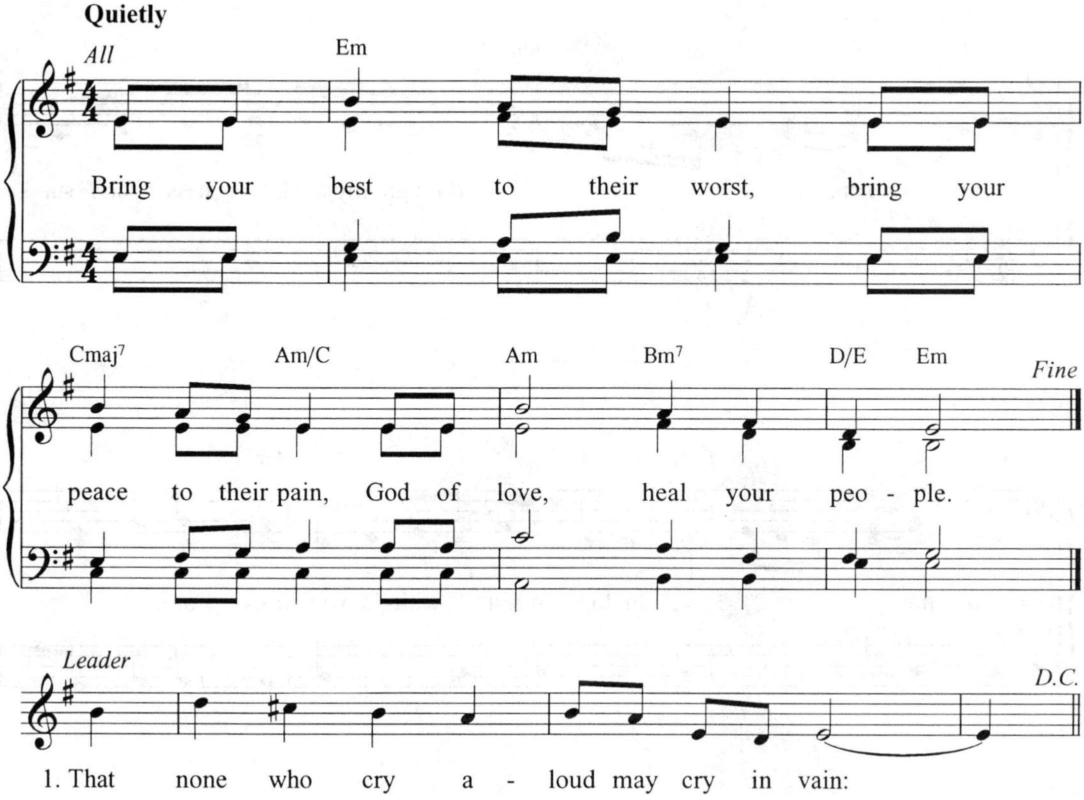
Quietly
All
Em
Bring your best to their worst, bring your
Cmaj7 Am/C Am Bm7 D/E Em
Fine
peace to their pain, God of love, heal your peo - ple.
Leader
D.C.
1. That none who cry a - loud may cry in vain:

2. That those who fear may never walk alone:

3. That those near death may see the light of day:

4. That guilty folk may find themselves forgiven:

5. That those who doubt may find a deeper faith:

6. That broken folk may know they will be whole:

1157 Broken, through my weakness *Simply loving you*

Words and Music: Adam Daubney

(♩ = 74)
C2 C Fm6/C
1. Bro - ken, through my weak - ness you sur -
C2 C Fm6/C Am7
round me, I long to rest with - in your arms, Lord,
F B♭ G
to find my com - fort with - in you.
C2 C Fm6/C C2 C
2. Peace - ful, though my spi - rit cries 'I need you,'
3. Joy - ful in the truth that you are with me,

Fm6/C
Am7
hold - ing on to what you pro - mise,
in this love that ne - ver leaves me,
F
B♭
G
Je - sus, that you'll al - ways be here by my side.
tak - ing up my cross and walk - ing in your ways.
Chorus
C
G/B
Am7
F
C/E
Dm7
G
Sim-ply lov - ing you, sim - ply breath-ing you.
C
G/B
Am7
1.
B♭
Fm6
Sim-ply one with you, it's all I de-sire, it's all I de-sire.
C
Fm6/C
C
Fm6/C

2.
B♭ G C G/B
Sim - ply lov - ing
Am7 F C/E Dm7 G
you, sim - ply breath - ing you.
C G/B Am7 B♭
Sim - ply one with you, it's all I de - sire,
Fm6 C Fm6/C
it's all I de - sire.
C Fm6/C C

For the Lord is good and his love endures for ever;
his faithfulness continues through all generations.

Psalm 100:5

1158 By your blood

Come to the table

Words and Music: Billy Funk

(♩ = 62)
Chorus
C/D G Gsus4 D/G D/F# Em7 G2
By your blood you have saved us, by your blood you have freed us, by your
C G2/B Am7 D C/D
blood we can en - ter in - to the ho - ly place. By your
G Gsus4 D/G D/F# D#dim Em7 G2
love you for-gave us, by your pow'r you have raised us, by your
To Verse
Last time
C Dsus4 D G C/D B/D# G
blood, pre-cious blood of the Lamb. Lamb.

Verse
Em Cmaj7 Dsus4 D G2
Fa - ther God in hea - ven, pre - cious Lamb of God, we
Em Cmaj7 C/D D C/D B/D#
hum - bly bow be - fore you and cry ho - ly, ho - ly.
Em Cmaj7 Dsus4 D G2 G
All of hea - ven's sing - ing the song of the re - deemed,
C C/D D G C/D
giv - ing glo - ry to the Lamb. By your
D.S.

1159 Can a thousand souls be won in a day?

Dreamers of impossible dreams

Words and Music: Robert Critchley

Rock style
D
Gsus4/D
G/D
1. Can a thou-sand souls be won in a day?
Could our tremb-ling hands bring your heal-ing grace?
2. We have prayed for re - vi - val flow-ing from a-bove,
As your peo-ple re-joice in the oil and the wine,
D
Gsus4/D
G/D
D
Gsus4/D
Can we win our ci-
And the words we speak
and our lives have been
will we see a great
G/D
D
Gsus4/D
G/D
- ties when we fast and pray?
have the pow'r to save?
changed by the Fa-ther's love.
har-vest ga-thered in our time?
B♭
C
Our heads are spin - ning, but our hearts say

B♭
C
yes. You've gi - ven us vis - ion, now we face the test.
B♭
C
The words of the pro - phets are with - in our grasp,
B♭
C
1.
F
when we risk it all to fol-low in your steps.
D
Gsus4/D
G/D
Our hearts say yes! Our hearts say
D
Gsus4/D
G/D
D.C. (verse 2)
2.
F
yes! 'Cause we are

C Dm B♭
dream - ers of im - pos - si - ble dreams,
F C Dm B♭
walk - ing by faith in what is yet un - seen.
F C Dm B♭
Num - ber us, Lord, with those who dare to be - lieve, that we can
C B♭ F
live in your im - pos - si - ble dream.
C Dm B♭
All things are pos - si - ble through Christ, who streng - thens me.

F
C
Dm
All things are pos - si - ble when
1.
2.
B♭
C
B♭
God says 'Let it be.'
God says 'Let it be.'
C
D
Gsus4/D
When God says 'Let it be.'
G/D
D
Gsus4/D
G/D
D

1160 Can't stop talking

Words and Music: Russell Fragar

A7
G
D
Can't stop talk - ing 'bout ev - 'ry - thing he's done, it's the
A7
D
best thing hap - pened since the world be - gun; it
A7
G
D
A7
did - n't come cheap but I got it for free, it's the hope of glo - ry
1.
2.
A
Fine
A
E
Christ in me. Christ in me. He helped me to see when my

F#m7 D
spi-rit was blind, it's a-maz-ing if you look just what you'll find.
E F#m7
Ev-'ry step I took, he took two, if he did it for me, he will
D A A7 D/A
do it for you. (He) Do you know him? (Yes, I do).
A7 D/A A7
Do you know what I say is true? Do you know him?
D/A A7 D/A
D.C. al Fine
(Yes, I do). If he did it for me, he will do it for you.

1161 Celebrate in the Lord *Dancing on holy ground*

Words and Music: Evan Rogers

Brightly
C F C G7
C F C
1. Ce - le - brate in the Lord, he is the rea - son we
2. This is our ju - bi - lee, no debt no bon - dage, we
3. free - dom you have set us free, no lon - ger bound to sla -
G7 C F
re - joice; for he has cast our sins a - way, for -
are free. We're free to give him ev - 'ry - thing for
- ve - ry. You've bro - ken ev - 'ry chain that binds; you've
C G7 C
got - ten now, for e - ver and al - ways,
we have no - thing, now it is all his,
con - quer'd sin for e - ver and all time,

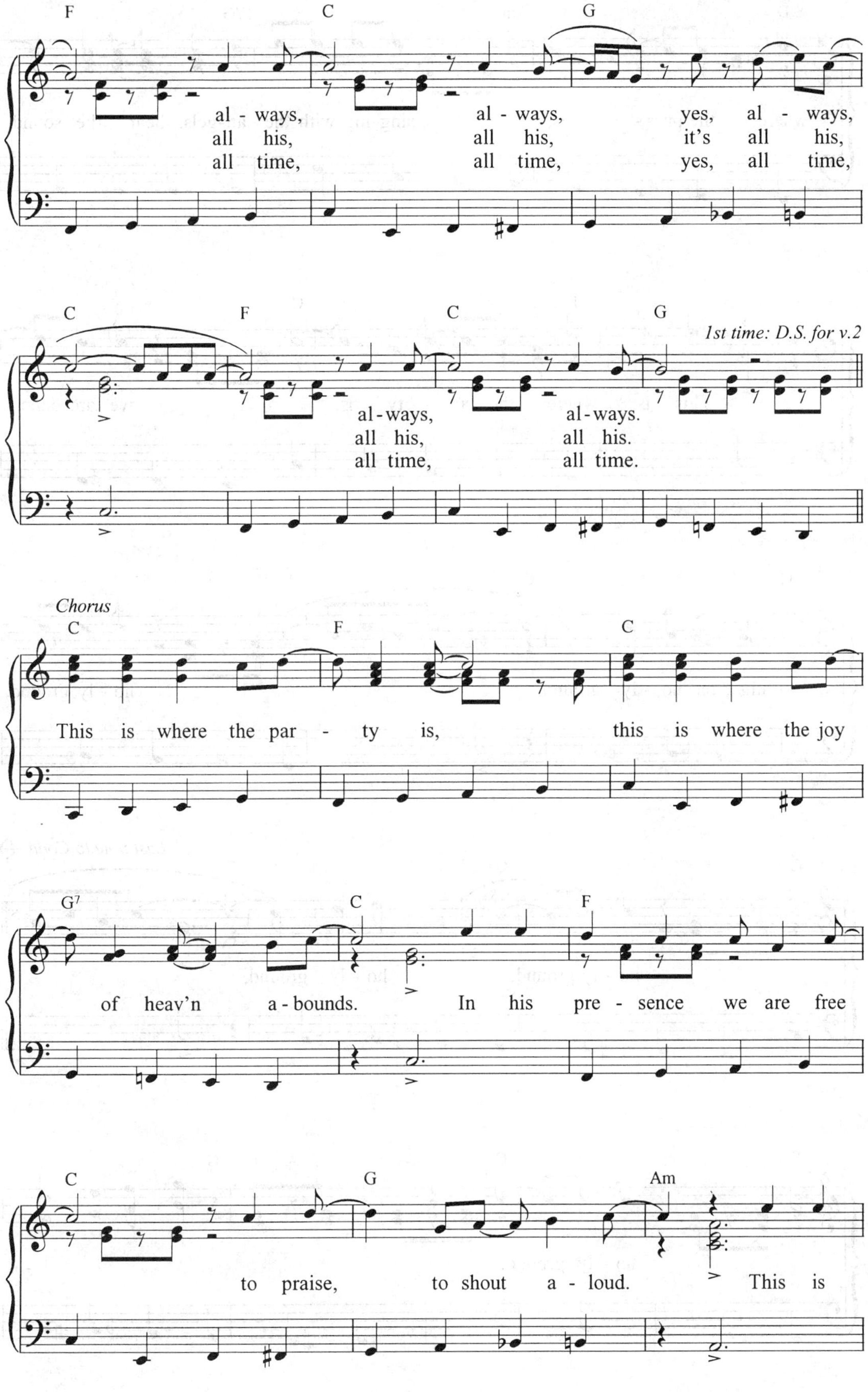
F C G
al - ways, al - ways, yes, al - ways,
all his, all his, it's all his,
all time, all time, yes, all time,
C F C G
1st time: D.S. for v.2
al-ways, al-ways.
all his, all his.
all time, all time.
Chorus
C F C
This is where the par - ty is, this is where the joy
G7 C F
of heav'n a - bounds. In his pre - sence we are free
C G Am
to praise, to shout a - loud. This is

D
Am
F/G
where the par - ty is, sing-ing with the an-gels, hear the sound.
C
F
C
This is where the par - ty is, we are danc -
G
C
F
- ing on ho - ly ground, ho - ly ground,
Last time to Coda
C
G
C
ho - ly ground, ho - ly ground,
F
C
G
ho - ly ground.

C F C G
D.S. al Coda
3. For
CODA
F C G
ho - ly ground, ho - ly ground. Si - ya - vu -
C F C
- ya, si - ya - vu - ya, si - ya - vu -
1. G 2. G C
- ya. Si - ya - vu - - ya. Ja - bu - la - ni,
Repeat and fade to end
F C G
ja - bu - la - ni, ja - bu - la - ni. Ja - bu - la -

1162 Chosen to go

Words and Music: Susie Hare

Brightly
D
D/C♯
Bm
1. Cho - sen to go, cho - sen to do,
2. Cho - sen to go, cho - sen to do,
3. Cho - sen to go, cho - sen to do,
D/A
G
G/B
D
cho - sen to speak your sal -
cho - sen to be on your
cho - sen to stir a de -
D/A
A
D/A
A
D
va - tion; we are your hands,
mis - sion; we want to give,
sire; we want to reach,
D/C♯
Bm
D/A
we are your feet,
we want to serve,
we want to build,

G G/B D G/A Asus4
we are your voice in the na - tion.
we want to fol - low your vi - sion.
we want to see hearts on fire.
A G D/F# Em7 D A D
You're the rock on which we stand,
Where lives hide in shades of night,
Voi - ces raised to fill the sky,
G D/F# Em7 D A D G D/F# Em7 D
make us faith - ful in this land to build up the
we will march in ar - mour bright, tak - ing to the
vic - t'ry's ban - ner we shall fly, lift - ing up the
A Bm Asus4 A
church that you have planned.
dark your shin - ing light!
name of Je - sus high!
Chorus
D D/F# G9 A D
Send us out to pro - claim your king - dom,

D/F♯ G9 A A/C♯ Bm
send us out to pro - claim your word.
D D/F♯ G9 A A/C♯ Bm
Send us out to pro - claim your free - dom,
1, 2.
G A D A/D G/D A/D
D.C.
send us in pow - er, O God.
3.
Bm A/B Bm A G A Bm A/B
God. Send us in pow - er, O God.
Bm A G A D
Send us in pow - er, O God!

1163 Christ be before me

Words: Attributed to St Patrick

Music: Phil Hart

1164 Christ is risen

Words and Music: Chris Rolinson

Joyfully (♩. = 76)
Chorus
Capo 3
G D/G C/G G Em Cmaj7 D
E B/E A/E E C♯m Amaj7 B
Christ is ri - sen, hal - le - lu - jah, hal - le - lu - jah!
G D/G C/G G Em D G
E B/E A/E E C♯m B E
Fine
Christ is ri - sen, ri - sen in-deed, hal - le - lu - jah!
C G/B C G/B Am D7
A E/G♯ A E/G♯ F♯m B7
1. Love's work is done, the bat - tle is won. Where now, O death, is your
2. Lord o - ver sin, Lord o - ver death, at his feet Sa - tan must
3. Tell it a - broad, 'Je - sus is Lord!' Shout it and let your praise
G B♭ E♭/B♭ B♭ E♭/B♭
E G C/G G C/G
sting? He rose a - gain to rule and to reign,
fall! Ev - 'ry knee, bow! All will con - fess
ring! Glad - ly we raise our songs of praise:

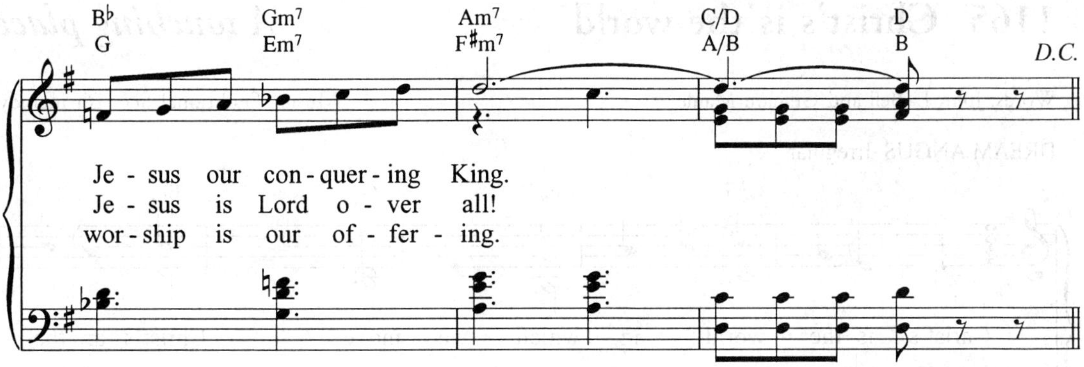
B♭ Gm7 Am7 C/D D
G Em7 F♯m7 A/B B
D.C.
Je - sus our con - quer - ing King.
Je - sus is Lord o - ver all!
wor - ship is our of - fer - ing.

1165 Christ's is the world *A touching place*

Words: John L. Bell and Graham Maule Music: Traditional Scottish melody

DREAM ANGUS Irregular

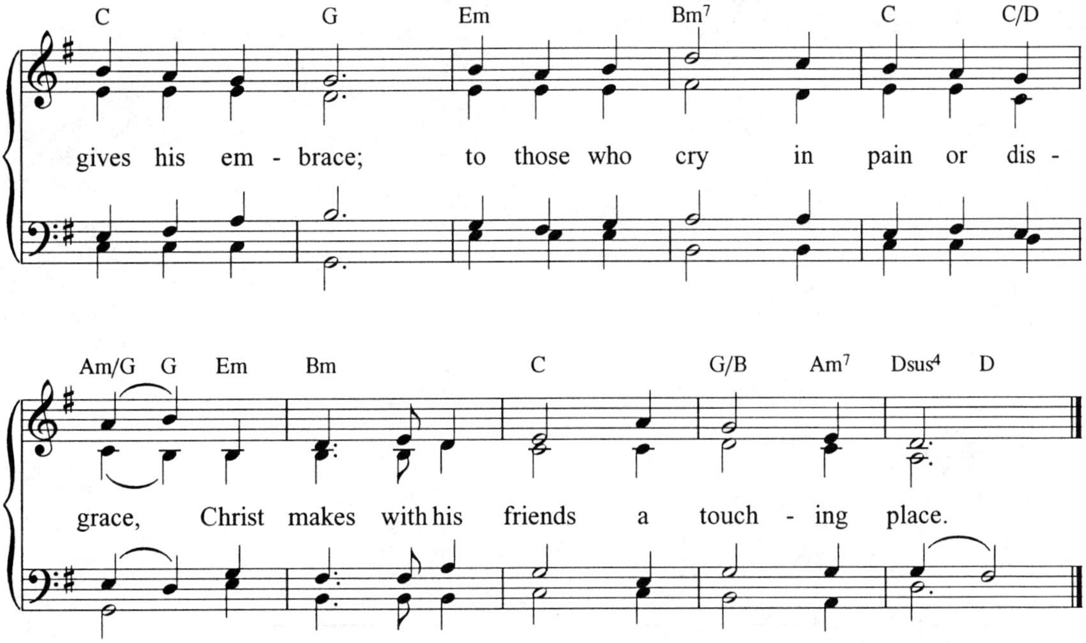
C G Em Bm7 C C/D
gives his em - brace; to those who cry in pain or dis -
Am/G G Em Bm C G/B Am7 Dsus4 D
grace, Christ makes with his friends a touch - ing place.

2. Feel for the people we most avoid,
strange or bereaved or never employed;
feel for the women, and feel for the men
who fear that their living is all in vain.

3. Feel for the parents who've lost their child,
feel for the women whom men have defiled,
feel for the baby for whom there's no breast,
and feel for the weary who find no rest.

4. Feel for the lives by life confused,
riddled with doubt, in loving abused;
feel for the lonely heart, conscious of sin,
which longs to be pure but fears to begin.

Shout for joy to the Lord, all the earth,
burst into jubilant song with music;
make music to the Lord with the harp,
with the harp and the sound of singing,
with trumpets and the blast of the ram's horn –
shout for joy before the Lord, the King.

Psalm 98:4-6

1166 Christ the Lord is risen again

Words: after Michael Weisse, Catherine Winkworth

Music: *Hundert Arien,* Dresden

WÜRTTEMBERG 77 77 with Alleluia

D A/C♯ A7 Bm A D G A7/E Bm G6 A D
1. Christ the Lord is ris'n a - gain, Christ has bro - ken ev - 'ry chain;
A A/C♯ D F♯7/C♯ B B/D♯ E A/C♯ A D F♯m
hear the an - gel voi - ces cry, sing - ing e - ver -
D6 E7 A A7 Bm G6 A D
more on high: al - le - lu - ia.

2. He who gave for us his life,
who for us endured the strife,
is our paschal lamb today;
we too sing for joy and say:
alleluia!

3. He who bore all pain and loss
comfortless upon the cross
lives in glory now on high,
pleads for us and hears our cry:
alleluia!

4. He who slumbered in the grave
is exalted now to save;
through the universe it rings
that the Lamb is King of kings:
alleluia!

5. Now he bids us tell abroad
how the lost may be restored,
how the penitent forgiven,
how we too may enter heaven:
alleluia!

6. Christ, our paschal lamb indeed,
all your ransomed people feed!
Take our sins and guilt away;
let us sing by night and day:
alleluia!

1167 Come, come let us return to the Lord

Come, let us return to the Lord

Words and Music: Matt Redman

To continue
Bm7 D G2
With the rend - ing of a heart, with the bow - ing of a
Bm7 D G2 Bm7 D
knee, Lord, we are re-turn - ing. With a pray'r and with a
G2 Bm7 D G2
fast, with a song in min - or key, Lord we are re-pent - ing.
Em7 D/F♯ G
E - ven now, e - ven now with all of our hearts
Em7 D/F♯ G2
D.C. al Coda
for you may turn and you may leave a bles-sing be-hind, O

CODA
C
G/B
In your mer - cy you will come, in your mer - cy you will
D
C
come
as sure-ly as the ris-ing
1.
G/B
D
sun, as sure-ly as the ris-ing sun.
2.
G
Asus4
A
D.C. al Fine
sun, as sure-ly as the ris-ing sun.
O

1168 Come, Holy Spirit

Words and Music: John L. Bell

Sustained
F Bb Eb2 Eb Am7 Dm Gm7
Capo 3 D G C2 C F#m7 Bm Em7
All
Come, Ho - ly Spi - rit, des - cend on us, des -
C F/A Bb C7/Bb F/A Gm7 Csus4 C7 C9
A D/F# G A7/G D/F# Em7 Asus4 A7 A9
cend on us; we ga - ther here in Je - sus'
Last time
F Gm7/F C/F F
D Em7/D A/D D
Leader
(Come, Ho - ly Spi - rit . . .)
(Come, breath of hea - ven . . .)
(Come, word of mer - cy . . .) Come!
name. (Hum) (hum)

Ascribe to the Lord the glory due to his name;
bring an offering and come into his courts.
Worship the Lord in the splendour of his holiness;
tremble before him, all the earth.

Psalm 96:8-9

1169 Come into his presence

Words and Music: Lynn Baird

1170 Come into the holy of holies

Words and Music: John Sellers

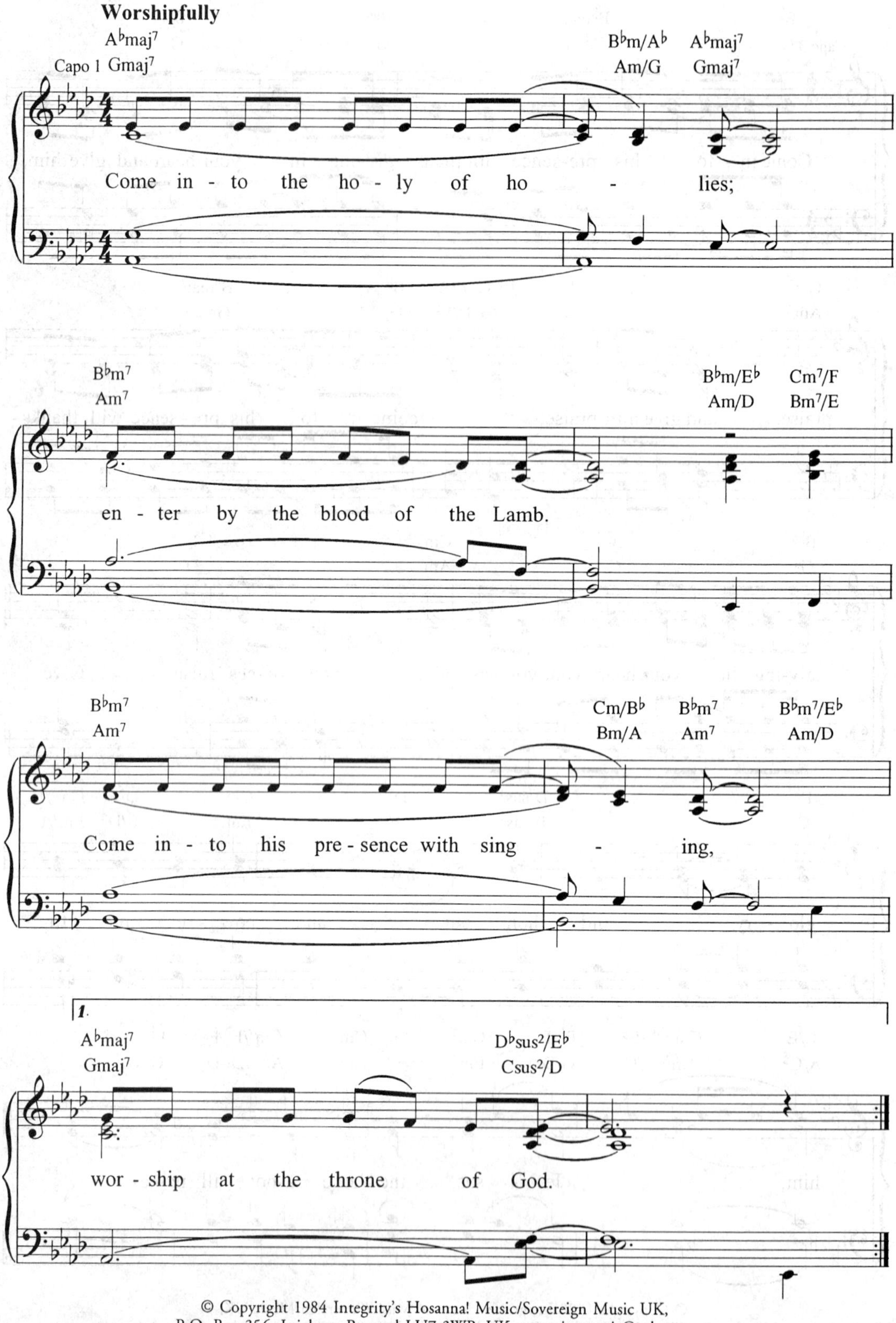

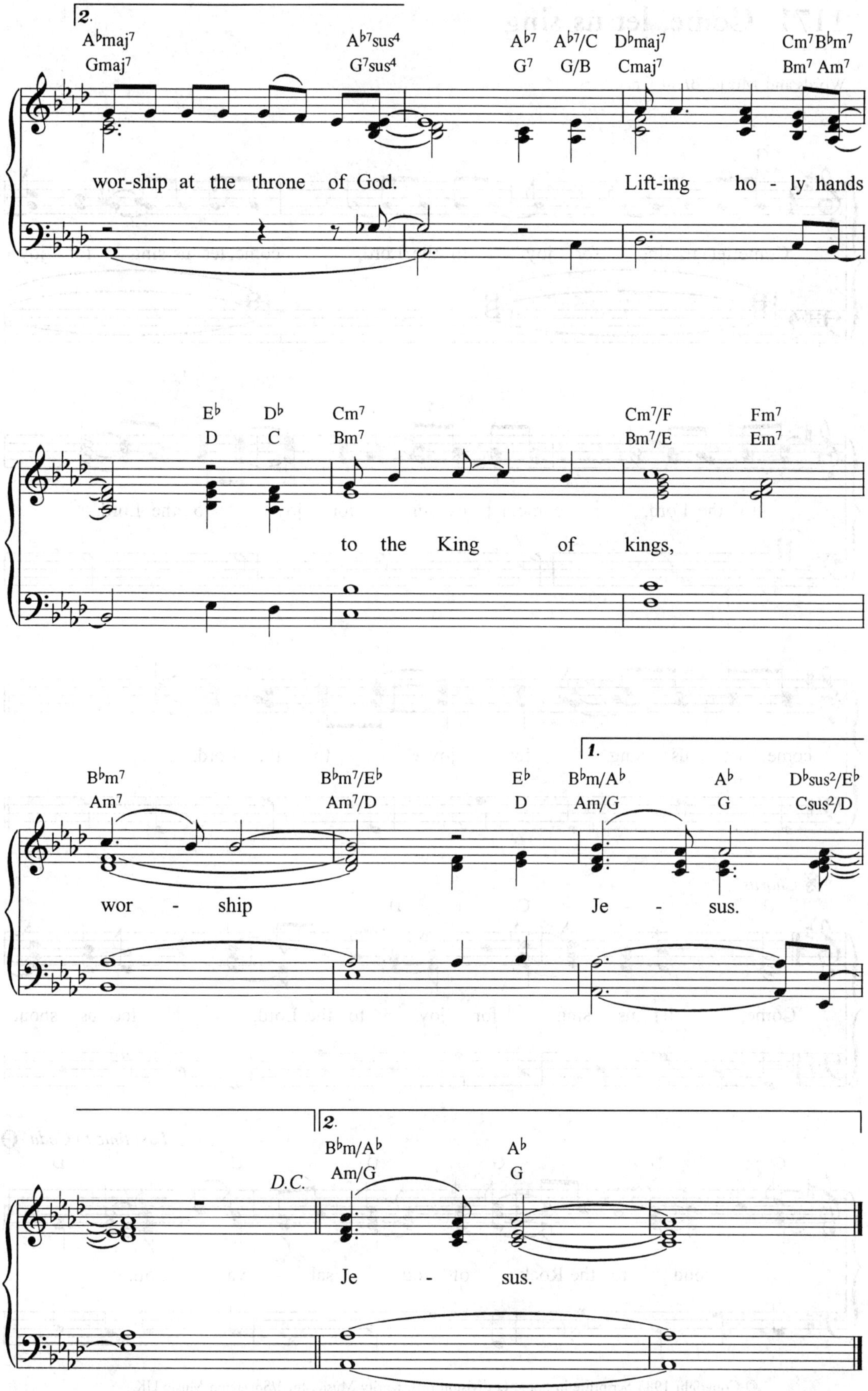
2.
A♭maj7 A♭7sus4 A♭7 A♭7/C D♭maj7 Cm7 B♭m7
Gmaj7 G7sus4 G7 G/B Cmaj7 Bm7 Am7
wor-ship at the throne of God. Lift-ing ho - ly hands
E♭ D♭ Cm7 Cm7/F Fm7
D C Bm7 Bm7/E Em7
to the King of kings,
1.
B♭m7 B♭m7/E♭ E♭ B♭m/A♭ A♭ D♭sus2/E♭
Am7 Am7/D D Am/G G Csus2/D
wor - ship Je - sus.
2.
D.C.
B♭m/A♭ A♭
Am/G G
Je - sus.

1171 Come, let us sing

Words and Music: Brent Chambers

2. Let us bow before him in our worship,
let us kneel before God, our great King;
for he is our God and we are his people
that's why we shout and sing.

1172 Come near to me

Words and Music: Alan Rose

With a rhythmic feel
Am7 Gsus2 Fsus2 Gsus2 Am7 Gsus2
1. Come near to me, as I come near to you;
2. Draw close to me, as I draw close to you;
Fsus2 Gsus2 Am7 Gsus2 Fsus2 C/E
pour out your mer - cy and your
re - lease your pow - er from a -
Dm7 Gsus4 G Am7 Gsus2
grace. I need your
bove. I'm dry and
Fsus2 Gsus2 Am7 Gsus2 Fsus2 Gsus2
(v.2)
love, I need your ten - der - ness;
thir - sty, Lord, come and fill me up;
Am7 Gsus2 Fsus2 C/E Dm7
I'm long - ing for your sweet em - brace.
I'm wait - ing for your touch of love.

Chorus
E7 F C D7
My heart cries out for more of you, Lord;
F G7sus4 F C
I'm so hun-gry for your pre - sence. Your love is wa-ter to my soul.
Dm7 G F C
I will be sa-tis - fied with you,
D7 F G7sus4 Dm7
Lord; you ful - fil my deep-est long - ing. Pour out your
C/E F E7
Spi - rit once a - gain.
1.
D.C.

2.
Gsus4
G
F
C/E
I've felt your pre-sence, Lord, I've
Dm7
C/E
F
tast - ed of your love. Now all I am
C/E
Dm7
C/E
cries out for more of you, I want more
F
C/E
F
of you; more of your Spi - rit
C/E
Dm7
E7
D.S.
poured from a-bove, more of your pow - er, more of your love.

Sing to the Lord a new song;
sing to the Lord, all the earth.
Sing to the Lord, praise his name;
proclaim his salvation day after day.
Declare his glory among the nations,
his marvellous deeds among all peoples.

Psalm 96:1-3

1173 Come, praise the Lord *Every breath*

Words and Music: Keith Getty and Kristyn Lennox

1. Come, praise the Lord, he is life in all its full - ness;
2. Come, praise the Lord, he is love that wel-comes sin - ners;

will you lift your voice? Come, praise the Lord, he is light
will you give your life? Come, praise the Lord, he is great

that shat - ters dark - ness; we have come to re-joice.
a - bove all o - thers; all his ways are right.

All a-round the world he is call - ing

peo - ple who would take up his call and fol - low him.

F D
Chorus
B♭/D G/B
C A
Dm Bm
Ev-'ry breath be praise, ev-'ry heart be raised
B♭ G
F/A D/F♯
Gm7 Em7
C7sus4 A7sus4
to the King of all cre - a - tion.
F D
B♭/D G/B
C A
Dm Bm
Ev-'ry breath be praise, ev-'ry heart be raised
B♭ G
C A
F D
F/E D/C♯
B♭2/D G2/B
to the Lord of all.
F D
Dm7 Bm7
F/C D/A
B♭2 G2
F D

1174 Come, see the Lord

Words: Martin E. Leckebusch

Music: Joseph Francis Thrupp

EPIPHANY 11 10 11 10

C G/B Am G/B G7/B C
1. Come, see the Lord in his breath - tak - ing splen - dour:
G7/F C/E G7/D C F Dm G
gaze at his ma - jes - ty: bow and a - dore!
C/E C G G7 Am D7/F♯ G
En - ter his pre - sence with won - der and wor - ship:
C Dm7 C/E F6 C/G G7 G6(7) C
he is the King, and en - throned e - ver - more.

2. He is the Word who was sent by the Father,
born as a baby, a child of our race:
God here among us, revealed as a servant,
walking the pathway of truth and of grace.

3. He is the Lamb who was slain to redeem us –
there at the cross his appearance was marred;
though he emerged from the grave as the victor,
still from the nails and the spear he is scarred.

4. He is the Lord who ascended in triumph –
ever the sound of his praises shall ring!
Hail him the first and the last, the Almighty:
Jesus, our Prophet, our Priest and our King.

5. Come, see the Lord in his breathtaking splendour:
gaze at his majesty – bow and adore!
Come and acknowledge him Saviour and Sovereign:
Jesus our King is enthroned evermore.

1175 Come, share his resurrection

I see the cross

Words and Music: Brian Doerksen

F
D
B♭2
G2
cross, and it's all I need to see;
cross, lift-ed high for all to see;
Dm
Bm
I see the cross, and it
I see the cross, it's the
B♭2
G2
F
D
calls me to be - lieve.
love the na - tions need.
No o - ther way to be
C
A
B♭2
G2
re - con - ciled, to re - ceive com-plete for-give - ness; no o - ther
F
D
C
A
B♭2
G2
choice could have set us free, could have paid the price of jus-

Gm
Em
F/A
D/F♯
- tice; so I come as I am to the
B♭
G
Csus4
Asus4
C/F
A/D
place where mer - cy meets me. I see the
F
D
C/F
A/D
F
D
1.
C/F
A/D
cross. 2. I see the
2.
C/F
A/D
F
D
C/F
A/D
F
D
Gm
Em
Bridge
You
F/A
D/F♯
B♭2
G2
C
A
Gm
Em
suf - fered and died, poured out your life; you

F/A D/F# Bb2 G2 C A Gm Em
showed us the way to truly be great; yet
F/A D/F# Bb2 G2 C A Gm Em
this just be-gins the Fa - ther's full plan; now
F/A D/F# Bb2 G2 C A
there is a way to share in your
Chorus 2 F D C/E A/C#
re - sur - rec - tion,
Bb2 G2 F/A D/F# C A F D
live for e - ver through your

C/E A/C♯ B♭2 G2
1, 2.
C A F/C D/A C7 A7
death and life.
We'll share your
3.
F/C D/A Gm/C Em/A B♭ G F/A D/F♯ C/G A/E F D B♭ G F/A D/F♯
We'll share your re - sur - rec - tion, live for
F2 D2 F D B♭ G F/A D/F♯ C/G A/E F/A D/F♯ B♭/F G/D
e - ver through your death and life;
C A F/C D/A C7 A7 Fsus4 Dsus4 B♭/F G/D C/E A/C♯ B♭2/D G2/B B♭2/D G2/B Dm7 Bm7
we'll share your re - sur - rec - tion, live for
C A F/C D/A B♭2/F G2/D F D C/E A/C♯ F D B♭ G F2 D2
e - ver through your death and life.

1176 Come, wounded Healer

Words: Martin E. Leckebuch

Music: Traditional Irish melody

SLANE 10 11 11 11

2. Come, hated Lover, and gather us near,
your welcome, your teaching, your challenge to hear:
where scorn and abuse cause rejection and pain,
your loving acceptance makes hope live again!

3. Come, broken Victor, condemned to a cross –
how great are the treasures we gain from your loss!
Your willing agreement to share in our strife
transforms our despair into fullness of life.

1177 Comfort me *You are the God that never sleeps*

Words and Music: Brenton Brown

A E F#m D A E
ing o - ver me. You've pro - mised mer - cy with no end,
B7 D F#m D
and I need your help a -gain! A God who's lived
A E F#m D A E
this life on earth; you know the heart - ache and the hurt.
F#m D A E B7
You said you'd com - fort those in pain; and I
D F#m D
need your help a -gain. Com-fort me; I

A E F#m D A E
need you right now. Com-fort me, 'cause I don't know how I'm in need,
F#m D A E B7
Je - sus, and there's no one else who will do. The
1.
D E F#m D A E F#m D
on-ly God I need is you. I need you.
A E
2.
D E F#m D
on-ly God I need is you, Je - sus. I
A E F#m D A E
need you right now; com-fort me, 'cause I don't know how I'm in need,
F#m D A E
Je - sus, and there's no one else who will

B7 D E F#m
Fine
do. The on-ly God I need is you.
D
My God, my God, why have you for-sak-en me? My
A E
God, my God, why have you a-ban-doned me? My
F#m D
God, my God, why have you for-sak-en me? My
A E/G# E F#m D
D.S. al Fine
God, my God, my God. Com-fort me, I

1178 Crown of glory, crown of thorns

Words and Music: Paul Field

Chorus
F F/A B♭ F Dm E♭
Capo 3 D D/F♯ G D Bm C
Crown of glo - ry, crown of thorns, Sa - viour of the world was
C F/A B♭ A Dm Gm F/A
A D/F♯ G F♯ Bm Em D/F♯
born; to die for us in sa - cri - fice, and rise and wear the
C C/B♭ C/A C/G
A A/G A/F♯ A/E
Last time
F
D
Fine
crown of life.
To verses
F Gm Csus4 C Am Dm
D Em Asus4 A F♯m Bm
life. 1. Prince of peace, a pau - per

Am F#m Dm Bm B♭ G
came, with ri - ches sure e - nough, to light the true, e -
F/A D/F# E♭ C Csus4 Asus4 C A Am F#m
ter - nal flame: the Fa - ther's heart of love. Son of God and
Dm Bm Am F#m Dm Bm B♭ G
Son of man, you walked a - mong us here, you knew the
Am F#m E♭ C Csus4 Asus4 C A
fra - gile hearts we are, you shared our joy and tears.

2. King of love, you bore our sin
that nailed you to the cross;
the tears of God, shed to reclaim
the broken and the lost.
Lord of light from darkness shone
in pow'r to rise again,
for death has no dominion now,
the King of life shall reign.

3. God with us, Emmanuel
the Shepherd and the Lamb;
from now until eternity
your faithfulness will stand.
Hallelujah! Living God, our hope
is in your name:
by your grace we come to you:
renew our faith again.

1179 Dance, dance

Joy is in this place

Words: John Newton adapted by Tim Hughes   Music: Tim Hughes

With a strong rhythm
Capo 3
B♭ G E♭ C Cm Am
1. Dance, dance, ev - 'ry-bo-dy dance, ev - 'ry-bo-dy sing, for joy
2. Shout, shout, ev - 'ry-bo-dy shout, ev - 'ry-bo-dy scream, for joy
E♭ C B♭ G E♭ C
is in this place now. Dance, dance, ev - 'ry-bo-dy dance, ev -
is in this place now. Shout, shout, ev - 'ry-bo-dy shout, ev -
Cm Am E♭ C B♭ G
- 'ry-bo-dy sing, for joy is in this place now.
- 'ry-bo-dy scream, for joy is in this place now.
Cm Am E♭ C
And ev - 'ry-bo-dy dance now.
Yeah, joy is in this place now.

B♭ G
Cm Am
And ev- Yeah, joy
Last time
To continue
E♭ C
B♭ G
Fine
B♭ G
-'ry-bo-dy dance now.
is in this place now.
Cm Am
E♭ C
Cm Am
A-maz-ing grace, how
B♭/D G/B
E♭ C
Cm Am
sweet the sound, to save a wretch like me; I once was lost, but
B♭/D G/B
A♭ F
F D
D.C. al Fine
now I'm found, was blind, but now I see.

1180 Day after day

Words and Music: Tim Hughes

Simply
E F♯m D
1. Day af - ter day, I'll search to find you;
2. che - rish your word, I'll seek your pre - sence, I'll
E F♯m D
day af - ter day, I'll wait for you. The
chase af - ter you with all I have. As
E F♯m D E F♯m
deep-er I go, the more I love your name.
one day I know I'll see you face to face.
D Chorus A E Bm
So keep my heart pure, and my ways true, as I

A E D A E Bm
fol - low you. Keepme hum - ble, I'll stay mind - ful of your
A E D
1. 2.
mer - cies, Lord. 2. I'll

1181 Deep in my heart

Words and Music: Silke Dürrkopf

E
F#m
1. Deep in my heart burns a de - sire, oh Lord,
2. On - ly in you is there a peace that lasts,
C#m
B/D#
and I run to you, in -
Fa - ther, in your arms, there
E
to your arms. No - thing holds, holds me back,
I find rest. Your love it heals,
B
F#m
B
no - thing holds, holds me back, I come to
your love it heals it heals my

This song was one of many written by foreign aid workers who were arrested by the Taliban and endured four months of imprisonment in various jails throughout the autumn of 2001. They were facing uncertainty regarding the safety of their lives but were miraculously rescued in November 2001 by allied forces in Afghanistan.

E
1.
2.
Chorus
you.
heart.
Oh
Je - sus, Je - sus, Je - sus you are won - der-ful, and a -
B/D♯
gain I lay my life in - to your hands. I
F♯m
bow my knees in awe of your ma - jes - ty;
C♯m/B
B
C♯m/B
B
deep from my heart you make me sing.

1182 Deep in my soul

Will you worship?

Words and Music: Brian Doerksen

Capo 3
F D
F2/A D2/F#
Deep in my soul is a tug of war, I'm
B♭ G
Csus4 Asus4
C A
strugg-ling to know what this life is for and
F D
F2/A D2/F#
I try so hard to stay in con-trol, to
B♭ G
Csus4 Asus4
C A
hold back the tears, to not let go, and
E♭ C
B♭2/D G2/B
I don't know why I hang on so long when I

Gm7 Em7 F2/A D2/F♯ Csus4 Asus4 C A
know the ques - tion you are ask - ing me.
F D Chorus F2/A D2/F♯
Will you wor - ship, will you bow down be- fore
B♭ G F D C A F D
your Lord and King? Will you love me,
F2/A D2/F♯ B♭ G 1. F D C A
will you give me your heart, your ev - 'ry-thing?
2. F D E♭ C B♭/D G/B
Right here and now I make my choice with

Gm7 F/A C
Em7 D/F# A
all my love I will ans - wer you.
G G2/B
E E2/G#
Chorus
I will wor - ship, I will bow down be- fore
C2 G D
A2 E B
my Lord and King.
G G2/B
E E2/G#
I will love you, I will give you my heart,
Last time
C2 G D G
A2 E B E
my ev - 'ry-thing.

1183 Do not be afraid

Words: Gerard Markland
based on Isaiah 43:1-4

Music: Gerard Markland

Chorus
D Em7 A7 D
Do not be a - fraid, for I have re-deemed you.
Bm Em7 A7
I have called you by your name; you are
D Fine Bm G
mine. 1. When you walk through the wa - ters, I'll be
A G A D D.C.
with you. You will ne - ver sink be - neath the waves.

2. When the fire is burning all around you,
you will never be consumed by the flames.

3. When the fear of loneliness is looming,
then remember I am at your side.

4. When you dwell in the exile of the stranger,
remember you are precious in my eyes.

5. You are mine, O my child, I am your Father,
and I love you with a perfect love.

1184 Draw us near

Words and Music: Paul Critchley

(♩ = 112)
E Chorus
B/D♯
A²
Draw us near, draw us near-er to you,
E
B/D♯
Je - sus. Draw us near, draw us near - er to
A²
Last time
E
you.
E
B/D♯
A²
1. Thank you for mak - ing a way, thank you, Lord,
2. Thank you for show - ing the way, thank you, Lord,

C♯m7
B
thank you, Lord. A way bought at a fate - ful cost, a way
thank you, Lord. A way to see your glo - ry more, a way
A2
B
you made to save the lost
to hear your heart - beat, Lord,
and as we come, O God
A2
D.C.
of heav'n, we lift our voice; hear us a - gain.

1185 Even if the world should fall around me

Words and Music: Phil Loose and John Winfieldale

E
A
A/B
E
1. E - ven if the world should fall a - round me, e - ven if a
sun is full of pro - mise, gen - tle as it
A
A/B
E
A
A/B
friend should turn a - way, though I work the fields but see no har -
drives the mist a - way, you a - lone the hope of our sal - va -
C#m
F#m7
A/B
1.
E
- vest, I will wait up - on your ho - ly name. 2. Like the dawn-ing
- tion, take me to the high - er place a - gain.
2.
E
Chorus
A
E/G#
O Je - sus, O

F♯m7 E/G♯ A
Sa - viour, you are my bro - ther,
E/G♯ F♯m E/G♯
you are my friend. O
A E/G♯ F♯m7
lead me, O change me,
E/G♯ A E/G♯
though it's not ea - sy, teach me to love.
F♯m7 1. E D.S. 2. E
3. When the land is

3. When the land is dry and I am weary,
when my body longs and thirsts for thee
I will worship in your sanctuary,
your power and your glory there to see.

4. Better than my life: your loving kindness,
I will fill my mouth with praise to thee,
satisfy my soul with food from heaven,
bless your holy name the days I live.

1186 Even when we turned our backs on you

Thank you for the cross

Words and Music: Brenton Brown

C D
1. E - ven when we turned our backs on you,
2. E - ne - mies of God with no ex - cuse,
Em C D
in wic - ked - ness and lies sup-pressed the truth.
know - ing what was right we turned from you.
Em C D
E - ven then you showed your love for us,
Giv - en up to sin, con-demned to die,
Em C D G
Chorus
giv-ing up your life up - on the cross. Je - sus,
e - ven then you chose to give us life.

Am G/B D Am G/B
thank you for the cross, for the blood that sets us free;
D Am G/B D
the crim - son stain of all our sin, washed a -
Am G/B C Fine A4/C#
way in your mer - cy. Ev - 'ry one
C G/B C A4/C#
of us de - serves to die, but you save all
C G/B C D.S. al Fine
who hope in your great love. Je - sus,

1187 Everlasting God

Yesterday, today, forever

Words and Music: Vicky Beeching

Rock style
Capo 3 G
B♭ Dm7 B♭
G Bm7 G
1. E - ver - last-ing God, the years go by but you're
2. Un - cre - at - ed One, you have no end and no
Dm7 B♭ Dm7
Bm7 G Bm7
un - chang - ing. In this fra-gile world, you
be - gin - ning. Earth - ly pow-ers fade, but
B♭ Dm7 Gm7(4)
G Bm7 Em7(4)
are the on - ly firm foun - da - tion.
there is no end to your king - dom.
Al-ways lov -
F/A B♭
D/F♯ G
- ing, al - ways true,
al - ways mer -

Dm7 C
Bm7 A
- ci - ful and good, so good.
Chorus
F/A B♭ Dm7 C F/A B♭
D/F♯ G Bm7 A D/F♯ G
Yes - ter - day, to - day and for e - ver, you are the same,
Dm7 C F/A B♭ Dm7 C
Bm7 A D/F♯ G Bm7 A
you ne - ver change. Yes - ter - day, to - day and for e - ver,
Gm7 B♭ C F/A B♭
Em7 G A D/F♯ G
1.
you are faith - ful and we will trust in you.
Dm7 C F B♭
Bm7 A D G
Last time
2.
Fine
We will trust in you,

F/A
D/F#
B♭
G
we will trust in you,
F/A
D/F#
Bridge
B♭2
G2
in you. Yah - weh,
F/A
D/F#
B♭2
G2
God un - chang - ing. Yah - weh,
F/A
D/F#
1.
2.
D.S. al Fine
3
firm foun - da - tion. You are da - tion.

How lovely is your dwelling-place,
O Lord Almighty!
My soul yearns, even faints,
for the courts of the Lord;
my heart and my flesh cry out
for the living God.

Psalm 84:1-2

1188 Ever living God

Words and Music: Raymond Badham

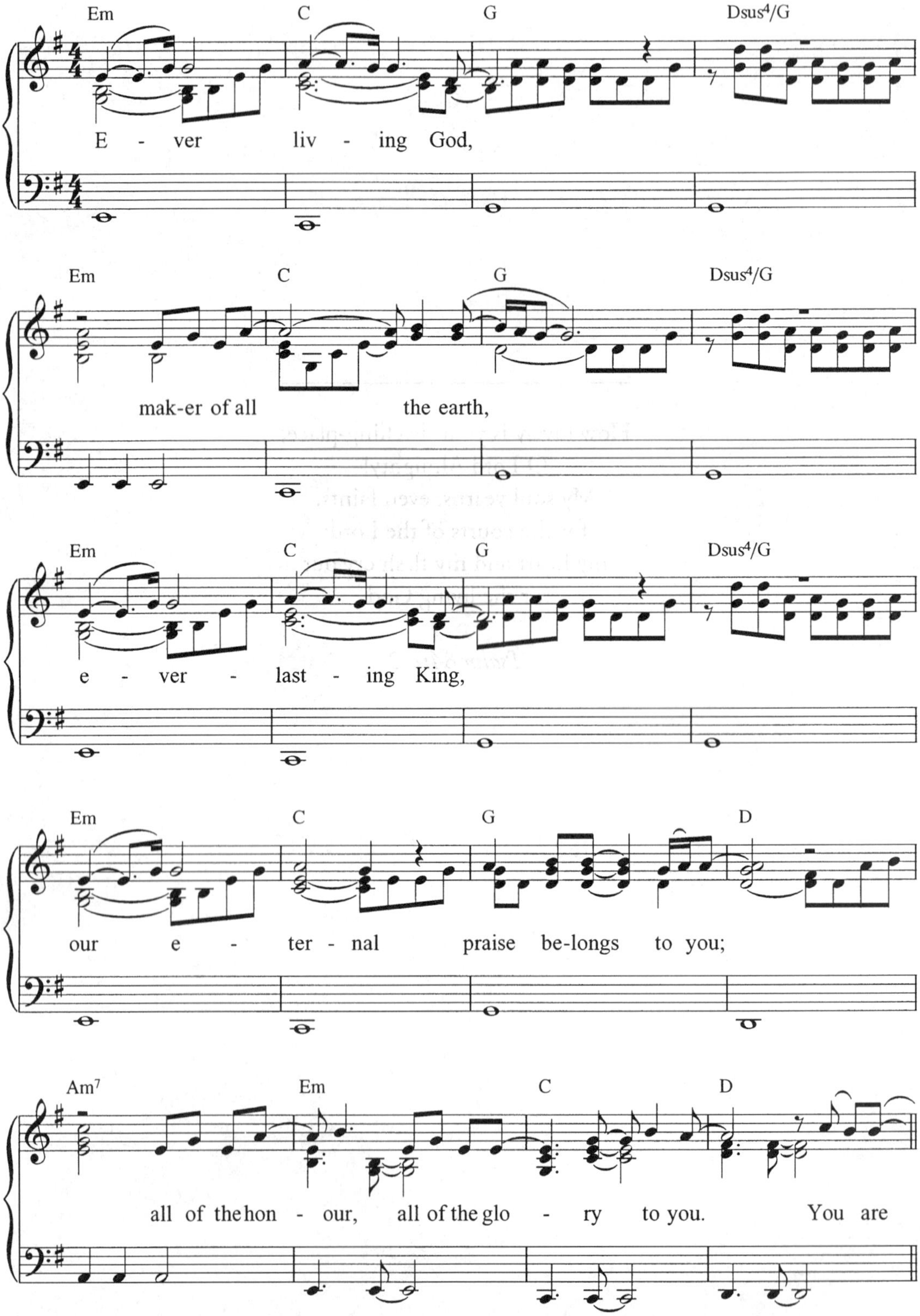
Em C G Dsus4/G
E - ver liv - ing God,
Em C G Dsus4/G
mak-er of all the earth,
Em C G Dsus4/G
e - ver - last - ing King,
Em C G D
our e - ter - nal praise be-longs to you;
Am7 Em C D
all of the hon - our, all of the glo - ry to you. You are

G G/B C Dsus4 D
wonder - ful, marvel - lous, for e - ver beau-ti-ful,
G G/B 1. C Dsus4
Prince of Peace, Faith-ful One, for e - ver.
Em C 2, 3. C Dsus4
One, for e - ver. Take the
C D C
place of all hon - our, take the place a-bove all thrones,
D C D
take the place of all pow - er; you are the
C 1. D D.S. 2. D G
One glo-ri-ous. You are

1189 Evermore

Words and Music: Geron Davis

Chorus
C
Dm7
E-ver-more, I will love you e-ver-more, I will serve you e-ver-more,
C/E
F
Am7
Gsus4
I will glo - ri-fy the name of the Lord. E - ver-more,
C
Dm7
Last time to Coda
I'll a-dore you e - ver-more, bow be-fore you. I will
Fmaj7
G
Am
G
1.
C
G
bless your name for e - ver - more. E - ver-more,
2.
C
Verse
F
more. You a-lone are glo - ri-fied and

C/E
Dm
C/E
of your good - ness tes - ti-fied. Your ban-ner I will lift on high for
F/G
G
F/G
G
F
e - ver and e - ver; and when my life on earth is done and
C/E
Dm
C/E
when my bat - tles have been won, I'll sing my praise a-round the throne for
F/G
G
F/G
G
D.S. al Coda
e - ver and e - ver. E - ver-more,
CODA
Fmaj7
G
Am
G
C
bless your name for e - ver - more.

1190 Every day

The eyes of my heart

Words and Music: Matt Redman

Rhythmically
C Csus4 C Csus4 Am7
Capo 3 A Asus4 A Asus4 F♯m7
1. Ev - 'ry day, I see more of your
2. Ev - 'ry day, I see more of your
G C Csus4 C Csus4
E A Asus4 A Asus4
beau - ty. Ev-'ry day, I
great - ness. Ev-'ry day, I
Am7 G B♭sus2
F♯m7 E Gsus2
know more of my frail - ty, Lord. And I can on-ly
know more of my weak - ness, Lord. And I can on-ly
F C Csus4 C Csus4
D A Asus4 A Asus4
hope that I'll be changed,
hope that I'll be changed,

B♭sus2
Gsus2
F
D
G
E
e-ven as I look up-on your face.
e-ven as I look up-on your face.
C
A
Chorus
For the eyes of my
Am7
F♯m7
B♭
G
heart, they are on you for e-ver,
F
D
1.
they are on you for e-ver. Yes, the eyes
2.
3.
D.C.
C
A

1191 Every day that I live

Words and Music: Belinda Horley, Doug Horley and Steve Whitehouse

B
C♯m7
F♯m
you, you are my friend, how I need you.
you, you are my life, lost with-out you.
You are my
E/G♯
B
A
Last time to Coda
1.
D.C.
strength, you are my hope, you are my song.
2.
3.
D.S. (chorus 2)
A
2. You are my
And I'm
ne-ver gon-na give up, give up on you;
B
C♯m7
ne-ver gon-na give up, give up on you; ne-ver gon-na give up, give up on you;
F♯m
D.S. (Chorus 1) al Coda
CODA
E
ne-ver gon-na give up.
You are my

1192 Every day with you, Lord

Sweeter

Words and Music: Israel Houghton, Meleasa Houghton and Cindy Cruse-Ratcliffe

E A/E B/E A/E E A/E
B/E E/A E E/A E E/A
1. What a priv-'lege to know you like I know you, to be loved
2. What a won-der to live life, real-ly live life, o-ver-com-
E A B/E E/A E E/A
like you love me, what an hon-our to wor - ship, tru-ly wor-
- ing a-ny-thing, what a rea-son to lift up, free-ly lift
E E/A E A B/E
- ship; from this heart that you have freed.
up ev-'ry day, my ev-'ry-thing.
From the ris-
Am B Chorus D.S.
- ing of the sun to the sett - ing of the same. Ev-'ry day with

Bridge
E A/E B/E A/E E A/E
B/E A/E E A/E B/E A/E
(Leader)
Ev - 'ry day, ev - 'ry day with you, Lord.
Ev - 'ry day is sweet - er than the day be-fore.
To repeat ad lib.
E A/E B/E A/E
(Echo)
Ev - 'ry day, ev - 'ry day with you, Lord.
Ev - 'ry day is sweet - er than the day be - fore.
To Chorus
E B/E
Chorus D.S.
Ev - 'ry day with you. Ev - 'ry day with
CODA
E A/E
B/E A/E E A/E B/E A/E E

I will praise you, O Lord, among the nations;
I will sing of you among the peoples.
For great is your love, reaching to the heavens;
your faithfulness reaches to the skies.
Be exalted, O God, above the heavens;
let your glory be over all the earth.

Psalm 57:9-11

1193 Every morning that breaks *Mercies anew*

Words and Music: Mark Altrogge and Bob Kauflin

2.
C/E F/A Gsus4 C
2. When I've new.
Bridge
G/B Am G F C
And your mer - cies, they will ne - ver end; for ten
Am G F G
thou - sand years they re - main. And when
Am G F Em
this world's beau - ty has passed a - way your
E♭ F B♭ Dm7 G
D.S.
mer - cies will be un - changed. 3. And when the

CODA
Dm7
C/E
F
G
new, I will sing of your mer - cies
C
a - new.

God has ascended amid shouts of joy,
the Lord amid the sounding of trumpets.
Sing praises to God, sing praises;
sing praises to our King, sing praises.
For God is the King of all the earth;
sing to him a psalm of praise.

Psalm 47:5-7

1194 Everything

Words and Music: Israel Houghton

C F/A B♭ F C B♭/D C/E F
A D/F♯ G D A G/B A/C♯ D
Great is the mea - sure of your roy - al - ty, O Morn-
Gm7 B♭m
Em7 Gm
- ing Star, you tru - ly are ev - 'ry-thing.
F F/A
D D/F♯
Last time
B♭maj9 C7sus4 F
Gmaj9 A7sus4 D
D.C.

1195 Everything's gonna be OK *My Father's here*

Words and Music: Tom Lane and Scott MacLeod

D
Dsus4
D
G
1.
D.C.
2.
D
So let the thun-der crack,
G
let the storm-clouds rain,
they may
D
G
push me back
but I'm gon - na face the pain.
D
Let the moun-tains shake,
let the

G
D
o-ceans scream, what-e-ver it takes
G
I'm gon-na live this dream. And if you've
D
3
reached the end and think you
G
D
can't go on let me tell you, my friend,
G
D.C. al Fine
you are not far gone.

Clap your hands, all you nations;
shout to God with cries of joy.
How awesome is the Lord Most High,
the great King over all the earth!

Psalm 47:1-2

1196 Fall, Holy Spirit, fall

Fall

Words and Music: Nicola Rodgers

G A D G A Bm
me with your love that it may o - ver-flow and touch
G A D G A D
your peo - ple's hearts. And I will give
G A D G A
you all the hon - our, I'll give you all the glo -
Bm G A Bm
- ry as o - ther lives are changed, as o -
G A D G A D
- ther lives are saved.

1197 Far across the world *All my fountains are in you*

Words and Music: Barry Hart

B♭ C Csus4 C
G A Asus4 A
you're the one who made our lives brand new.
F C F B♭ F Gm7 C7
D A D G D Em7 A7
This one, that one born a-gain; glo-rious things we will pro-claim,
Dm B♭2 Csus4 C7 F B♭ C
Bm G2 Asus4 A7 D G A
all my foun-tains are in you.
F B♭ C F/A B♭ C7
D G A D/F♯ G A7
All my foun-tains, all my foun-tains,
To repeat/To Verses/To Coda
Last time
Dm B♭2 Csus4 C7 F B♭ C F B♭ F
Bm G2 Asus4 A7 D G A D G D
Fine
all my foun-tains are in you. you.

CODA
F/A D/F#
Bb G
C7 A7
Got to get the news a-round,
got to get the news a - round,
got to get the news a-round con-cern - ing Zi - on.
F D
C A
(combine this melody with previous eight bars)
Got to get the news a-round,
got to get the news a-round,
got to get the news a - round con - cern - ing Zi -
1.
- on.
2.
D.S. al Fine
- on.
We

1198 Father, into your courts I will enter *All the earth*

Words and Music: Wayne Huirua and Andrew Ulugia

Am G Fmaj7 C/E
is ev - 'ry-where. The fields will ex - alt,
C/F Gsus4 G Gsus4 G Gsus4 G
seas re-sound. Hear the trees'
C Dm7 C/E Gsus4 G Am7 G
joy-ful cry, prais-ing you and so will I.
Fmaj7 C/E Dsus4 D
A new song I'll sing, Lord, I will
1.
Fmaj7 G C Dm7
glo - ri - fy and bless your ho - ly name.

C/E G7sus4 Am7 Gsus4 F
D.C.
2.
Fmaj7 G F/A
glo - ri - fy and bless your name, glo - ri - fy and
A/B C Dm7 C/E Gsus4 G C
bless your ho - ly name.

1199 Father, let me dedicate *Be glorified*

Verses: Laurence Tuttiet, adapt. Matt Redman
Chorus: Chris Tomlin, Louie Giglio and Jesse Reeves

B♭ G
C7sus4 A7sus4
F D
Fsus4 Dsus4
be my prayer: glo-ri-fy thy name.
fu-ture brings, glo-ri-fy thy name.
F D
Chorus
B♭ G
F D
C A
Be glo-ri-fied in me, be glo-ri-fied.
B♭ G
F D
C A
B♭ G
F D
C A
Be glo-ri-fied in me,
B♭ G
F D
C A
1.
D.C.
be glo-ri-fied.
2.
Chorus
D.S.
3.
F D
Be glo-ri-fied

1200 Father, make us one

Words and Music: Rick Ridings

D♭ E♭ D♭ E♭
C D C D
dwell in u - ni - ty, for there the Lord com -
A♭ Fm E♭ D♭ E♭ D♭/A♭ A♭
G Em D C D C/G G
mands the bles - sing, life for e - ver - more.

Who may ascend the hill of the Lord?
Who may stand in his holy place?
He who has clean hands and a pure heart,
who does not lift up his soul to an idol
or swear by what is false.

Psalm 24:3-4

1201 Father of heaven, whose love profound

Words: Edward Cooper

Music: John Bacchus Dykes

RIEVAULX 88 88 (LM)

D A7/C# D G A7/G D D/F# G G6 D/F#
1. Fa - ther of heav'n, whose love pro - found a ran - som for our
Em7 A7/E D G Bm/F# F#7 Bm D/A A7
souls has found: be - fore your throne we sin - ners
D G/B Aadd4 G D/F# A7/E D A6 A7 D
bend – to us your par - d'ning love ex - tend.

2. Almighty Son, incarnate Word,
our prophet, priest, redeemer, Lord:
before your throne we sinners bend –
to us your saving grace extend.

3. Eternal Spirit, by whose breath
the soul is raised from sin and death:
before your throne we sinners bend –
to us your living power extend.

4. Transcendent Father, Spirit, Son –
mysterious Godhead, three in one:
before your throne we sinners bend –
grace, pardon, life to us extend.

1202 Father of love *Your loving-kindness*

Words and Music: Billy Funk

(♩ = 104)
Capo 3
F D
Gm7 Em7
Fa - ther of love, Lord of all cre - a - tion,
C A
B♭/F G/D
F D
I will bless your name for e - ver and e - ver;
Gm7 Em7
I will de - clare your grace and your mer - cy, and
C A
F D
Gm7 Em7
C A
tell of your un - fail - ing love.

Chorus
F C/F F F/A B♭ F/A Gm7
D A/D D D/F♯ G D/F♯ Em7
Your lov - ing - kind - ness is good to all,
B♭/C C B♭2/D C/E F
G/A A G2/B A/C♯ D
your wings of mer - cy lift me when I fall;
C/F F F/A F/B♭ B♭ F/A Gm7
A/D D D/F♯ D/G G D/F♯ Em7
your lov - ing - kind - ness meets my ev - 'ry need, you
B♭/C C Gm7 Am/C C F
G/A A Em7 F♯m/A A D
cleanse me from un - right - eous - ness and you give new life to me.

1203 Father, we have sinned against you

Words and Music: Geoff Twigg

G
3
law, we're re - turn - ing once more home to
A
you; we have sinned, we have sinned, we are
C
G
seek - ing your face, we re - turn by your
3
A
grace home to you.

1204 Father, your love

Words and Music: Robert Critchley

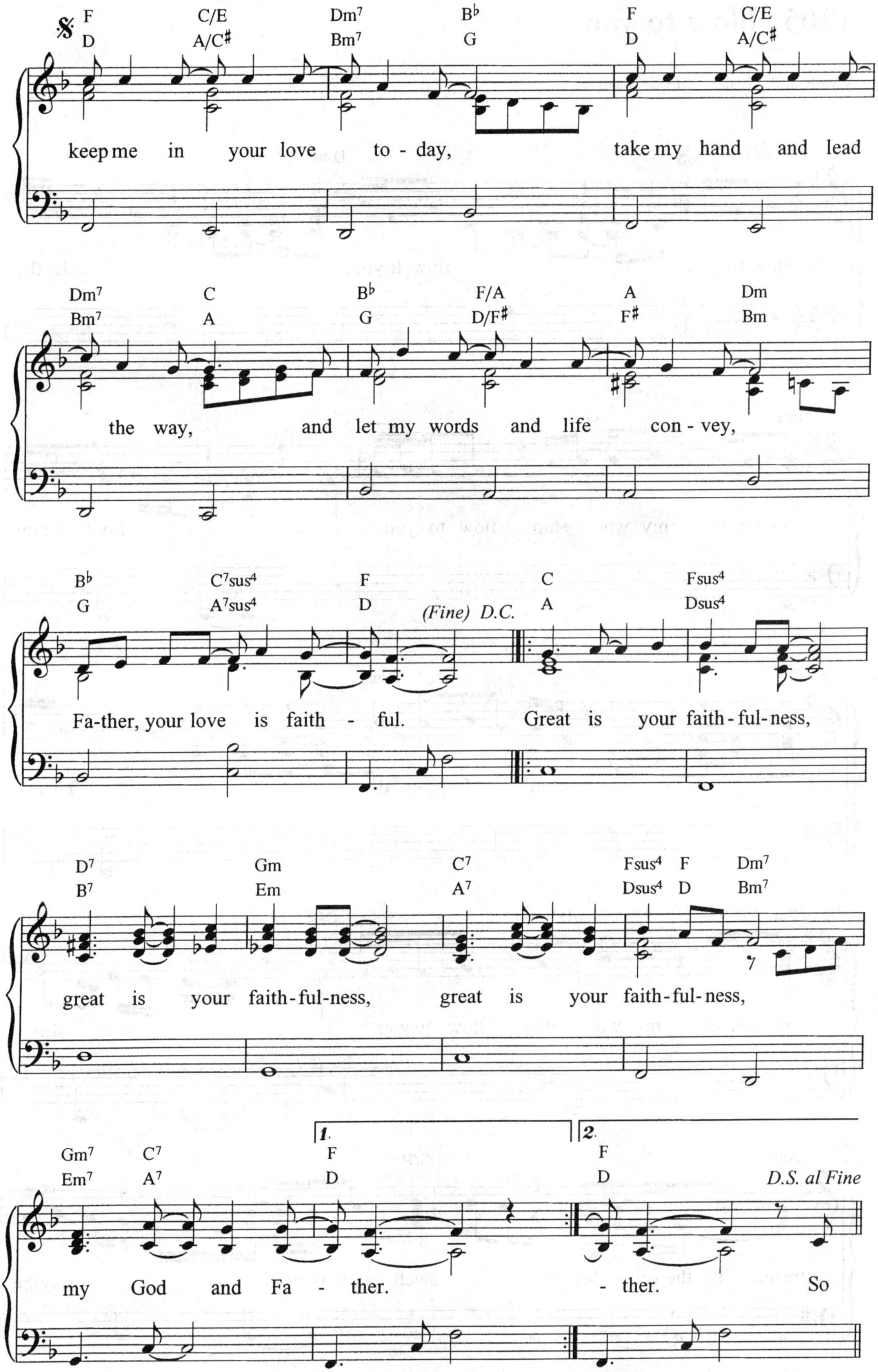
F C/E Dm7 B♭ F C/E
D A/C♯ Bm7 G D A/C♯
keep me in your love to - day, take my hand and lead
Dm7 C B♭ F/A A Dm
Bm7 A G D/F♯ F♯ Bm
the way, and let my words and life con - vey,
B♭ C7sus4 F C Fsus4
G A7sus4 D A Dsus4
(Fine) D.C.
Fa-ther, your love is faith - ful. Great is your faith-ful-ness,
D7 Gm C7 Fsus4 F Dm7
B7 Em A7 Dsus4 D Bm7
great is your faith-ful-ness, great is your faith-ful-ness,
1. 2.
Gm7 C7 F F
Em7 A7 D D
D.S. al Fine
my God and Fa - ther. - ther. So

1205 Flow to you

Words and Music: Lynn deShazo

(♩ = 62)
G
Dsus4
Flow to you,
flow to you,
let the
Em
G/D
C2
ri - ver of my wor - ship flow to you.
Lord, I pray
G
Dsus4
in all I do
let the
Em
G/D
C2
ri - ver of my wor - ship flow to you.
Like
Am7
G/B
streams in the val - ley
swell with the rain
may the

C2
Dsus4
D
songs of my heart rise to bless your name and flow to you,
C2
Last time to Coda
Em7
Dsus4
3
Am7
Dsus4
flow to you, let my wor-ship flow to you.
1.
G
C/G
G
C/G
Flow to you,
2.
G
D/F#
Em7
C2
Dsus4
G
D/F#
I love you, Lord, and ev - 'ry-thing a-bout you;
Em
C2
D
Am7
I wor - ship you with all my heart. Let all my
Dsus4
D
D.S. al Coda
heart flow to you,

CODA
Em7
Dsus4
Am7
Dsus4
let my wor - ship flow to you,
Em7
Dsus4
Am7
Dsus4
let my wor - ship flow to you.
G
C2/G
G
C2/G
G
C2
Flow to you, flow to you, let it
G
C2
Em7
Dsus4
D
G
flow to you.

O Lord, our Lord,
how majestic is your name in all the earth!
You have set your glory
above the heavens.

Psalm 8:1

1206 Forever in my heart

The promise of your cross

Words and Music: Matt Redman

Dm7 C B♭maj7 C
Capo 3 Bm7 A Gmaj7 A
1. For - e - ver in my heart, and writ - ten on my soul,
2. Em-bed - ded in my heart, and root - ed in my soul,
Dm7 C B♭maj7 C
Bm7 A Gmaj7 A
the pro - mise of your cross.
the pro - mise of your cross.
Dm7 C B♭maj7 C
Bm7 A Gmaj7 A
I have no o - ther claim, I have no o - ther plea:
It seals me as your own, and tells me I am yours:
Dm7 C B♭maj7 B♭ F/A Gm
Bm7 A Gmaj7 G D/F♯ Em
the pro-mise of your cross; the hope for ev - 'ry heart.
the pro-mise of your cross; the hope for ev - 'ry heart.
Chorus
F
D
Where mer - cy e - ver flows, and

Dm7
Bm7
G7sus4
E7sus4
shame's no lon - ger known, I'll praise you for the cross, the
B♭
G
F
D
pro - mise of your cross to me. It
Dm7
Bm7
ne - ver fails to bring the cleans - ing that I need,
G7sus4
E7sus4
B♭
G
I'll praise you for the cross, the pro - mise of your cross to me.
1.
Last time
2.
F
D
C
A
D.C. (v.2)
F
D
Fine
F
D
C
A

Dm7 Bm7 C A B♭maj7 Gmaj7 C A
3. Tell it in all the earth, sing it through-out the world,
Dm7 Bm7 C A B♭maj7 Gmaj7 C A Dm7 Bm7 C A
the pro-mise of the cross. There is a high-er way,
B♭maj7 Gmaj7 C A Dm7 Bm7 C A
there is a high - er hope: the pro - mise of your
B♭maj7 Gmaj7 B♭ G F/A D/F♯ Gm Em
cross; the hope for ev - 'ry heart. Where
D.S. al Fine

1207 For every disappointment *The cross still stands*

Words and Music: David Hind

Prayerfully
D G
1. For ev - 'ry dis - ap - point - ment, for
ev - 'ry wound - ed per - son, for
ev - 'ry one who's des - p'rate, for
ev - 'ry pain - ful ques - tion, for
A/C♯ D A/C♯ Bm
ev-'ry bro - ken heart, for ev - 'ry one in dark -
ev-'ry tir - ed mind, for hope-less si - tu - a -
ev-'ry one who's lost, for ev - 'ry one who's fear -
ev-'ry one's re - grets, for ev - 'ry cry of 'Why,
1, 3.
G A/C♯ Bm A/C♯
- ness; a light. 2. For
- ful; a shel - ter. 4. For
2, 4, 5.
Em A/C♯ Bm A/C♯
Last time to Coda
- tions; a hope. The
God?' an ans - wer. (And)

D G A/C♯ D A/C♯
cross still stands, the cross still tow - ers, his
Bm G A
blood still clean - ses, e - ter - nal - ly the same.
1, 3.
2.
D
(3rd time Instrumental) D.C.
Bm G
3. For Grace and peace,
Em A Bm G
mer - cy and joy, all un - de - served,
Em A/C♯ G/B A/C♯
D.S.
I bow down. The

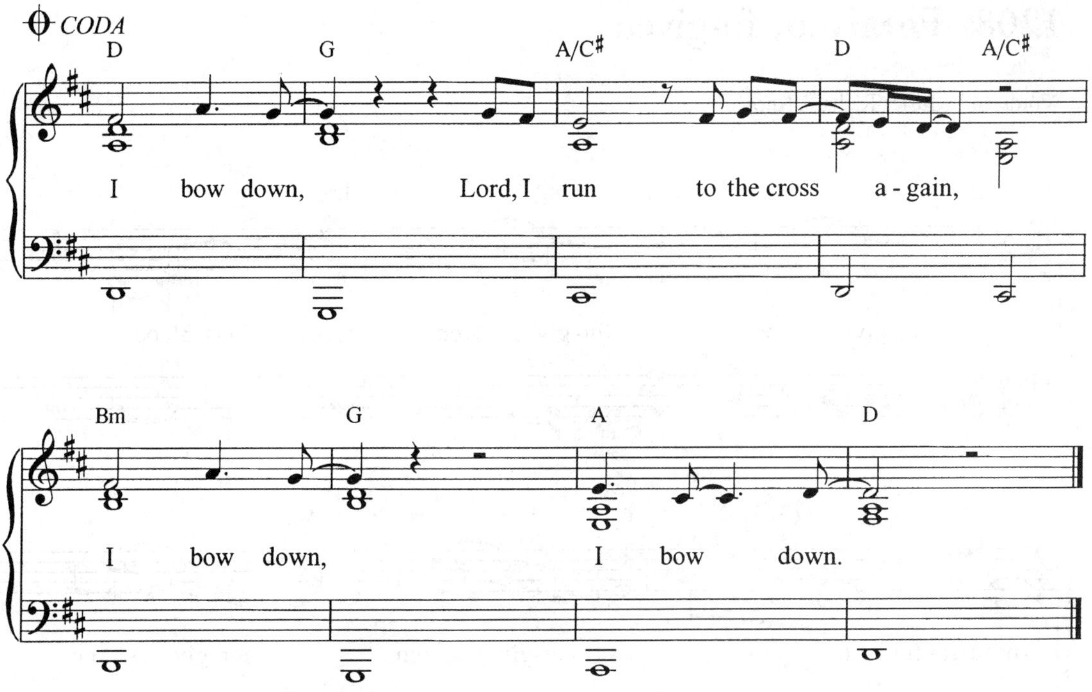
CODA
D G A/C♯ D A/C♯
I bow down, Lord, I run to the cross a - gain,
Bm G A D
I bow down, I bow down.

1208 Forgiven, forgiven

Words and Music: Richard Knott

C Am7 B♭
For-giv - en, for-giv - en, your pre-cious blood,
F G C Am7
beau-ti - ful love. For-giv - en, for-giv - en,
B♭ F G F/A G/B Chorus
un-end-ing grace, o-pened a way, a way for me. My
C Em7 F
love, my ev - 'ry - thing, my hope, the pro -
G C Em7 F
- mised King, my love, my ev - 'ry - thing is Je - sus,

1.
G
D.C.
Je - sus.
2.
G
Chorus
Je - sus. My
3.
G
Je - sus,
F G F/A G
Chorus
Je - sus, Je - sus. My
4.
G F G F/A
Je - sus, Je - sus, Je -
G F/A G/B C
sus, Je - sus. I am free, all hon-
G B♭
- our and praise to the King,
1.
F
to the King of all kings, I am free
2.
F C
King of all kings. I am free.

1209 For riches of salvation *Give thanks*

Words: Martin E. Leckebusch

Music: Susie Hare

FROYLE 75 75 777 7

Brightly
G G/B C Bm7 Am7 D
1. For rich - es of sal - va - tion give thanks to the Lord; re -
Am7 D C Am7 D G
lease from con - dem - na - tion, give thanks to the Lord; for
Bm7 Em Am7 D
love which tru - ly frees us be - cause the Fa - ther sees us i -
G B/F# Em C#m7b5 G/D D7
den - ti - fied with Je - sus – give thanks, give thanks to the Lord!

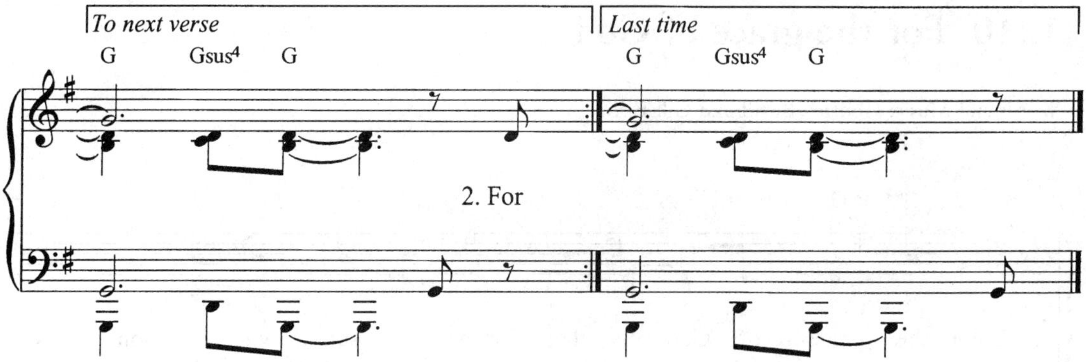

2. For courage and endurance
give thanks to the Lord;
the Spirit's reassurance,
give thanks to the Lord;
for fatherly correction,
the call to share perfection,
the hope of resurrection –
give thanks, give thanks to the Lord!

3. For life in all its fullness
give thanks to the Lord;
for all that leads to wholeness,
give thanks to the Lord;
he knows our ev'ry feeling
and speaks in grace, revealing
his comfort and his healing –
give thanks, give thanks to the Lord!

4. For justice with compassion
give thanks to the Lord;
and freedom from oppression,
give thanks to the Lord;
for holiness unending,
a kingdom still extending,
all earthly pow'r transcending –
give thanks, give thanks to the Lord!

1210 For the grace of God

Words and Music: Godfrey Birtill and Gill Birtill

G D/F#
1. For the grace of God that brings sal - va - tion has
Em C G
come for ev-'ry-one in ev - 'ry na - tion, and it teach-es us to say
D/F# Em C
no to all un - god - li - ness. And the
G D/F# Em
peace of God beats all un - der-stand - ing, re - new-ing our minds, free
C G D/F#
from en-tang - ling, and it teach - es us to be still in all our

Em C Chorus G
bu - sy - ness. While we wait
wait,
C G C2
for the bles - sed hope, for the glo - ri - ous ap-
we can rest as - sured of the glo - ri - ous ap-
Em7 C2 Am7 1. D
pear - ing of our great God and Sa - viour. While we
pear - ing of our great God and
Last time 2.
D G D G
Sa - viour. Sa - viour.
Gsus2 G Gsus2
2. For the

G D/F♯ Em
love of God, be - yond all mea - sure, pours in - to our hearts the joy
C G D/F♯
of hea - ven, and it teach - es us to add faith to see his
Em C G
king - dom come. And the pow'r of God at work
D/F♯ Em C
with - in us is great-er than a - ny force of e - vil, and it
G D/F♯ Em C
teach-es us to press in and to stand, stand strong. While we
Chorus D.S.

The eternal God is your refuge,
and underneath are the everlasting arms.
He will drive out your enemy before you,
saying, 'Destroy him!'

Deuteronomy 33:27

1211 For the life of the world

Words and Music: David Haas

Chorus
C/E F G C Em7 F C/E Am7
Capo 3 A/C# D E A C#m7 D A/C# F#m7
For the life of the world, we will stand to - ge-ther,
Dm7 G C/E F G C Em7
Bm7 E A/C# D E A C#m7
we will serve the Lord. For the life of the world,
F C/E D D/F# G C/E F Dm7 Gsus4 G
D A/C# B B/D# E A/C# D Bm7 Esus4 E
we will cry for jus - tice, and ev-'ry heart will sing that Je - sus Christ is
C Em7
A C#m7
Lord!
To continue
F Gsus4 G
D Esus4 E
Last time
F Gsus4 G C
D Esus4 E A
Fine

B♭ F/A C
G D/F# A
1. We walk to - ge - ther to be child - ren of light,
B♭ F/A Gsus4 G
G D/F# Esus4 E
our God calls each of us by name!
B♭ F/A C
G D/F# A
Christ moves with - in us; we are God's work of art!
B♭ F Gsus4 G
G D Esus4 E
D.C.
We live no long - er for our - selves.

2. We are empowered by the love of Christ,
whose life has conquered sin and death!
There is no other name but Jesus the Lord!
We live no longer for ourselves!

3. The lost and broken will be healed from their shame,
the poor will see the face of God!
Sent by the Spirit we are called to serve!
We live no longer for ourselves!

1212 For the Lord is good

Words and Music: Lynn DeShazo and Gary Sadler

Brightly
Chorus
D E A
For the Lord is good, and his love
D E A D E
endures for e - ver; he's a faith - ful God
F♯m Dsus2 Esus4 E
to all gen - er - a - tions. For the Lord
D E A D E
is good, and his mer - cies will not fail
A D E F♯m
us; they are new each day. O, lift

D E A Dsus2
your voice and say, 'The Lord is good!'
Last time
To continue
F#m E A A D/A E/A
Leader:
Great is your faith - ful - ness, O Lord.
A D/A E/A A
All:
Great is your faith - ful - ness, O Lord.
Leader:
Your lov - ing - kind-
D/A Bm7 E A
- ness fills our hearts to o - ver - flow - ing.
All:
Leader:
Songs of re - joic-
D/A E/A F#m Dsus2
- ing and sweet praise, songs of praise!
All:
Leader:
They fill our hearts,
All:
they fill
E
our hearts, they fill our days.
D.S.
For the Lord

1213 From everlasting *Everlasting*

Words and Music: Brian Doerksen and Matt Unruh

(♩ = 136)
A Chorus
E/G♯
From e - ver - last - ing
to e - ver - last -

D
- ing
you
are

A
God;
from e - ver - last -

E/G♯
- ing
to e - ver - last - ing

3rd time to Bridge
Last time to Coda
D
A
you are God.
D/A
A
Verse
E
1. In ho - li - ness you stand
2. In faith - ful - ness your love
E/B
Bm7
se - cure through cul - ture's shift - ing sands,
ex - tends through times of tur - bu - lence,
A
E
un - changed by all the va -
a - dopt - ing those who call
E/B
D2
- ni - ties of man; and
up - on your name; and

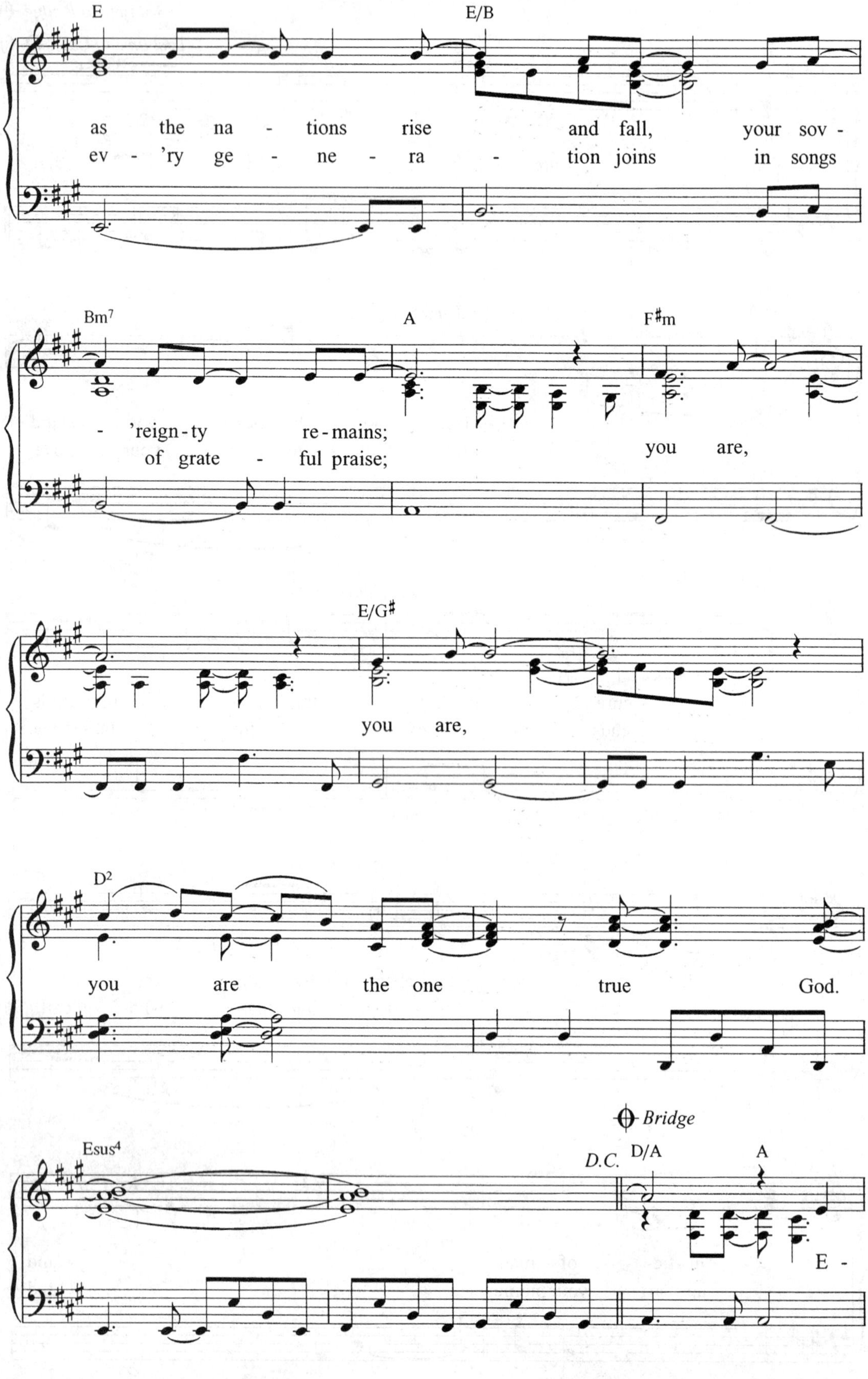
E
E/B
as the na - tions rise and fall, your sov -
ev - 'ry ge - ne - ra - tion joins in songs
Bm7
A
F#m
- 'reign - ty re - mains;
of grate - ful praise;
you are,
E/G#
you are,
D2
you are the one true God.
Bridge
Esus4
D.C.
D/A
A
E -

A
E/G♯
ter - nal, im - mor - tal,
D²
in - vi - si - ble
1, 2.
3.
A
D/A
A
D/A
A
D.C. al Coda
God. E -
CODA
D
A
You are God,
D/A
A
D
A
you are God.

1214 From the heights of glory *What a gift*

Words and Music: Susie Hare

Unhurried
Capo 3
B♭2 F/A Gm7 Dm/F E♭ B♭/D
G2 D/F♯ Em7 Bm/D C G/B
1. From the heights of glo - ry, to a hum - ble birth, the Lord of hea - ven came
Cm7 F7sus4 F7 B♭2 F/A Gm7 Dm7
Am7 D7sus4 D7 G2 D/F♯ Em7 Bm7
down to earth. And the great - est sto - ry that is known to man, in a
Cm7 Dm7 E♭maj7 E♭/F B♭ B♭/D E♭ F
Am7 Bm7 Cmaj7 C/D G G/B C D
Chorus
sta - ble room be - gan. What a gift, what a gift we are
B♭ B♭/D Cm7 F F/A B♭ B♭/D
G G/B Am7 D D/F♯ G G/B
giv - en; sac - ri - fice of the Fa - ther for us. What a
E♭ F7 D7/F♯ Gm Cm7 E♭maj7 E♭/F
C D7 B7/D♯ Em Am7 Cmaj7 C/D
gift, what a gift we are giv - en; King of kings, Lord of lords, Je -

To next verse
Last time
B♭ N.C. B♭ B♭/D E♭ F
G D.S. G G/B C D
sus! 2. From a sus! What a hope, what a hope we are
B♭ B♭/D Cm7 F F/A B♭ B♭/D
G G/B Am7 D D/F♯ G G/B
giv-en; sac-ri-fice of the Fa-ther for us. What a
E♭ F D/F♯ D7/F♯ Gm Cm7 E♭maj7 E♭/F
C D B/D♯ B7/D♯ Em Am7 Cmaj7 C/D
song to pro-claim: 'He is ri - sen! King of kings, Lord of lords, Je -
B♭ Gm7 Cm7 E♭maj7 E♭/F B♭
G Em7 Am7 Cmaj7 C/D G
sus! King of kings, Lord of lords, Je - sus!'

2. From a humble stable, to a world of shame,
the friend of sinners, who calls my name
brought the love of heaven to the hearts of men
and it gave lives hope again.

3. From a life, so perfect, to a cruel cross,
the world's redemption, the Father's loss;
and the nails were driven and the blood flowed free
in the hands outstretched for me.

4. From the grave he's risen, ever glorified,
to take his place at his Father's side;
and the greatest glory will be ours to own
when he comes to take us home.

1215 From the rising of the sun

Words and Music: Paul Deming

With a swing feel (♩ = 138)
Capo 1
Verse
Ab2/Bb G2/A
Eb D
From the rising of the sun,
from the rising of the sun to the going down
Eb/D D/C# Cm9 Bm9 Cm/Bb Bm/A Fm7 Em7 Fm7/Ab Em7/G Bb A Bb13 A13
of the same, the Lord's name is to be praised.
Eb D Ab G Ab2/Bb G2/A Eb D
From the rising of the sun,
from the rising of the sun to the going down
Eb/D D/C# Cm9 Bm9 Cm/Bb Bm/A
of the same, the Lord's name

Fm7 Fm7/A♭ B♭ B♭13 E♭ Fm7 F♯dim E♭/G E♭
Em7 Em7/G A A13 D Em7 Fdim D/F♯ D
is to be praised.
Chorus
A♭ A♭/E♭ A♭ E♭/G Fm7 E♭
G G/D G D/F♯ Em7 D
Praise ye the Lord, praise him, all ye ser-vants of the
G A♭ Fm7 Gm7/B♭ B♭13 B♭ E♭ E♭/B♭
F♯ G Em7 F♯m7/A A13 A D D/A
Lord, praise the name of the Lord.
E♭9 E♭ E♭/F E♭/G A♭ A♭/E♭ A♭ E♭/G Fm7
D9 D D/E D/F♯ G G/D G D/F♯ Em7
Bles-sed be the name of the Lord,
E♭ G A♭ Fm7 Gm7/B♭ B♭13 B♭ E♭
D F♯ G Em7 F♯m7/A A13 A D
from this time forth and for e - ver - more.

1216 From the squalor of a borrowed stable *Immanuel*

Words and Music: Stuart Townend

With a 'celtic' feel
Domit3
Bm
1. From the squa-lor of a bor-rowed sta - ble, by the Spi-rit and a
Em7 D/G A7sus4
Domit3
vir - gin's faith; to the an-guish and the shame of scan - dal
Bm
A7sus4
Domit3
came the Sa-viour of the hu - man race! But the
D/F#
G
D
skies were filled with the praise of heav'n, shep-herds lis - ten as the

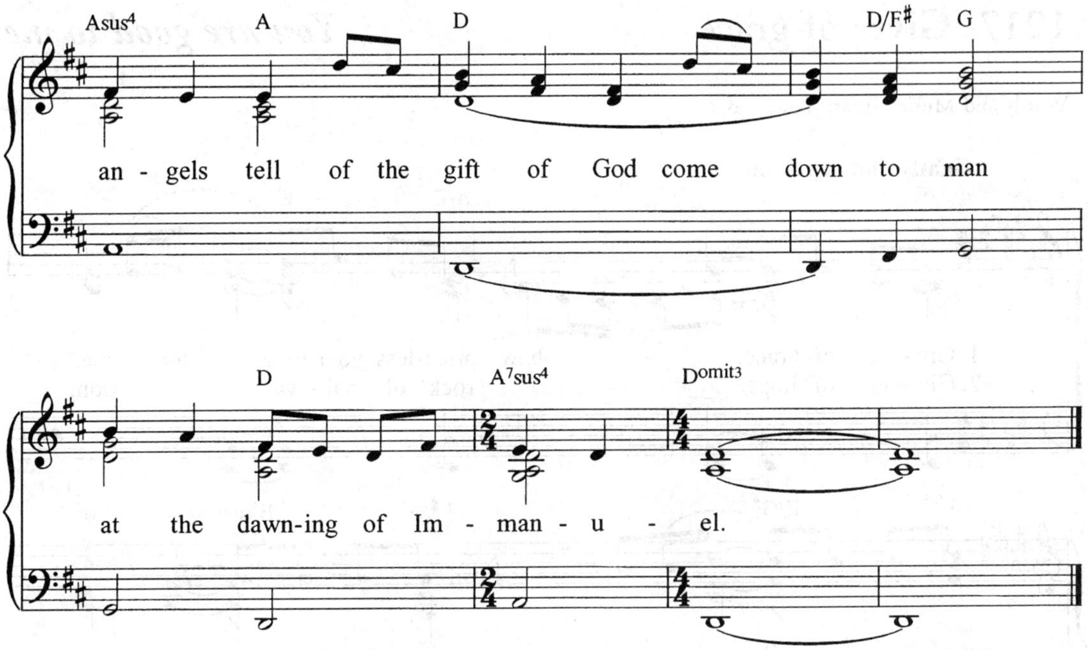
Asus4 A D D/F# G
an - gels tell of the gift of God come down to man
D A7sus4 Domit3
at the dawn-ing of Im - man - u - el.

2. King of heaven now the friend of sinners,
humble servant in the Father's hands,
filled with power and the Holy Spirit,
filled with mercy for the broken man.
Yes, he walked my road and he felt my pain,
joys and sorrows that I know so well;
yet his righteous steps give me hope again –
I will follow my Immanuel!

3. Through the kisses of a friend's betrayal,
he was lifted on a cruel cross;
he was punished for a world's transgressions,
he was suffering to save the lost.
He fights for breath, he fights for me,
loosing sinners from the claims of hell;
and with a shout our souls are free -
death defeated by Immanuel!

4. Now he's standing in the place of honour,
crowned with glory on the highest throne,
interceding for his own belovèd
till his Father calls to bring them home!
Then the skies will part as the trumpet sounds
hope of heaven or the fear of hell;
but the Bride will run to her Lover's arms,
giving glory to Immanuel!

1217 Giver of grace *You are good to me*

Words and Music: Stuart Townend

B E A F#m7 B C#m7
good to me. Oh, you are good, so good to me. Yes, you are
A F#m7 B E
Fine
good, so good to me.
Bm7 A E B
I've ne-ver known a love so per-fect in its faith - ful-ness;
D A A/E E A
it lifts me up to the high - est place.
Bm7 A E B
A glimpse of hea-ven and a taste of my in - he - ri-tance,
D A B7sus4 B7
D.C. al Fine
I know that one day I'll be with you.

1218 Giver of life

Words and Music: Tim Hughes

(v.2)
Gm7
Capo 3 Em7
F/A
D/F♯
B♭2
G2
1. Giv - er of life, you ne - ver change, all that is per -
new ev - 'ry day; your mer -
E♭
C
Gm7
Em7
F/A
D/F♯
- fect comes from you, your won - ders ne - ver cease.
- cies will ne-ver fail, so great is your faith - ful - ness.
E♭
C
Gm7
Em7
Not e - ven life,
Your love is kind,
F/A
D/F♯
B♭2
G2
E♭
C
not e - ven death, nor a - ny pow'r in hea - ven or earth
your love is pure, your love will al - ways per - se - vere,

Gm7 Em7 F/A D/F# E♭ C
could se - pa-rate us from your love.
for ev - 'ry bles - sing comes from you.
Chorus
E♭ C F D
For you are good, and your mer-
Dm Bm Gm7 Em7 E♭ C
- cies last a life - time, you are good,
F D Dm Bm Gm7 Em7 E♭ C
al - ways, al - ways. Ev-'ry day,
F D Dm Bm Gm7 Em7
your love is ne - ver - end - ing, for you are good,

E♭ C F D Dm Bm
1.
al - ways, al - ways.
Gm7 Em7 D.S.
2, 3. Dm Bm E♭ C Fine
2. Free - ly you give, al - ways.
Gm Em Bridge F D
You de - light to pour your good - ness down.
E♭ C Gm Em
You de - light to
C/E A/C♯ E♭ C Chorus D.S.S. al Fine
pour your good - ness down. For you are good,

1219 Glory and gratitude and praise

Words and Music: John L. Bell

1220 Glory to him who has saved us *We crown you now*

Words and Music: Lara Martin and Mark Stevens (Abundant Life Ministries, Bradford, England)

A2
E2
Glo - ry to him who has saved us and
A2
E2
freed us from sin by his blood.
F♯m7
Bsus4
B
G♯m7
A
Je - sus the ra - di-ance of God, the
F♯m7
A
Bsus4
1.
B
glo - ry of the Fa - ther in us.

2, 3.
Chorus
B E/G♯ A Bsus4
We crown you now with wor - ship and hon - our,
B E/G♯ A Bsus4
King of kings, Lord of lords, there's no o - ther.
B A/C♯ F♯m7
Ho - ly, ho - ly, God al - migh - ty,
A Bsus4 B
1.
D.C.
Je - sus Lord of all.
Last time
2.
B E B A
Fine

C#m
Bsus4
B
You are
A
C#m7
high and lift - ed up,
high and lift - ed up,
A
you are high and lift - ed up,
Son of
1.
2.
E
Bsus4
B
D.S. al Fine
God.
You are God.
We crown you

1221 God holds the key of all unknown

Words: Joseph Parker

Music: George C. Stebbins

PARKER 84 884 extended

2. What if tomorrow's cares were here
without its rest!
I'd rather he unlocked the day,
and, as the hours swing open, say,
my will is best.

3. I cannot read his future plans;
but this I know:
I have the smiling of his face
and all the refuge of his grace
while here below.

4. Enough; this covers all my wants
and so I rest;
for what I cannot, he can see
and in his care I saved shall be
for ever blest.

1222 God is good

Words and Music: Russ Hughes

E/G#
thank you, Je - sus; thank you, thank you, thank you, Je - sus;
F#m
D
thank you, thank you Lord, for lov - ing me.'
A/C#
Bm7 D/E
A
Yes, I sing: 'Thank you, thank you, thank you, Je - sus, the
E/G#
F#m
love you bring it comes and frees us; thank you, thank you,
1.
D
Lord, for lov - ing me.'
2.
D
A
'For lov - ing me.'

I will proclaim the name of the Lord.
Oh, praise the greatness of our God!
He is the Rock, his works are perfect,
and all his ways are just.
A faithful God who does no wrong,
upright and just is he.

Deuteronomy 32:3-4

1223 God is so good

Words and Music: Traditional

GOD IS SO GOOD Irregular

2. He cares for me,
he cares for me,
he cares for me,
he's so good to me!

3. I love him so,
I love him so,
I love him so,
he's so good to me!

4. I praise his name,
I praise his name,
I praise his name,
he's so good to me!

1224 God of glory, God of wonder *Dwelling-place*

Words and Music: Tommy Walker

God of glo - ry, God of won - der, God of beau - ty, you reign through all e - ter - ni - ty. Be-fore the moun - tains or the earth had been formed you were our e - ver-last - ing Lord. You've been our home, you've been our shel - ter safe for young and old to ge-ne-

A E A D/A D A/C# Bm7 A
G D G C/G C G/B Am7 G
ra-tions past; we stand in awe of a God so great; we stand in
E B/D# B#dim7 C#m7 F#
D A/C# A#dim7 Bm7 E
thanks for your faith - ful-ness. O
1, 2.
A B2 B7 Esus4 B7
G A2 A7 Dsus4 A7
Lord, you've been our dwel - ling - place. God of
Last time
C#m E/F# F# A Bsus4 G#/B# C#m E/F# F#
Bm D/E E G Asus4 F#/A# Bm D/E E
place. O Lord, you've been our dwel - ling - place, O
A E/B B Esus4 E/G# A B7 E
G D/A A Dsus4 D/F# G A7 D
Lord, you've been our dwel - ling-place.

Speak to one another
with psalms, hymns and spiritual songs.
Sing and make music in your heart to the Lord,
always giving thanks to God the Father for everything,
in the name of our Lord Jesus Christ.

Ephesians 5:19-20

1225 God of grace

Words and Music: Keith Getty and Jonathan Rea

A7 D D/F# Gmaj7 D/F# Em A7 D A7
1. God of grace, a-maz-ing won-der, ir-re-sis-ti-ble and free. Oh, the
D D/F# Gmaj7 D/F# Em A7 D A7
mi-ra-cle of mer-cy; Je-sus reach-es down to me. God of
D D/F# G D/F# G2 Bm Em7 Asus4 A A7
grace, I stand in won-der, as my God re-stores my soul: his own
D D/F# Gmaj7 D/F# Em A7 D
blood has paid my ran-som; awe-some cost to make me whole.

2. God of grace, who loved and knew me
long before the world began;
sent my Saviour down from heaven:
perfect God and perfect man.
God of grace, I trust in Jesus,
I'm accepted as his own.
Ev'ry day new grace sustains me,
as I lean on him alone.

3. God of grace, I stand astounded,
cleansed, forgiven and secure.
All my fears are now confounded
and my hope is ever sure.
God of grace, now crowned in glory,
where one day I'll see your face;
and forever I'll adore you
in your everlasting grace.

1226 God of holiness *Glorious one*

Words and Music: Ken Riley

Steadily
D A
1. God of ho - li-ness, God of faith, God of
D A Bm7
right-eous-ness, God of grace, God of all I am,
D F#m7 D Bm7
ev - 'ry - thing, how I long to gaze up - on your shin - ing
E Chorus D E
face. Beau-ti - ful Sa - viour, glo - ri - ous
A F#m7 D E
one, awe-some in splen - dour, won-der - ful

2. God of purity, God of might,
God of mystery, clothed in light.
Through eternity we will sing
heaven's song of love unto our glorious King.

1227 God of restoration

I am yours

Words and Music: Matt Redman

A E/G♯ Bsus4 B
to-day and ev-'ry day. I am
E B2/D♯ A/C♯
yours, I am yours, ev-'ry breath that I breathe, ev-'ry
B/D♯ E B2/D♯
mo-ment that's lived. I am yours, I am yours, you're the
A/C♯ Last time to Coda B/D♯ B
rea-son to breathe, you're the rea-son to live. And now ev-'ry-one that you
C♯/E♯ A E/G♯ Bsus4 B
have saved will come to be your praise, I am
1. E B/D♯ A/C♯ E B/D♯ A/C♯ D.C.
yours.

2.
E
A
yours. And if my food is to do your will,
E/G#
B
E/G#
then I'm hun - gry, still hun - gry; there's so much more
1.
A
E/G#
B
that I need to give to thank you, to thank
2.
E/G#
E/G#
A
E/G#
Bsus4
you. Yes, if my food to - day and ev-'ry day.
CODA
B
D.S. al Coda
B/D#
E
I am rea-son to live, I'm yours.

I will pour out my Spirit on all people.
Your sons and daughters will prophesy,
your old men will dream dreams,
your young men will see visions.
Even on my servants, both men and women,
I will pour out my Spirit in those days.

Joel 2:28, 29

1228 Great and mighty

Words and Music: Nicola Rodgers

Great and migh - ty, you are wor - thy. Ho - ly God, we come to bow be - fore you, sing your prai - ses, raise your name a - bove the earth. For you are al - migh - ty, our sov-'reign Sa - viour; so wor - thy

A G F#m7 Em7 G#sus4 F#sus4 G# F# Chorus
of glory, we raise you high. Ho-
Amaj7 Gmaj7 B A C#m Bm B A
sanna! We extol your glorious name,
A G G#m7 F#m7 F#m7 Em7 G#m7 F#m7
we cry hosanna! Let the
C#m Bm B A A G G#m7 F#m7 F#m7 Em7 G#m7 F#m7
earth groan with the praises of our God, our God and
C#m Bm A G F#m7 Em7 G#m7 F#m7 C#m Bm
King.

Come, let us bow down in worship,
let us kneel before the Lord our Maker;
for he is our God
and we are the people of his pasture,
the flock under his care.

Psalm 95:6-7

1229 Great God of wonders!

Words: Samuel Davies, alt. Music: Henry Carey

SURREY 88 88 and Refrain

2. Pardon from an offended God!
Pardon for sins of deepest dye!
Pardon bestowed through Jesus' blood!
Pardon that brings the rebel nigh!

3. O may this glorious, matchless love,
this God-like miracle of grace,
teach mortal tongues, like those above,
to raise this song of lofty praise:

1230 Great is the Lord God Almighty *Glory*

Words and Music: Reuben Morgan

G2
D/F#
E2
E
glo - ry to the Son, glo-ri-ous
G2
D
Son. Lift up your heads, o-pen the
Bm
doors, let the King of glo-ry come in and for -
G2
Bm
Asus4
e - ver be our God.
1.
2.
A
A
D
2. Ho-ly is the

1231 Great is your faithfulness *Unchanging*

Words and Music: Chris Tomlin

With praise
F Fmaj7 F6 F Fmaj7 F6 B♭ B♭(♮4) B♭
Capo 3 D Dmaj7 D6 D Dmaj7 D6 G G(♮4) G
1. Great is your faith-ful - ness, great is your faith-ful - ness.
2. True are your pro - mi - ses, true are your pro - mi - ses.
3. Wide is your love and grace, wide is your love and grace.
B♭(♮4) B♭ C B♭
G(♮4) G A G
You ne - ver change, you ne - ver fail, O God.
1. 2, 3.
F Fmaj7 F6 F Fmaj7 F6 F
D Dmaj7 D6 D Dmaj7 D6 D
Chorus
So, we raise
Dm7 F B♭
Bm7 D G
up ho - ly hands to praise the ho - ly one;

Dm7 Bm7
B♭ G
C A
who was and is, and is to come.
F D
Dm7 Bm7
Yeah, we raise up ho - ly hands
F D
B♭ G
Dm7 Bm7
to praise the ho - ly one; who was,
B♭ G
C A
Last time to Coda
F D
D.C.
and is, and is to come.
Dm7 Bm7
B♭ G
F/A D/F♯
Csus4 Asus4

Dm7
Bm7
B♭
G
F/A
D/F♯
You were, you are, you will al - ways be.
Csus4
Asus4
Dm7
Bm7
B♭
G
You were, you are,
CODA
F/A
D/F♯
Csus4
Asus4
D.S. al Coda
F
D
you will al - ways be. So, we raise

Therefore go and make disciples of all nations,
baptising them in the name of the Father
and of the Son and of the Holy Spirit,
and teaching them to obey
everything I have commanded you.
And surely I am with you always,
to the very end of the age.

Matthew 28:19-20

1232 Hallelujah, for the Lord our God

Hallelujah, our God reigns

Words and Music: Dale Garratt

Triumphantly
Capo 3
F D Bb G F D Dm Bm
Hal-le-lu-jah, for the Lord our God the Al-
F/C D/A C A F D
1.
migh-ty reigns. Hal-le-
2.
F D F7 D7 Bb G
reigns. Let us re-joice and be
F D G7 E7
glad and give the glo-ry un-to

C7 A7 F D
him. Hal - le - lu - jah,
B♭ G F D Dm Bm
for the Lord our God the Al -
F/C D/A C7 A7 F D
migh - ty reigns.

1233 Hallelujah, there will be no other

There will be no other

Words and Music: Matt Redman

G
Gaug
Em7
Hal - le - lu - jah, there will be no o-ther, hal - le - lu - jah,
Asus4
G
Gaug
there will be no o-ther, hal - le - lu - jah, there will be no o-ther,
Em7
Asus4
G
there will be no o-ther but you. In the north and in the south, ev-'ry
Gaug
Em7
cor - ner of the globe, for the weak and for the strong, with the
Asus4
G
young and with the old, on and on your prai - ses run. It's an

Gaug
Em7
e - ver - last - ing song.
There will be no o - ther but you.
Asus4
G
Your song will be heard in all of the earth,
Asus4
G
Fine
you will have your praise.
G
Gaug
Em7
Hal - le - lu - jah, there will be no o - ther, hal - le - lu - jah,
Asus4
G
Gaug
there will be no o - ther, hal - le - lu - jah, there will be no o - ther,
1.
2.
Em7
Asus4
Asus4
D.S. al Fine
there will be no o - ther but you.

1234 Hark! the voice of love and mercy

Words: Jonathan Evans and in this version Jubilate Hymns

Music: Henry Smart;
last verse arrangement and descant John Barnard

REGENT SQUARE 87 87 87

Capo 3 G
1. Hark! the voice of love and mer-cy sounds a-loud from Cal-va-ry;
2. Fi-nished all the types and sha-dows of the ce-re-mo-nial law;
see, it tears the tem-ple cur-tain, shakes the earth and veils the sky:
God ful-fils what he has pro-mised: death and hell shall reign no more:
'It is fi-nished, it is fi-nished!' hear the dy-ing Sa-viour cry.
'It is fi-nished, it is fi-nished!' Christ has o-pened hea-ven's door.
Descant
3. Saints and an-gels shout his prai-ses, his great fi-nished work pro-claim;
Unison

Gm/D D Gm D Gm B♭maj7/C C7 F
Em/B B Em B Em Gmaj7/A A7 D
all on earth and all in hea - ven join to bless Em - ma-nuel's name:
B♭ B♭7 E♭ G7/D Cm Ddim7 Cm/E♭ Gm Fsus4 F B♭
G G7 C E7/B Am Bdim7 Am/C Em Dsus4 D G
'Al - le - lu - ia, al - le - lu - ia, end-less glo - ry to the Lamb!'

1235 Have mercy on me

Words and Music: Graham Kendrick

(♩ = 110)
Em Am/E Em Am/E Em
Have mer-cy on me, O God (have mer-cy on me, O God), and
D Em Am/E
hear my prayer. Have
Em Am/E Em Am/E Em
mer-cy on me, O God (have mer-cy on me, O God), and
D C
hear my prayer.
Em D/E Em D/E

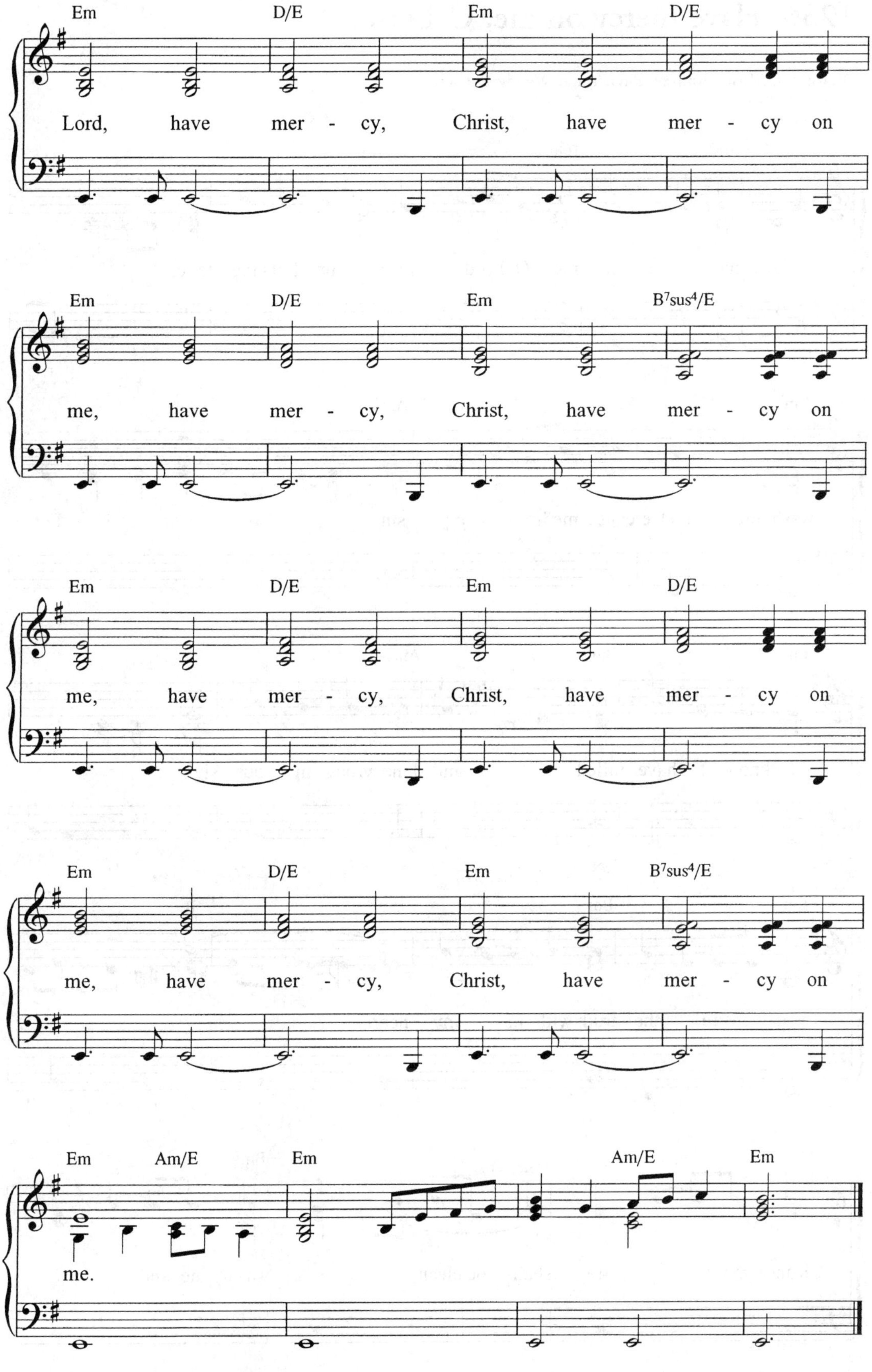
Em D/E Em D/E
Lord, have mer - cy, Christ, have mer - cy on
Em D/E Em B7sus4/E
me, have mer - cy, Christ, have mer - cy on
Em D/E Em D/E
me, have mer - cy, Christ, have mer - cy on
Em D/E Em B7sus4/E
me, have mer - cy, Christ, have mer - cy on
Em Am/E Em Am/E Em
me.

1236 Have mercy on me, O Lord

Words and Music: Andrew Rayner and Wendy Rayner

Em7
Bm7
Am7
Have mer-cy on me, O Lord, in your un-fail-ing love,
Em7
Bm7
Am7
wash me and cleanse me from my sin. For
Em7
Bm7
Am7
I know I have failed and done wrong in your sight,
Em7
Bm7
Bsus4
B
you de-sire the truth with-in my heart.
Cmaj7
Bm7
Cleanse me and I shall be clean, wash me and I

Am7
will be new, for - give me and my soul will re -
Bsus4
B
Cmaj7
joice. Cre - ate in me a
Bm7
pure heart, keep me in your pre - sence, re -
Am7
Bm7
Em7
new your Ho - ly Spi - rit with - in me.
Am7
Bm7
Em7

1237 Have you not known *Eagles' wings*

Words and Music: Steve James

(♩ = 154)
A D E A D E
A
1. Have you not known there's an e - ver-last - ing
2. Lift your eyes and see his vast e - ter - ni -
F#m C#m E
God? O give thanks, O give thanks to the Lord!
ty: O give thanks, O give thanks to the Lord!
Bm F#7/B
Have you not heard, he is
Like the stars, he knows our name, by his
Bm F#7/B Bm
Lord of all the earth? O give
pow - er we re - main. O give

D/E A D E
thanks to the Lord! The
thanks to the Lord! For
A
wa - ters and the land are in the hol-low of his hand.
all that he has done, our sal - va-tion he has won.
F♯m C♯m E
O give thanks, O give thanks to the Lord!
D E/D C♯m
For he is the one who makes the wea-ry
F♯m A/E Dmaj7 D/E A D/E
strong: let our joy in the Lord be our song!

Chorus
A A/C♯ D
We will run and not grow wea - ry in the race,
B B/D♯ E
we will rise up on ea-gles' wings and soar be-fore his face;
C♯ C♯/E♯ F♯m
he is God, and he has saved us by his
B7/D♯ A/E E7 A
grace. Hal-le - lu - jah, he is God!
D E A D E A
D.S.

Salvation is found in no one else,
for there is no other name under heaven given to men
by which we must be saved.

Acts 4:12

1238 Healer, heal me

Words and Music: Lamont Hiebert

(♩= 88)
G C Em7 Dsus4
G C Em7 Dsus4
1. Heal - er,
G C2 Em7
heal me; Sa - viour, save me;
Dsus G C2
Ma - ker, change me; Lov - er,
Em7 Dsus4 G
love me; 'cause I'm so tired of liv-ing for

C2
Em7
2nd time to Dsus4
the kind of love that on - ly lasts for a while;
G
C2
Em7
the pain, the shame
Dsus4
Chorus
G
C
tear me up in-side. So I fall on my knees to get back on
Dsus
G
Em7
my feet a-gain; and I cry out for
C
Am7
G
you to hear you speak to me.

C
Em7
Dsus4
G
C
Em7
Dsus4
D.S.
2. Heal - er,
Dsus4
G
C2
- ly comes and goes;
but your love,
your love
Em7
Dsus4
Chorus
lasts for e - ver.
So I
G
C
Dsus4
fall
on my knees
to get back on
my feet

G Em7 C
a-gain; and I cry out for you to
Am7 G
hear you speak to me. Yes, I fall on my
C Dsus4 G
knees to get back on my feet a-gain; and I
Em7 C Am7 G
run hard for you to en - ter your rest.
C Em7 Dsus4 G

1239 Heal me, O Lord

Words and Music: Don Moen

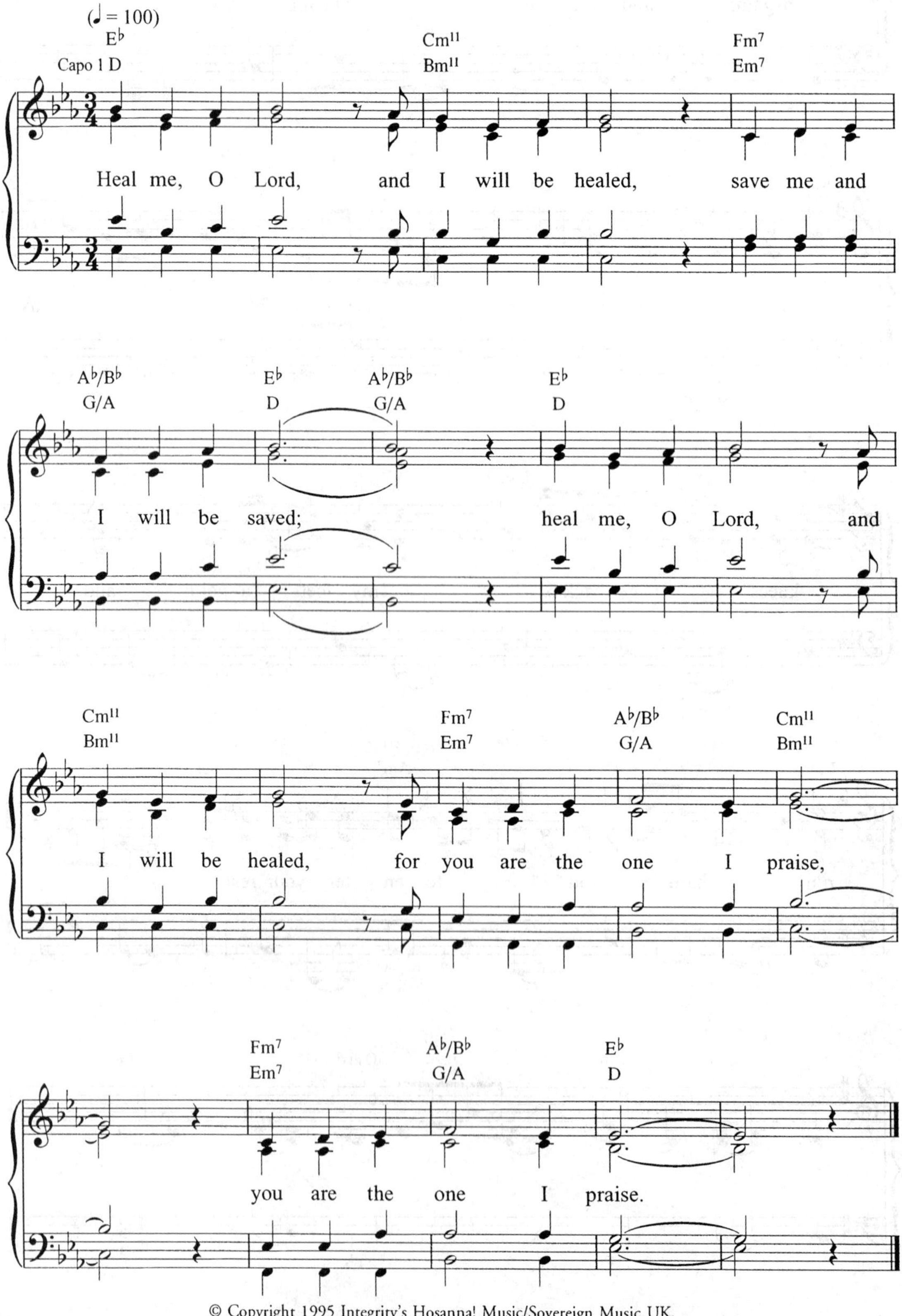
(♩ = 100)
Capo 1 D
E♭ D
Cm11 Bm11
Fm7 Em7
A♭/B♭ G/A
Heal me, O Lord, and I will be healed, save me and
I will be saved; heal me, O Lord, and
I will be healed, for you are the one I praise,
you are the one I praise.

1240 Hear all creation

Words and Music: Margaret Becker and Keith Getty

Brightly
Capo 3
E♭ A♭/E♭ B♭/E♭ A♭maj7/E♭
C F/C G/C Fmaj7/C
1. Hear all cre - a - tion lift its voice, the
mends our hearts, he keeps our ways: he
E♭ A♭/E♭ B♭/E♭ E♭ E♭maj7/G
C F/C G/C C Cmaj7/E
moun - tains sing and the ri - vers re - joice for the
lights our nights and he leads our days, all
A♭ E♭
F C
name of Je - sus, for his name.
for his glo - ry, for his name.
A♭/E♭ E♭ A♭/E♭ B♭/E♭ A♭maj7/E♭
F/C C F/C G/C Fmaj7/C
And we his peo - ple saved by grace, we
There's no-thing great - er than to be his, to

E♭ A♭/E♭ B♭/E♭ A♭maj7/E♭
C F/C G/C Fmaj7/C
bow our hearts and we bring our praise to the
bring him glo - ry and to ful - ly live for the
A♭ E♭
F C
sweet Re - deem - er, for his name.
name of Je - sus, for his name.
Chorus
Cm7 E♭/G Cm7 E♭/G
Am7 C/E Am7 C/E
So with ev-'ry-thing we are, and ev-'ry-thing we have we
A♭ A♭/B♭ B♭ E♭ E♭/G A♭ B♭
F F/G G C C/E F G
pour out our of - fer - ings. And if e - ver we should fail, the

Cm7 Am7 E♭/G C/E A♭ F A♭/B♭ F/G B♭ G E♭ C A♭/E♭ F/C
rocks will rise up and crown him the King of kings.
B♭/E♭ G/C A♭/E♭ F/C
1.
E♭ C A♭/E♭ F/C
B♭/E♭ G/C A♭/E♭ F/C
2. He
2.
B♭/E♭ G/C A♭/E♭ F/C A♭/E♭ F/C E♭ C

1241 Hear the sound

We speak to nations

Words and Music: Israel Houghton

(♩= 72)
G² A/G G² A/G G
1. Hear the sound,
2. Hear the sound,
Am⁷ C² C/D
the sound of the na - tions cal - ling;
the sound of the na - tions wor - ship-ping;
G Am⁷
hear the sound, the sound of the fa -
hear the sound, of sons and daugh -
C² C/D C/E D/F♯
- ther-less cry - ing; who will go for us,
- ters sing - ing; we will go for you,
G C/E D/F♯ Am/G
who will shout to the cor -
we will shout to the cor -

1.
G Am/G G F Dsus4 D
-ners of the earth that Christ is King?
-ners of the earth that Christ is King.
2, 3.
Dsus4 D
Chorus
G G/D C
We speak to na - tions, be o-pen;
G G/D C G/B
we speak to na - tions, fall on your knees; we speak to na - tions, the
C Am/E G Am7 Am7/D
king-dom is com - ing near to you; oh,
G G/D C/D G/D
we speak to na - tions, be bro-ken; pow-ers of dark - ness,

C
G/B
C
Am/E
G
Am7
you have to flee;
we speak to na - tions,
the king-dom is com - ing near
Am7/D
G/C
1.
to you;
we speak to you,
be free,
yeah;
G2
be free.
2.
D.S.
G/C
yeah;
E♭maj7
G
be free,
yeah;
be free!

1242 He is high and exalted *High and exalted*

Words and Music: Kyle Rasmussen

Capo 3
Dm7 Bb2 Dm7 C Bb2
Bm7 G2 Bm7 A G2
He is high and ex-alt - ed and wor - thy of praise, with our hearts
F/A C F/A Bb2
D/F# A D/F# G2
we will love and a- dore; he is high and ex-alt - ed and wor-
Dm7 C Bb C F
Bm7 A G A D
- thy of praise, ho - ly is the Lord.
Fine
Bb C F/A Bb C Dm
G A D/F# G A Bm
Ho - ly, ho - ly, ho - ly is the Lord;
D.S. al Fine
Bb C F/A Bb C Bb/F F Dm7 Bb2
G A D/F# G A G/D D Bm7 G2
ho - ly, ho - ly, ho - ly is the Lord. He is high

1243 He is the King

Words and Music: Tom Ewing, Don Moen and John Stocker

(♩ = 80)
Chorus
G G/B C G/B Am7
He is the King, he is the Lord, he is the one
G Em7 F C/D D G G/B
who de - li - vers me; he is the King, he is the Lord,
C G/B Am7 G/D Em7 Am9 D G C/D D
he is the one who de - li - vers me. Hail to the King,
G G/B C G/B Am7 G Em7
hail to the Lord, hail to the one who de - li - vers

F C/D D G G/B
me; hail to the King, hail to the Lord,
C G/B Am7 G/D Em7 Am9 D G
Fine
hail to the one who de - li - vers me.
Verse
C/D G G/B Am/C Am Bm/D Bm Em Am7 D
Je - sus, strong and migh - ty King, rul - ing o - ver all the king - doms of this
Bm7 Am7 D G G/B Am/C Am Bm/D Bm Em Am7
world; lift your voice to him and sing, he is Lord
Am7/G Fmaj9 Dsus4 D
Chorus D.S. al Fine
of ev - 'ry - thing, he is the King of kings. He is the King,

1244 He is the King of kings

Words and Music: Virgil O. Meares

(♩= 128)
D G C/G G C/G G D G Em7
He is the King of kings, he is the Lord of
Am7 D G G/F C/E C♯dim/E
lords; his name is Je - sus, Je - sus, Je - sus, Je - sus.
Dsus4 D 1. G C G/B Am7 D 2. G
Oh, he is the King. He is the King.

1245 Here I am

Majesty

Words and Music: Stuart Garrard and Martin Smith

Worshipfully, with strength
Gm F E♭ B♭/D
Capo 3 Em D C G/B
1. Here I am, hum-bled by your ma - jes - ty,
hum-bled by the love that you give,
E♭ B♭/D F/A D/F♯
C G/B D/F♯ B/D♯
cov-ered by your grace so free.
for-giv - en so that I can for - give.
Gm F E♭ B♭/D
Em D C G/B
Here I am, know-ing I'm a sin-ful man,
Here I stand, know-ing that I'm your de - sire,
E♭ B♭/D F/A D/F♯
C G/B D/F♯ B/D♯
cov-ered by the blood of the Lamb.
sanc - ti - fied by glo - ry and fire.

Gm F/A B♭ Gm F/A
Em D/F♯ G Em D/F♯
Now I've found the great-est love of all is
B♭ C/E
G A/C♯
mine, since you laid down your life, the great-est sac - ri -
E♭ B♭
C Chorus G
fice. Ma - jes -
Ma - jes -
F Gm7 E♭
D Em7 C
ty, ma - jes - ty. Your
ty, ma - jes - ty. For-
B♭ F
G D
grace has found me just as I am, emp - ty -
e - ver I am changed by your love, in the

Gm
Em
E♭
C
hand - ed but a - live in your hands.
pre - sence of your ma - jes - ty.
1.
2.
Gm F E♭
Em D C
D.S.
B♭
G
2. Here I am,

Hear my voice when I call to you.
May my prayer be set before you like incense.

Psalm 141:1b-2a

1246 Here I stand

Words: John L. Bell, from Revelation 3:20

Music: John L. Bell

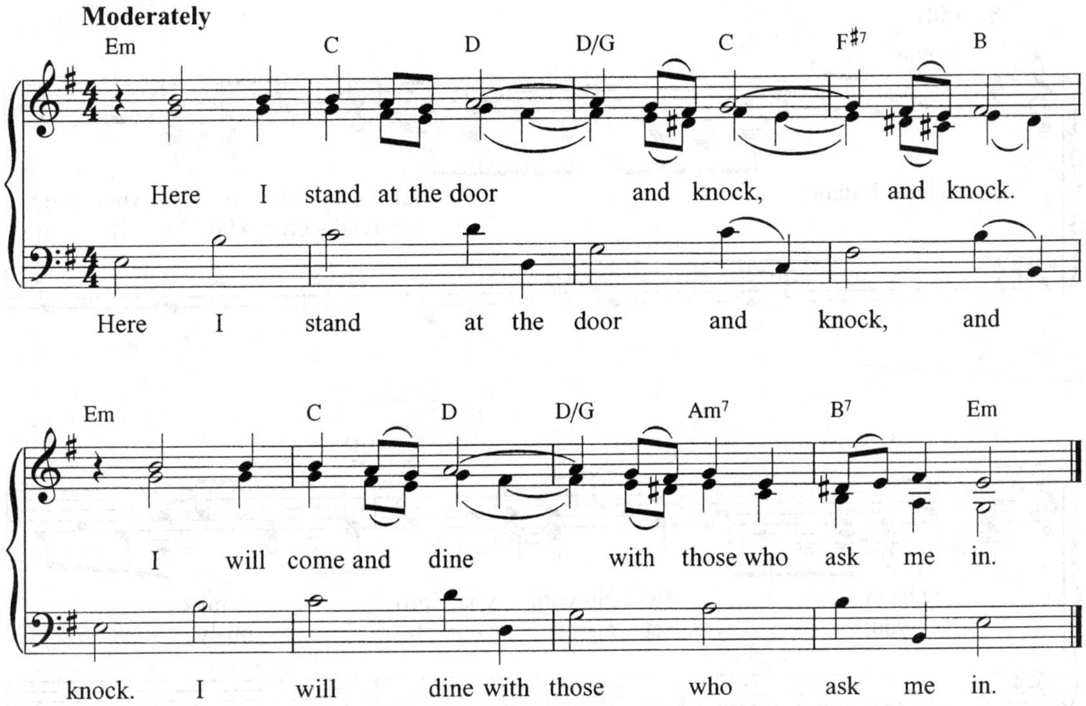

1247 Here I stand

Words and Music: Darlene Zschech

To you

Here I stand, for-e-ver in your migh-
sur-rend-ered whol-ly to

-ty hand, liv-ing with your pro — mise
you, you set me in your fa — mi-ly,

writ-ten on my heart. I am yours,
call-ing me your own.

Now I, I be-long to you, all I need,
I will lift my hands to the King,

D
G
C
your Spi - rit, your word, your truth. Hear my cry, my deep de - si -
this an - them of praise I bring. Hea - ven knows I long to love
1.
Em7
G/F
F
D
- re to know you more. In your name
2.
Em7
Dsus4
Last time to Coda
1.
D
you with all I am: I be - long to you.
C
G
D.C.
Here I stand,
2.
D
D.S.
3.
D
C
In your name I be - long to you.

D
Am7
D
1.
2.
D.S.
Now I,
CODA
D
G
Am7
In your name I will lift my hands to the King,
D
G
C
this an-them of praise I bring. Hea-ven knows I long to love
Em7
Dsus4
D
C
you with all I am, I be-long to you.
1.
G
2.
G

After this I looked
and there before me was a great multitude
that no one could count,
from every nation, tribe, people and language,
standing before the throne
and in front of the Lamb.
They were wearing white robes
and were holding palm branches in their hands.

Revelation 7:9

1248 Here I stand before you, Lord *King of love*

Words and Music: Evan Cooper

Gm7 Eb Bb F Eb Gm F
Em7 C G D C Em D
King of love, here on my knees I give my-self to thee,
Gm Eb Gm F Bb
Em C Em D G
I give my-self to thee.

1249 Here I stand in your presence *My desire*

Words and Music: Robert Critchley, Darlene Dunn and Kelley Warren

Worshipfully
Verse
D
Em
Here I stand in your pre - sence, call-ing out to you:
A
G
D
more of you and less of me, cleanse my heart, set me free. I
Em
want to look in-to your eyes, know the sec-rets of your heart, but
A
Em
G
most of all this is my cry: I want to be loved by
Asus4
A
Chorus
D
G/D
D
F#7/C#
you. My de - sire is to see your face. My de -

Bm Bm/A G D/F♯
sire is to feel your em-brace. My de-
Bm A G D/F♯
sire is to know with-out a doubt that you will ne-ver let me go;
G D/A A D
this is the de - si - re of my heart.

1250 Here we are *Song from the heart*

Words and Music: Kelly Bennett

D Em7 C2 Dsus4
ho - ly, wor - thy, mag - ni - fied.
Chorus
G
Call - ing out, cry - ing out a sound
C2
to please your ear, a song from our
G D G
hearts. We're call - ing out,
cry - ing out a sound to bring you near,

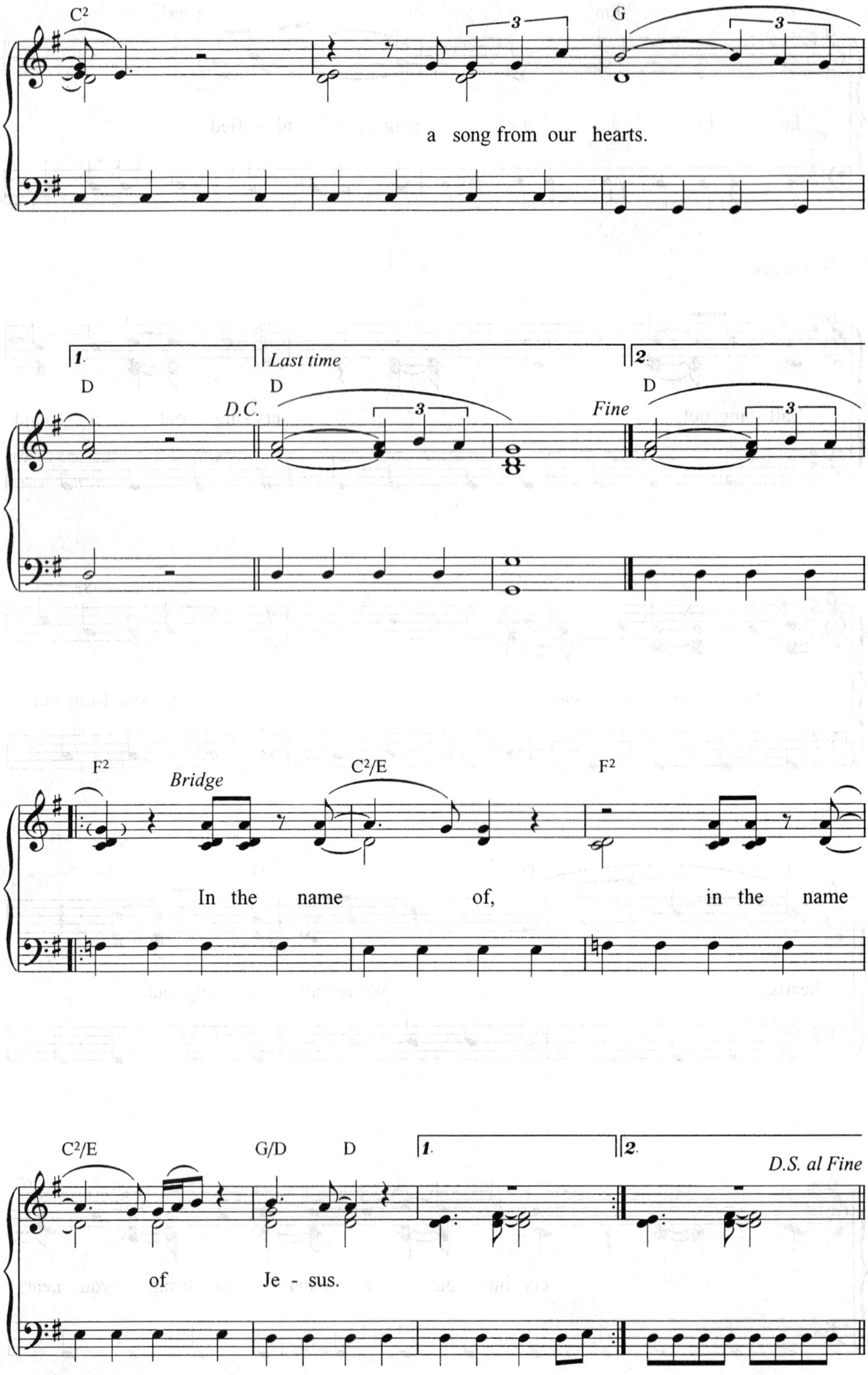
C2
G
a song from our hearts.
1.
Last time
2.
D
D.C.
D
Fine
D
F2
Bridge
C2/E
F2
In the name of, in the name
C2/E
G/D
D
1.
2.
D.S. al Fine
of Je - sus.

1251 Here we stand *Lead us, Lord*

Words and Music: Brian Doerksen

A E/B A/C#
to-ward what is still to come. We
E/G# Bsus4 B
want to dream a-gain.
Chorus
A E E/G# Bsus4 B
Lead us, Lord, in-to a life of fruit-
C#m B A E E/G#
-ful-ness; pre-pare our hearts to risk a-gain.

Bsus4 B A
And as we
E E/G♯ Bsus4 B C♯m B
trust, tak-ing sim - ple steps of o - be - di-ence, we know
A Bsus4 B E F♯m/E
that you will lead us, Lord.
E/G♯ A B 1, 2. E 3. E
Here we

1252 Here we stand in your presence *You're my God*

Words and Music: Jacky Jensen Brigstock

A
C#m
E/B
Lord, we come before your throne and worship you.
A
Bsus4
E
You're my shelter from the storm,
F#m7
E/G#
A
my Redeemer and my God, you bring com-
C#m
A
Bsus4
E
F#m7
-fort to my soul, you're my God.
E/G#
A
1st time D.C.
E
Hal-le-lu-jah,
F#m7
E/G#
A
Repeat ad lib.
E
you're my God, hal-le-lu-jah, you're my God.

1253 He's the Lily of the Valley

I believe

Words and Music: Alvin Slaughter

1. He's the Li - ly of the Val - ley, he's the bright and mor - ning star; he's the fair - est of ten thou - sand, Lord, you are.

See this migh - ty God of glo - ry lives with-in my heart to - day, with a song of praise I lift my voice and

2. He's my light and my salvation,
he's my strength, no need to fear;
a friend and help in times of trouble, he's always near.
Though a host may rise against us,
with assurance we can say
we're victorious through the pow'r of Jesus' name.

3. See the angels up in glory
gather 'round the throne to sing,
singing holy, holy, holy eternally.
But the angels cannot fathom
what it means to be redeemed,
so from the depth of my whole being I will sing.

1254 Hide me now *Still*

Words and Music: Reuben Morgan

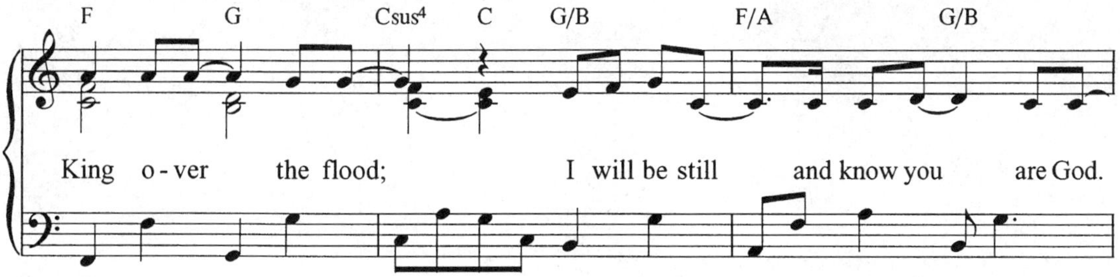

2. Find rest, my soul, in Christ alone.
Know his power in quietness and trust.

The Spirit of the Sovereign Lord is on me,
because the Lord has anointed me
to preach good news to the poor.
He has sent me to bind up the broken-hearted,
to proclaim freedom for the captives
and release from darkness for the prisoners . . .

Isaiah 61:1

1255 His wounds, my healing

Words and Music: Gareth Robinson

1256 Holiness, holiness

Take my life

Words and Music: Scott Underwood

1. Ho - li - ness, ho - li - ness is what I long
2. Faith - ful - ness, faith - ful - ness is what I long
3. Right-eous-ness, right-eous-ness is what I long

for; ho - li - ness is what I need,
for; faith - ful - ness is what I need,
for; right-eous-ness is what I need,

ho - li - ness, ho - li - ness
faith - ful - ness, faith - ful - ness
right-eous-ness, right-eous-ness

is what you want from me.
is what you want from me.
is what you want from me.

2, 3.
D2 D G C2
D2 D Chorus G C2
Take my heart and form
D G C2
it, take my mind and trans-form
D G C2
it, take my will, con-form
D G C2
it to yours, to yours O Lord.

1.
2.
D
D
D.C.
D
To yours,
G
C2
D
D.S.
to yours
O
Lord.
Take my
3.
D
G
To
yours,
to
yours
C2
D
G
O
Lord.

And I pray that you,
being rooted and established in love,
may have power, together with all the saints,
to grasp how wide and long and high and deep
is the love of Christ,
and to know this love that surpasses knowledge –
that you may be filled to the measure
of all the fullness of God.

Ephesians 3:17-19

1257 Holy God

Faithful, mighty, glorious

Words and Music: Kate Simmonds and Miles Simmonds

E/G# A F#m7
is wor - thy; all hon - our and glo -
is strong - er, and your rest is sweet -
E/G# F#m7 E/G# B
Chorus
- ry be - long to you. (For) You are
- er than a - ny o - ther.
A/C# B/D# E A/C# B/D#
faith - ful, migh - ty, glo - ri - ous, awe-some and vic - to -
Now our hearts are re - so - lute; our con - fi - dence is all
E A/C# B/D# E
- ri - ous, beau - ti - ful and won - der - ful, Lord.
in you, ev - 'ry-thing is pos - si - ble, O Lord,
B 1. 2. A
my Lord.
E B 1. 2. E
D.S.
2. When trou - bles come

1258 Holy, holy

Words and Music: Nathan Fellingham

Chorus
B
E
A
come. Lift up his name with the sound of sing -
Bsus4
B
E
A
ing, lift up his name in all the earth.
B
B/A
E/G#
A
Lift up your voice and give him glo -
B
A
F#m7
ry, for he is wor - thy to be
Bsus4
B
D.C.
Last time
E2
praised.

1259 Holy, holy are you, Lord *All the heavens*

Words and Music: Reuben Morgan

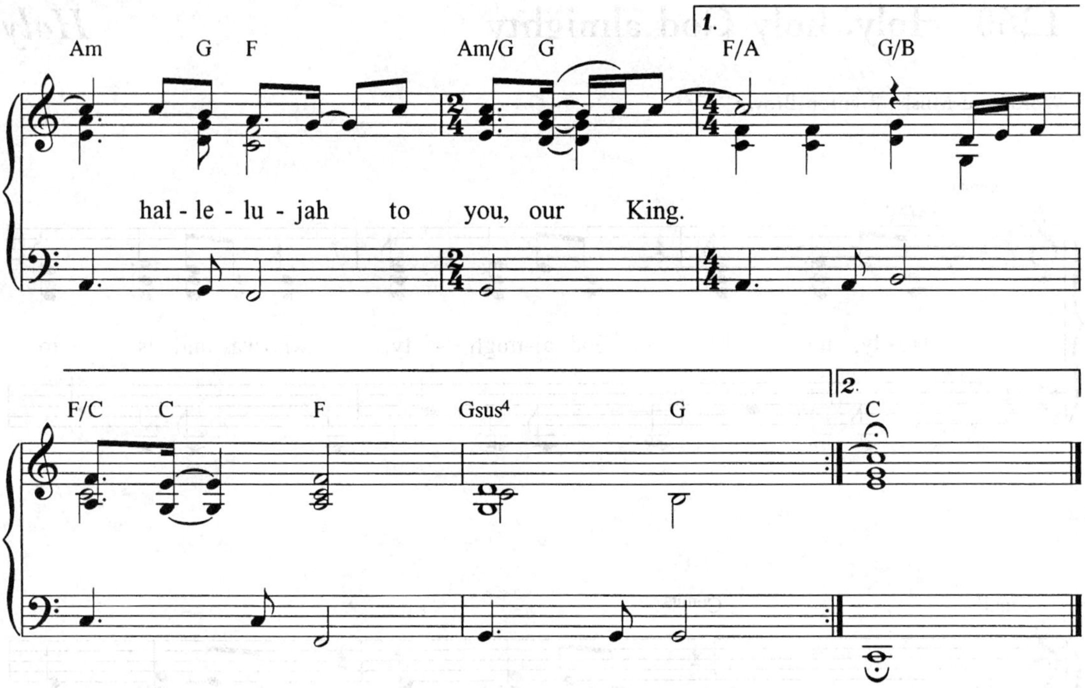
1.
Am G F Am/G G F/A G/B
hal - le - lu - jah to you, our King.
2.
F/C C F Gsus4 G C

1260 Holy, holy God almighty

Words and Music: Brenton Brown

G G/F C F G
done is just and true; ho - ly, ho - ly God are you,
C F G C
Fine
ho - ly, ho - ly God are you.
Am Bridge G F
All bles - sing, all hon - our be - longs to
C Csus4 C Am G
you, all pow - er and wis - dom is
1. 2.
C Csus4 C
D.S. al Fine
yours. Ho - ly is your

1261 Holy, holy, holy Lord *Forgiven*

Words and Music: Keith Getty, Emma Vardy and Noel Robinson

F2 Gm7sus4 Am7 Dm7 Gm7 B♭/C C7
D2 Em7sus4 F♯m7 Bm7 Em7 G/A A7
lift our hands, sur - ren - der to grace so un - de -
last home with the Fa - ther, our ho - ly dwel - ling -
Fsus4 F Cm7 F7
Dsus4 D Am7 D7
Chorus
served. Be - fore you, Lord, for - giv - en, we
place.
B♭2 Bdim F2 Dm7 B♭maj7 B♭/C C7
G2 G♯dim D2 Bm7 Gmaj7 G/A A7
bow be - fore your throne. At your cross, we
A7 Dm7 F/G G7 B♭/C C7
F♯7 Bm7 D/E E7 G/A A7
find in you our right - eous - ness re - stored. Be -

F Cm7 F7 B♭2 A7
D Am7 D7 G2 F♯7
fore you, Lord, for - giv - en, we stand in your great
Dm7 B♭2 A7 Dm
Bm7 G2 F♯7 Bm
love, and live our lives in hon - our to
1. 2.
F/G G7 Gm/C C7 Gm7 F2/A B♭maj7 Gm7 B♭/C F
D/E E7 Em/A A7 Em7 D2/F♯ Gmaj7 Em7 G/A D
your for - giv - ing blood. blood.

1262 Holy, holy Lord

I rejoice in your love

Words and Music: Gary Sadler

1. Ho-ly, ho-ly Lord, you are my strength and my high tow-er; holy, ho-ly Lord, you're the rock on which I stand. Ho-ly, ho-ly Lord, I put my trust in your great pow-er; ho-ly,

2. Ho-ly, ho-ly Lord, you are my God, there is no o-ther; holy, ho-ly Lord, I will hide be-neath your wings. Ho-ly, ho-ly Lord, you are my shield, you're my de-fend-er; ho-ly,

C Dm B♭ C F
A Bm G A D
Chorus
ho - ly Lord, my sal - va - tion is in your hands.
ho - ly Lord, when trou - ble comes you will co - ver me.
O
C Dm B♭maj7 C Dm B♭
A Bm Gmaj7 A Bm G
Je - sus, your faith - ful - ness is to me a migh - ty fort - ress,
Gm C F/A B♭ Dm C/E
Em A D/F♯ G Bm A/C♯
I re - joice in your love, I re - joice in your love;
C Dm B♭maj7 C
A Bm Gmaj7 A
O Je - sus, your vic - to - ry is the truth that
Dm B♭ Gm C F/A B♭
Bm G Em A D/F♯ G
sets me free, I re - joice in your love,

Dm Bm
Csus4 Asus4
F D
1, 3.
2.
Fine
I re-joice in your love.
Though
B♭ G
F D
C A
Dm Bm
B♭ G
Csus4 Asus4
dark - ness sur - rounds me I will not be a-fraid;
C A
B♭ G
Dm Bm
B♭ G
my faith is in you, O God, and the
Gm Em
F/A D/F♯
Csus4 Asus4
C A
D.S. al Fine
pro - mi - ses you've made.
O

1263 Holy, holy Lord God Almighty

Words and Music: Mary MacLean

who was and is and is to come.

Lord most Ho-ly, wor-thy of glo-ry,

pow-er and ma-jes-ty are yours. Ho-ly,

2.
C F C
yours. Bles-sing and hon - our to you for
F C Dm C/E F Am
e - ver un-to the Lamb up - on the
Gsus4 G C F C
throne. Strength and sal - va - tion be-long to the
F C Dm C/E F/G
Sa - viour, ho - ly, ho - ly is the Lord.
1.
C
Ho - ly, Lord.
D.S.
2.
C

Great and marvellous are your deeds,
Lord God Almighty.
Just and true are your ways,
King of the ages.
Who will not fear you, O Lord,
and bring glory to your name?
For you alone are holy.
All nations will come
and worship before you,
for your righteous acts have been revealed.

Revelation 15:3-4

1264 Holy one

Words and Music: Charmaine Ford

1265 Holy Spirit, hear my prayer

Words and Music: Andrew Crookall

C C/E F Gsus4 G C C/E
Take a - way my heart of stone, fill me with the
F Gsus4 G C C/E F C/E Dm
breath of life, help me be what I should tru - ly
F/G G C C/E F Gsus4 G
be. Take a - way my sin and
C C/E F G Am
shame, o - pen up my shut - tered soul.
Dm7 F/G C F/G
1. 2.
Ho - ly Spi - rit, come. 2. Ho - ly

1266 Holy Spirit, we wait on you

Words and Music: Andrew Rayner

1267 Holy words long preserved

Ancient words

Words and music: Lynn DeShazo

1. Ho - ly words long pre - served for our
 words of our faith hand - ed

walk in this world; they re - sound with God's own
down to this age, came to us through sac - ri -

heart, O, let the an - cient words im - part;
fice; O, heed the faith - ful words of Christ;

words of life, words of hope, give us strength,
ho - ly words long pre - served for our walk

C D Em D/F#
help us cope; in this world wher-e'er we
in this world; they re-sound with God's own
G G/B Am/C G/D D G
roam, an-cient words will guide us home.
heart; O, let the an-cient words im-part.
Chorus
G G/B D
An-cient words, e-ver true, chang-ing
Am G/B C D G D/F#
me, chang-ing you; we have come with o-pen
1.
G Am/C G/D D G D/F#
hearts, O, let the an-cient words im-part.

G G/B C G/D D G C/G G
2. Ho - ly
2.
Am/C G/D D G
D.S.
3.
Am/C G/D D
an - cient words im - part. An - cient an - cient words im -
G Em D/F#
part. We have come with o - pen
G G/B Am/C G/D D Em
hearts, O, let the an - cient words im - part.
D Am/C G/D D G
O, let the an - cient words im - part.

1268 How awesome is your name

Words and Music: Matthew Fallentine

(♩ = 69)
Chorus
G A D A7/E D/F#
How awe - some is your name,
G A Bm
how awe-some is your name in all the earth;
Last time to Coda
G A D A/C# Bm
we give you all the glo - ry,
Em7 Asus4
as we wor - ship at your throne.
D A/C# Bm F#m7
1. Ho - ly is the name of Je - sus,
2. In your pre - sence there is heal - ing,

C2 Em7 Asus4 A G/B A/C♯
ho - ly is the great 'I Am';
as we call up - on your name;
D A/C♯ Bm F♯m7
e - ver wor - thy to be wor-shipped and a-dored,
through you the u - ni-verse ex - pe - ri - enced its birth,
C2 Em7 Asus4 A D/A D.C.
Lord of hea - ven and of earth.
and for e - ver we'll pro - claim.
CODA
Em7 Asus4 A/B Bm7
as we wor - ship at your throne,
Em7 F♯m/A A7 D
as we kneel where we be - long.

1269 How could I but love you

Words and Music: Tommy Walker

1. How could I but love you, my Sa - viour and my God; how could I but serve you, when on the cross you were the ser - vant of

2. How could I but love you, my Com - for - ter, my strength; how could I but serve you, when in this life you've been so faith - ful and

Csus4 C F/B♭
Asus4 A D/G
all; how could I but
true; how could I but
F/A Dm
D/F♯ Bm
fol - low you, when all your ways lead to free - dom and life;
fol - low you, when some day soon you'll o - pen hea - ven for me;
B♭ F F/B♭ Gm/B♭
G D D/G Em/G
how could I but love you, my
C7sus4 C F F/B♭ Gm/B♭
A7sus4 A D D/G Em/G
Sa - viour and my God.

Chorus
F D
F/B♭ D/G
Gm/B♭ Em/G
Leader
How could I,
All How could I but love you;
how could I but love you;
how could I but love you;
how could I but fol - low you, my God.
B♭ G
F/B♭ D/A

1270 How good is the God we adore

Words: Joseph Hart | Music: *Lancashire Sunday School Songs*

CELESTE 88 88

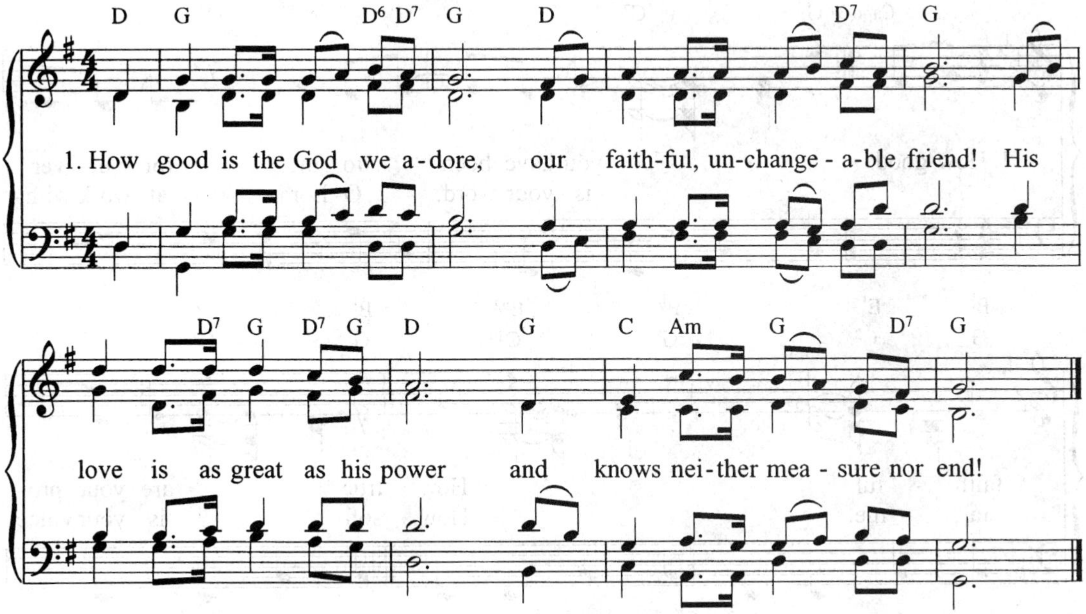

2. 'Tis Jesus the first and the last,
whose Spirit shall guide us safe home;
we'll praise him for all that is past;
we'll trust him for all that's to come.

1271 How good you have been to me

Words and Music: Lara Martin (Abundant Life Ministries)

Chorus
B♭ F/A Gm7 E♭
G D/F♯ Em7 C
I live for you, I place no one a-bove you.
B♭ F/A Gm7 E♭
G D/F♯ Em7 C
I'll walk with you, al - ways, al - ways.
B♭ F/A Gm7 E♭
G D/F♯ Em7 C
To talk with you, and feel your breath on my face, how a-maz -
Gm7 Gsus2(4) Gm E♭ F
Em7 Esus2(4) Em C D
- ing, how a-maz - ing you are!
B♭ E♭2 B♭ E♭2 B♭ E♭2 B♭ E♭2 B♭
G C2 G C2 G C2 G C2 G
1.
2.
2. How rich

1272 How matchless is your love

Words and Music: John Hartley and Gary Sadler

Moderate pace

1. How match-less is your love, how
 price-less is your blood, how

beau-ti-ful your grace, for one so just to
beau-ti-ful your name, for one so clean to

bear a cross to take my guilt a-way.
die for me, to take my sins a-way.

2. How

Chorus

Je - sus, Je -

3. How matchless is your heart,
how great your faithfulness,
for Christ, so true and pure as you
to call me as your friend.

1273 How sweet the name of Jesus sounds

Words: John Newton
adapted by Lucy Bunce

Music: Lucy Bunce

(♩ = 80)
C F G C
1. How sweet the name of Je - sus sounds in
makes the wound - ed spi - rit whole, and
Gsus4 G C F
a be - lie - ver's ear! It soothes our sor - rows, heals
calms the trou - bled breast; 'tis man - na to the hun-
G Am F C/G G
our wounds, and drives a - way, and drives a - way our
- gry soul, and to the wea - ry, to the wea - ry,
1. 2.
C F/C C G/B Chorus Am G
fear. 2. It rest. Je - sus, my shep - herd,

© Copyright 2005 Kevin Mayhew Ltd.

F2 C Gsus4 G
Sa-viour, friend, my pro-phet, priest, and King. My
Am G F2 C
Lord, my life, my way, my end, ac-
To next verse
Last time
F C/G G C F/C D.S. C
cept the praise, ac-cept the praise I bring. 3. Dear bring.

3. Dear name! the rock on which I build,
my shield and hiding-place,
my never-failing treas'ry filled
with boundless stores,
with boundless stores of grace.

Chorus

4. Weak is the effort of my heart,
and cold my warmest thought;
but when I see thee as thou art,
I'll praise thee as,
I'll praise thee as I ought.

5. Till then I would thy love proclaim
with ev'ry fleeting breath;
and may the music of thy name
refresh my soul,
refresh my soul in death.

Chorus

1274 I behold your power and glory *Irresistible*

Words and Music: Darlene Zschech

G2
Cmaj7
D
Morn-ing by morn - ing your mer-cy a-wak - ens my soul.
E
A2
I lift up my eyes to see the
C#m7
B/D#
E
A2
won-ders of hea - ven o-pen-ing o-ver me, your
C#m7
B/D#
E
G2
good-ness a-bounds; you've tak-en my breath a - way with your
Cmaj7
D
E
ir-re-sis - ti-ble love.

1275 I believe in Jesus

Words and Music: Chris Storey

2. I belong to Jesus, the only Son of God.
He alone has saved me and paid with his own blood.
I belong to Jesus, the Lamb who once was slain.
Through his blood shed for me I have been born again.

1276 I belong to you

Words and Music: Trish Morgan

Steady 4
D
Bm
A
G
D
Bm
I be-long to you, keep-er of my ways. I be-long to you,

A
G
D
Bm
plan - ner of my days, through this walk of life,

A
A♯dim
Bm
D/A
Em7
A
to my fin - al breath, oh I, oh I, I be-long to

D
A7/E
you. You reign for e - ver, high-ly ex-alt - ed,

D/F♯
Gmaj7
Gm/B♭
Gm
hea - ven is hear - ing e - ter - nal love songs.
D
A7/E
Praise to our Mak - er, our God and Sa - viour, cre -
D/F♯
G
A
D
a - tion a - waits the com - ing King.

1277 I can do all things

Words and Music: Paul Smith

2.
F B♭/F F B♭2
D G/D D G2
I re-joice, Lord,
me. I re - joice, Lord, in your
F/A Dm7 Gm11 C
D/F♯ Bm7 Em11 A
in your pre - sence,
pre - sence, as your pow - er sup - plies all my
F B♭2
D G2
I re-joice, Lord,
needs. I re - joice, Lord, in your
F/A Dm7 Gm11 F/A
D/F♯ Bm7 Em11 D/F♯
in your pre - sence,
pre - sence, as your strength is made per - fect in
CODA
Gm/B♭ Csus4 C F/A F B♭/F F
Em/G Asus4 A D/F♯ D.S. al Coda D G/D D
me. I can do me.

1278 I come before you

Father of life

Words and Music: Craig Smith

E♭/G
C/E
C2
A2
Chorus
B♭2
G2
cleanse me from my sin.
Fa - ther of life,
Csus4
Asus4
F2
D2
please have mer - cy,
B♭2
G2
C2
A2
F2
D2
take this heart and give it pu - ri - ty;
B♭2
G2
Csus4
Asus4
Fa - ther of life, pour your mer-
F2
D2
B♭2
G2
- cy o - ver me, and re-new a stead - fast spi-

C2
A2
F2
D2
Last time to Coda
2nd time to Bridge
-rit with-in me.
2. Wea-thered and worn, my life has been
Bb2
G
Csus4
Asus4
F2
D2
torn, my gaze has been drift - ing. I call your name,
Bb2
G
search me, my Lord; my heart needs your
Csus4
Asus4
Eb/G
C/E
mend - ing; please re-move my trans-gres-

B♭2
G2
E♭/G
C/E
C2
A2
Chorus D.S. then Bridge
- sions, for-give me, O God.
Bridge
D♭2/A♭
B♭2/F
E♭2
C2
D♭2/F
B♭2/D
Re-ceive my sa - cri-fice, a bro-ken spi-
E♭/G
C/E
Csus4
Asus4
Chorus D.S. then Coda
- rit, bro-ken heart.
CODA
B♭2
G2
C2
A2
And re-new a stead-fast spi - rit with-in me.
F2
D2

1279 I come to bow down

Heart and soul

Words and Music: Kate Simmonds

D Bm7 A/C#
Lord. Wonder of heaven,
Rock of salvation,
C/D G/D Em7 Bm7
joy of my heart; strength of my being, I love
love of my life; God of all comfort, draw
A 1. 2. G
you.
near.
Heart and soul
Em7 D F#7
I seek you, Lord; heart and
G Em7 D
soul I seek you, Lord.

1280 I come to you

Your love

Words and Music: Nathan Fellingham and Louise Fellingham

1. I come to you, to sit at your feet,
2. Now look-ing clos - er, I see the scars,

I hear you call, I'm long-ing to meet
sto - ries of love, you paid the great-

you. I lift my face to you, and catch your eye,
- est price, so that I may have life. Thank you, my friend,

oh, how you sa - tis - fy.
you're show-ing me once a - gain.

Chorus
D D/C G/B Em7 D D/C
Je - sus, your love sur - rounds me.
G/B Em7 D D/C G/B Em7
Je - sus, your love com -
Last time to Coda
2nd time D.S.
D D/C G/B Em7 Bm A
- pletes me. There's no - thing
G#dim G Bm7 A G Em7 Bm A
like it, there's no - thing like it, there's no - thing
G#dim G D Dsus4 D
like the love of God.

D D7 Bm/D Daug D D7
No long-er search - ing, I've found the One, just touched the sur-
Bm/D Daug D D7 Bm/D Daug
- face, on - ly be-gun; this love goes deep - er than a - ny I've
D.S. al Coda CODA
D D7 Bm/D Daug D
known.

Worthy is the Lamb, who was slain,
to receive power and wealth and
wisdom and strength
and honour and glory and praise!

Revelation 5:12

1281 I dream of tongues of fire *Believer*

Words and Music: Matt Redman

2. I hope to see you come down,
rend the mighty heavens,
and let your glory cover all the earth;
to see your sons and daughters
come to know and love you,
and find a purer passion in the church.
These are the things my heart will pursue:
when will all the dreams come true?

3. May your church now reach out,
sowing truth and justice,
learn to love the poor and help the weak.
When your kingdom's coming
it will touch the broken,
place the lonely in a family.
So many hopes and longings in you:
when will all the dreams come true?

1282 I enter the Holy of holies *For your name is holy*

Words and Music: Jim Cowan

Am
Em
G
wor - ship you; Lord, I wor - ship
D
Am
Em
D
you, I wor - ship you; for your name is
C
D
Em
D/E
ho - ly, ho - ly, Lord.
Em
D
C
For your name is ho - ly,
D
Em
D/E
Repeat ad lib.
Em
ho - ly, Lord.

1283 If I could have one desire *One desire*

Words and Music: Lenny LeBlanc

(♩ = 78)
Chorus
D D/F♯ G A D D/F♯
If I could have one de-sire be-fore my life is
G A F♯m Bm G D/F♯
through, e-ven in my dark - est night my
Em Em/D A/C♯ A D D/F♯
light would shine for you. If I could stop the hands
G A D D/F♯ G A
of time, or make a wish come true, I would

Bm D/A G D/F♯ A A♯dim7
tell my heart to burn with fire for no one else but you.
2nd time to ⊕
Bm F♯m/A G2 Asus4 D D/F♯ G D2/F♯
This is my one de-sire.
G2 Asus4 A F♯m7 Bm G A7sus4
1.You are my sav - ing grace, an-chor of my soul
Dsus4 D A/C♯ G/B
and in a world that's turned up-side down
Gm/B♭ D/A Asus4 A
I want you to know:

* May be transposed up an octave if more comfortable for singers.

Chorus
E E/G# A B E E/G#
If I could have one de-sire be-fore my life is
A B G#m C#m A E/G#
through, e-ven in my dark - est night my
F#m F#m/E B/D# B E E/G#
light would shine for you. If I could stop the hands
A B E E/G# A B
of time, or make a wish come true, I would

C#m E/B A E/G# B Cdim7
tell my heart to burn with fire for no one else but you.
C#m G#m/B A2 B7sus4 C#m G#m/B
This is my one de-sire, this
A2 B7sus4 B
is my one de-sire.
E E/G# A Bsus4 B E

Oh, the depth of the riches
of the wisdom and knowledge of God!
How unsearchable his judgements,
and his paths beyond tracing out!

For from him and through him
and to him are all things.
To him be the glory for ever! Amen.

Romans 11:33, 36

1284 If it wasn't for your mercy

Where angels fear to tread

Words and Music: Matt Redman and Tom Lane

E/B A E/G♯
an - gels fear to tread, where I would ne - ver dare to come,
2nd & 3rd times to Coda
A E/B F♯m7
but for the clean-sing of your blood. 3. With
A E/G♯
you there is for-give - ness, and there-fore you are feared.
A
Je - sus, it's your lov - ing kind - ness that
CODA
E/G♯ D.S. al Coda Chorus F♯m7
brings me to my knees. And I In the

E/G♯ A E/B
beau-ty of your ho - li-ness, in the beau-ty of your ho - li-ness,
A/C♯ E/G♯ A
in the beau-ty of your ho - li-ness, in the
E/B F♯m7
1. D.S. al Coda
Chorus
2. E
beau-ty of your ho - li-ness. And I

In the year that King Uzziah died,
I saw the Lord seated on a throne,
high and exalted,
and the train of his robe filled the temple.
Above him were seraphs, each with six wings:
with two wings they covered their faces,
with two they covered their feet,
and with two they were flying.
And they were calling to one another:
'Holy, holy, holy is the Lord Almighty;
the whole earth is full of his glory.'

Isaiah 6:1-3

1285 I fix my eyes on you

All the days of my life

Words and Music: Tommy Walker and Bob Wilson

(♩ = 112)
F2
Capo 3 D2
I
F2
D2
fix my eyes on you,
C
A
the au - thor of my faith,
B♭
G
cast-ing a - side ev - 'ry sin and ev - 'ry weight;
C
A
F
D
F2
D2
I fix my eyes on you,

C
A
I lay my bur - dens down,
B♭
G
C
A
F
D
let-ting the cares of this world now fade a - way.
Chorus
F/B♭
D/G
C/E
A/C♯
One thing I ask, this
B♭/F
G/D
F
D
Am7
F♯m7
Dm
Bm
F/B♭
D/G
one thing I seek, that I may dwell in your house,
C/E
A/C♯
F
D
Gm7
Em7
F/A
D/F♯
O Lord, my King;

F/B♭ C/E B♭/F F
D/G A/C♯ G/D D
all the days of my life I want to gaze up-on your beau-
Am7 Dm7 B♭ C
F♯m7 Bm7 G A
Last time to Coda
-ty and seek you in this ho - ly place.
1.
F C/E
D A/C♯
B♭ Csus4 C
G Asus4 A
I
2.
F
D
D.S. al Coda
CODA
F
D

F/B♭ D/G C/E A/C♯
All the days of my life I want to gaze
B♭/F G/D F D Am7 F♯m7 Dm7 Bm7 B♭ G
up-on your beau - ty and seek you in this ho -
C A 1. F D 2. F D
- ly place.

1286 If you're looking for somebody *Look my way*

Words and Music: Lindell Cooley and Lenny LeBlanc

(♩ = 123)
Capo 3
F/A B♭ C Dm F/A B♭ C F
D/F♯ G A Bm D/F♯ G A D
1.
2.
C F F/A B♭
A D D/F♯ G
Chorus
If you're look - ing for some - bo - dy who loves
C Dm F/A B♭ C F
A Bm D/F♯ G A D
you, look my way, look my way; if you're
F/A B♭ C Dm
D/F♯ G A Bm
look - ing for some - bo - dy to praise you, won't you
(Je - sus)

F/A D/F♯ B♭ G C A Dm Bm
look my way, look my way; won't you
F/A D/F♯ B♭ G
1. C A F D
look my way, look my way. If you're
2, 3, 4. C A F D
look my way.
3rd time to Bridge
Gm7 Em7 B♭ G F D
1. I don't have ma - ny things to of - fer, just a pas - sion for
2. Lord, I want to give glo - ry and hon - our to your
C A Gm7 Em7 B♭ G
you; and ev - 'ry day I get a lit - tle bit clo - ser,
name; I just want to see your migh - ty pow - er

F C Gm7
D A Em7
clo-ser to you; Lord, you have my heart, you
fall like rain;
F/A B♭ C
D/F♯ G A
Chorus D.S.
have my soul, and one more thing that I want you to know. If you're
Bridge
F/A B♭ C Dm F/A B♭ C F
D/F♯ G A Bm D/F♯ G A D
F/A B♭ C Dm F/A B♭
D/F♯ G A Bm D/F♯ G
Je - sus, won't you look my way,
1. 2.
C Dm C Dm
A Bm A Bm
look my way, look my way.

Praise the Lord.
How good it is to sing praises to our God,
how pleasant and fitting to praise him!

Psalm 147:1

1287 If your presence doesn't go with us

May your presence go with us

Words and Music: Don Moen

(♩ = 76)
Chorus
C/D
C/G
G
G/B
If your pre-sence does-n't go with us, we don't want to
D/C
C
G/B
Am7
leave this place; Lord, we need you near, as we go from
D
C/G
G
C/D
here, to lead us by your love and grace. May your pre-sence fill us
C/G
G
G/B
D/C
C
ev - 'ry day, may your Spi - rit lead the way;
3rd time to
4th time to
G/B
Am7
D
Lord, to you we call, let your glo-ry fall, and may your pre-sence

1.
D.S.
2.
C/G G C/D C/G G
go with us. If your pre-sence does-n't go with us.
D/F♯ Em Em/D C G/B
Verse
If we have found fa - vour in your sight,
Am7 D G F♯m7(♭5) B7 Em Em/D C
show us your ways, O Lord; 'cause we want to know you and live
G/B Am7 G2/B C/D D
in your light, for all of our days show us your ways.
3.
G C/D D.S. C/G G Am7 Gmaj7/B
If your pre-sence does-n't go with us.

C D/C Bm7 Em
We have all our hopes and we have our dreams; but
Am7 G/B C C/D
we can - not go where you will not lead.
D.S. C/G G
4.
If your pre - sence does - n't go with us.

Lord, I have heard of your fame;
I stand in awe of your deeds, O Lord.
Renew them in our day,
in our time make them known;
in wrath remember mercy.

Habakkuk 3:2

1288 I have come to worship *Surrender*

Words and Music: Dave Lubben

A
I have come to wor-ship the God of won - ders;
I am here to drink from the stream of
E
D2
A
El Shad - dai; I have come to
2
lis-ten to my Cre - a - tor;

E D²
I am here to lift up the name of Je - sus
A
Christ.
D² E D²
If you are search-ing you'll find peace in
E D² E
him; if you are search-ing you'll find true
D² E
Chorus
love from him. Let's give him our hearts,

A
E/A
let's give him our breath, let's take time to thank
F♯m
D
him for dy - ing our death; let's give him our voice,
A
E/A
Last time to Coda
let's lift up our hands, let's give him our lives,
F♯m
D2
let's sur-ren - der to him.
Bridge
Bm
E
D2
I sur - ren - der to you;

F#m
E
Fa - ther, I sur - ren - der to
D2
Bm
E
you; Je - sus, I sur - ren - der to
D2
F#m
you; Ho - ly Spi - rit, I sur -
E
D2
D.S. al Coda
ren - der to you. Let's give him our hearts,
CODA
F#m
D2
A
let's sur - ren - der to him.

1289 I have found exceeding joy *Exceeding joy*

Words and Music: Miriam Webster

(♩ = 75)
F2 F C/F B♭/F
Capo 3 D2 D A/D G/D
1. I have found ex - ceed - ing joy,
2. Mer - cy, grace, e - ter - nal life,
3. I will lift my eyes up high,
F2 F C/F B♭/F
D2 D A/D G/D
Je - sus ans - wered when I called. This name
brought from dark - ness to his light; while lost
prais - ing Je - sus through each trial; though I
Gm7 Csus4 C Gm7
Em7 Asus4 A Em7
that has saved me, pure love that em -
in my sin he raised me and
have not seen him I love him com-
1.
2, 3.
F/C C Csus4 B♭/C F E♭/F
D/A A Asus4 G/A D C/D
Chorus
braced me.
made me live.
plete - ly.
My soul mag-ni-fies

B♭ F E♭/F B♭ F/A
G D C/D G D/F♯
the Lord, my heart joys in God my Sa - viour, for
Gm7 F/C C Gm7
Em7 D/A A Em7
he lifts the low - ly, he's done great
F/C C F E♭/F B♭
D/A A D C/D G
Last time to Coda
things for me; I will sing, prais-ing e - ver-more. He is
1.
Gm7 Csus4 C F2 F
Em7 Asus4 A D2 D
D.C.
migh - ty and ho - ly is his name.
2.
Csus4 C F2 F C F
Asus4 A D2 D A D
ho - ly is his name. Though

Gm7 Csus4 C B♭/D Dm
Em7 Asus4 A G/B Bm
I have not seen him I love him com -
CODA
Csus4 C Gm7 B♭/C
Asus4 A D.S. al Coda Em7 G/A
plete - ly. My migh - ty, migh - ty, he is
Gm7 B♭/C Gm7
Em7 G/A Em7
migh - ty, migh - ty. He is migh - ty and
Csus4 C F2 F F2 F
Asus4 A D2 D D2 D
ho - ly is his name.

Praise be to the God and Father
of our Lord Jesus Christ!
In his great mercy
he has given us new birth into a living hope
through the resurrection of Jesus Christ from the dead.

1 Peter 1:3

1290 I have heard so many songs *The Father's song*

Words and Music: Matt Redman

Gently
E♭sus2 E♭sus2/D E♭/D♭
Capo 1 Dsus2 Dsus2/C♯ D/C
I have heard so many songs, listened to a
The Father's song, the Father's love, you sung it over
A♭/C Fm7 B♭7sus4
G/B Em7 A7sus4
1.
thousand tongues, but there is one that sounds above them all.
me, and for eternity it's
Cm B♭/D A♭ B♭7sus4 B♭
Bm A/C♯ G A7sus4 A
2.
written on my
E♭ E♭sus2 E♭ A♭/C
D Dsus2 D G/B
Chorus
heart. Heaven's perfect melody,
mystery,

B♭/D A/C♯ E♭/G D/F♯ A♭ G
the Cre - a - tor's sym-pho-ny, you are sing - ing
the King of Love has sent for me, and now you're sing - ing
1.
Fm7 Em7 B♭sus4 Asus4 Cm7 Bm7
o - ver me the Fa - ther's song.
o - ver me
2.
B♭/D A/C♯ E♭/G D/F♯ B♭sus4 Asus4 B♭ A E♭ D
Hea-ven's per-fect the Fa - ther's song.

1291 I have his word

Words and Music: Lex Loizides

Brightly
D G A
1. I have his word, his great and precious pro-
D D/C♯ Bm G
-mi-ses. He took my sin, his
D A D
right-eous-ness is mine. I am in Christ,
G A D D/C♯ Bm
se-cure for all e-ter-ni-ty: no pow'r can
Bm/A G Bm
se-ver me, nor cast me off from his a-

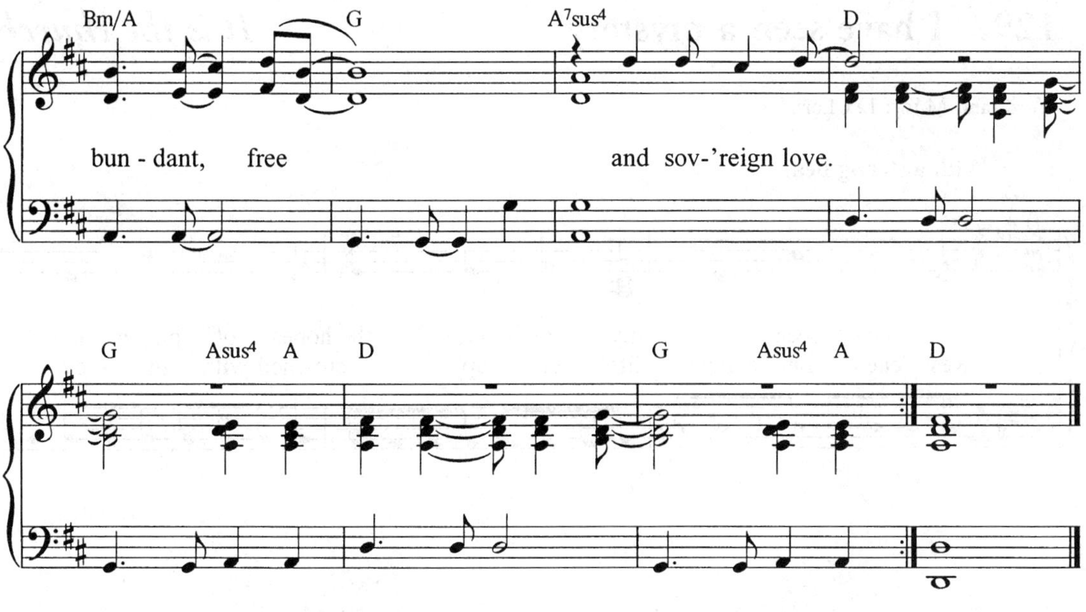

2. I have his word,
the Master Builder will succeed.
The gates of hell,
they never will prevail.
Throughout the earth
the joy of Jesus is his church;
she is the mystery
that stirred his heart,
drawing him out of heaven
to shed his blood.

3. I have his word,
a day is fixed when all the world
in sudden awe
the Son of God shall see.
And in that day
our eyes shall see his majesty;
what then of sufferings?
What then of tears?
We shall see perfectly
when he appears!

4. I have his word
that every race shall reign with him,
we'll reach our home,
the new Jerusalem.
The Triune God
shall dwell with man eternally,
more joys than eye has seen
or ear has heard
wait for us certainly,
I have his word.

1292 I have seen a mystery *It is the church*

Words and Music: Lex Loizides

With a strong beat
Verse D A Bm
I have seen a my - ste - ry, the hopes of prayer and
Res - cued, ran - somed, lift - ed up, crowned with mer - cy,
G A D A/C#
pro - phe - cy, and ris - ing from all peo - ples see, she comes.
clothed in hope, the ob - ject of all hea - ven's love, she comes.
Bm 1. G A 2. A Chorus
It is the church,
D A Bm
the hope of all the world, and
the pas - sion of God's Son, the

A
Bm
G
here I fix my heart and hand, I can - not turn a - way!
goal of his - t'ry, come. You'll see we've near - ly reached the day.
Asus4
1.
A
2.
A
3
It is the church, And she will
Em7
G
A
3
be all glo - ri-ous; fit-ting for
Em7
1.
G
A
him whose bride she is.
2. and Last time
G
A
1st time D.C.
D
Fine
bride she is.

3.
G A G
bride she is. In that day,
A G A G
in that day, in that day,
A G/B A/C# Chorus D.S. al Fine
in that day. It is the church,

Not to us, O Lord, not to us
but to your name be the glory,
because of your love and faithfulness.

Psalm 115:1

1293 I heard the sound of voices

Words and Music: Robin Mark

D
Em7
1. I heard the sound of voi - ces from ev - 'ry tribe
2. & 3. Where are the chains that bound me, the cords of my
G
and na - tion as they were walk - ing, sing - ing
op - pres - sion? Je - sus the Lamb had loosed them;
A
D/A
D
songs of de - li - ve - rance. For go - ing on
he's my de - li - ve - rance. My heart cries 'Ab -
Em7
be - fore them a lit - tle lamb was lead - ing
- ba, Fa - ther', for he has led me to you
G
A
and I could hear him sing - ing songs of de -
and I can hear you sing - ing songs of de -

1.
D
2, 3.
D
li - ve - rance.
li - ve - rance.
D
Em7
For out of E - gypt you have called your sons,
G
your daugh - ters that they might be a wit - ness
A
D
to your sav-ing name. So Fa - ther, I
Em7
am walk - ing, Lord, can you see me walk - ing?
Last time to Coda
G
A
D
1st time D.C.
O my de - liv - 'rer, I am fol-low-ing the Lamb.

G/D
D
A
As for me
D
and my house, we will serve the Lord. As for me
Em7
and my house, we will serve the Lord. As for me
G
D
and my house, we will serve the Lord al - ways.
1.
2.
CODA
D.S. al Coda
A
D
As for me
fol-low-ing the Lamb.

In that day you will say:
'Give thanks to the Lord, call on his name;
make known among the nations what he has done,
and proclaim that his name is exalted.
Sing to the Lord, for he has done glorious things;
let this be known to all the world.'

Isaiah 12:4-5

1294 I just want to love *I'll always love you*

Words and Music: Tim Hughes

A
E
F#m
1. I just want to love, I just want to
D
A
E
sing to the one a - bove who has
F#m
1.
D
Repeat verse
2.
D
touched this thirs - ty soul. And now I'll
Bm
A
Chorus
ne - ver be the same. I'll al-ways love
E
F#m
D
you, I'll al-ways sing to you, Je-sus.

A
E
F#m
I long to wor - ship you in spi - rit and in truth.
1, 3.
D
2.
D
(Fine)
D.C.
4.
D
Bm
C#m
And with this song we'll lift the name of Je -
D
Bm
- sus high - er. And with a shout
C#m
D
D.S. al Fine
we'll raiseup one voice.

2. Ev'ry day I'll come,
spend my life with you,
learning of your heart,
and what you're calling me to do.
(Repeat)
My ev'ry breath belongs to you.

1295 I lay my life down at your feet *One way*

Words and Music: Joel Houston and Jonathon Douglass

With life
A
F♯m7
1. I lay my life down at your feet, you're the on - ly
In trou-bled times it's you I seek, I put you first, that's
2. You are al - ways, al - ways there, ev - 'ry how and
You will ne - ver, e - ver change; yes - ter - day, to -
1.
E
one I need. I turn to you, and you are al - ways there.
all I need.
ev - 'ry - where, your grace a-bounds so deep - ly with - in me.
day the same,
D
2.
E
I hum - ble all I am,
for e - ver, till for e -
D
Chorus
all to you. Here we go.
- ver meets no end.

A
E
F♯m7
One way, Je - sus, you're the on - ly one that
D
A
E
Last time to Coda
I could live for. One way, Je - sus,
F♯m7
1.
G
F♯m7
you're the on - ly one that I could live for.
D
F♯m7
D
D.C.
2.
G
D.S.
I could live for.

3.
G A E
I could live for. You are the way, the truth and the life: we live
F#m7 D F#m7 E
by faith and not by sight for you, we're liv - ing all for you.
D
1, 2, 3.
4.
D.S. al Coda
Here we go.
CODA
F#m7 G2 A
you're the on-ly one that I could live for.

‘Where, O death, is your victory?
Where, O death, is your sting?’
The sting of death is sin,
and the power of sin is the law.
But thanks be to God!
He gives us the victory through our Lord Jesus Christ.

1 Corinthians 15:55-57

1296 I lift my voice

Words and Music: Chris Orange

(♩= 120)
G C G
1. I lift my voice to the King of hea - ven, wor - thy is
a song of free - dom, you have set
C D G C
his name. This will be our glo - ri - ous
us free. Let the sound of a migh - ty
G Am7 D
an - them, Christ has come to reign.
ar - my pro - claim the vic - to - ry.
Chorus
G C
We give you the high praise for you
G C G
have made a way. You've con - quered sin and tak -

C D
- en all our shame, Je - sus,
G C G
the high - est name a - bove all o - ther names.
C G C
We ce - le - brate your vic - t'ry in this place.
D G C
We give you praise.
G 1. D G 2. D G
2. We will sing

1297 I live for you

U.R.Y.

Words and Music: Kate Spence (Wray)

Em D C G/B C
1. I live for you, all that I am and
Dsus4 D Em D C
all that I do. My heart beats with you and each
G/B C Dsus4 D
day I wake I think of you. You are
Chorus
G
why I sing, you are
Em C Dsus4
why I live and ev - 'ry - thing of me I place at your feet. You are

G Em C D
why I love, you are why I give and ev-'ry-thing of me be-longs to
Em C D G/B C
you, ev-'ry-thing of me be-longs to you.
Last time
Fine
Dsus4 D G Em D C
2. I live for you, and
G/B C Dsus4 D Em D
you are my God, you are the truth. You're all I need,
C G/B C Dsus4 D D.S.al Fine
my soul, it longs for more of you. You are

1298 I live my life to worship you *Just to be with you*

Words and Music: Gareth Robinson

Em7
C
G
more of your love; just to be with you,
D/F#
Cmaj7
1.
Am7
D.S.
and to love you. I live my
2.
Am7
Em
Am7
And here you know me,
Em7/B
Am7
Em7/B
and here you love me, and here I know
Am7
Em7/B
Am7
Em7
you, and here I love you.

1299 I long for freedom

Change me on the inside

Words and Music: Brian Doerksen

1. I long for free-dom to live in the truth,
2. Just like King Da-vid I cry out to you,

I want to be more like you. But
cre-ate in me a clean heart. I've

ev-'ry time I try to bring a - bout change I
grieved you a - gain, I need your re-lease from

on-ly touch the vi - si - ble me;
pat-terns that keep me in sin;

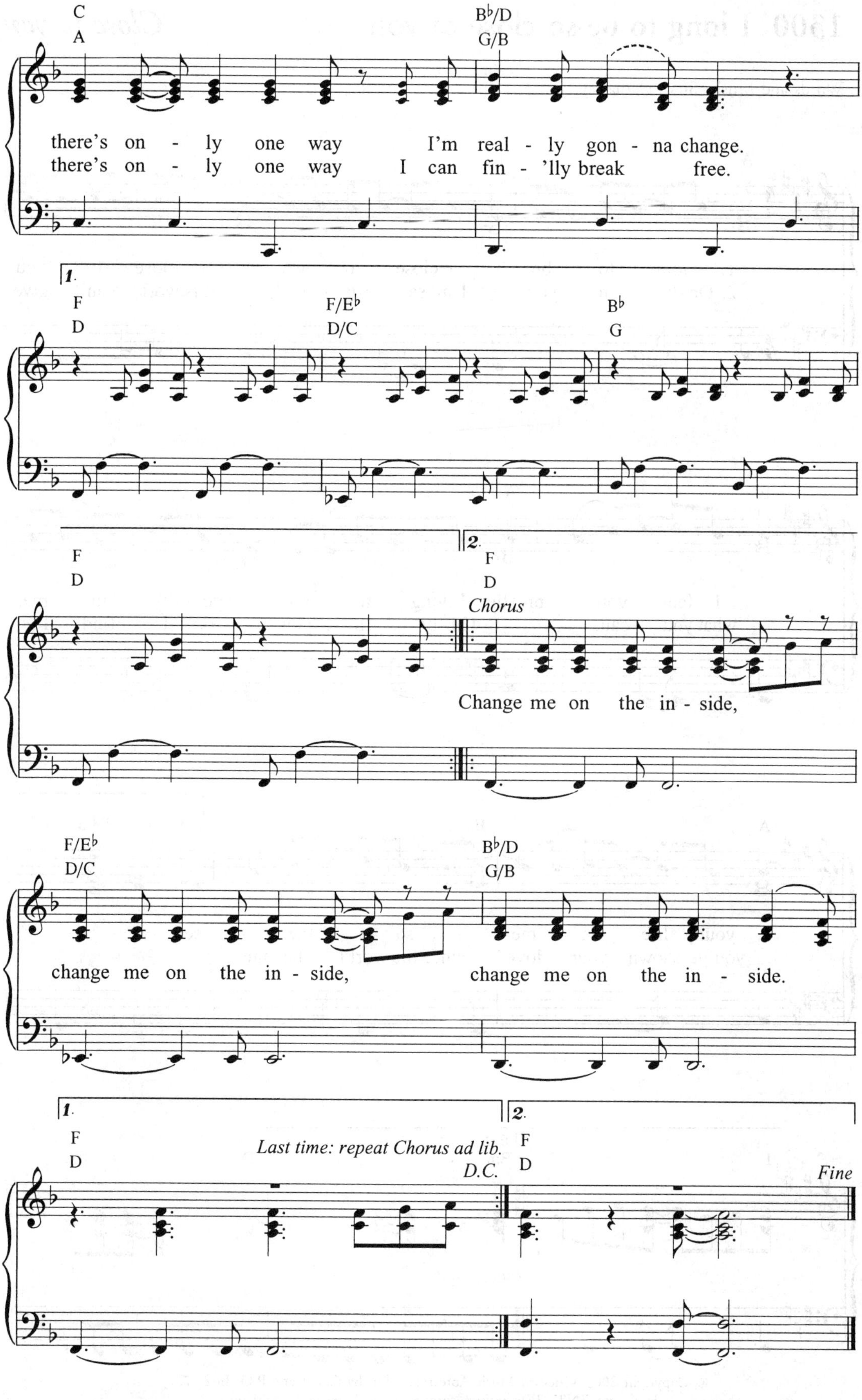
C
A
B♭/D
G/B
there's on - ly one way I'm real - ly gon - na change.
there's on - ly one way I can fin - 'lly break free.
1.
F
D
F/E♭
D/C
B♭
G
F
D
2.
F
D
Chorus
Change me on the in - side,
F/E♭
D/C
B♭/D
G/B
change me on the in - side,
change me on the in - side.
1.
F
D
Last time: repeat Chorus ad lib.
D.C.
2.
F
D
Fine

1300 I long to be so close to you *Close to you*

Words and Music: Steve Hathaway

1. I long to be so close to you, so close to you
2. On-ly in you I'm sa - tis - fied, this world can't give

I feel you breathe. I long to see your life in me,
what you can. On - ly in you do I find life,

your life in me so o - thers see.
you've shown your love since the world be - gan.

(v.1)
(see.)

Chorus
D F#m E A
Bet - ter one day in your house, O Lord,
F#m D E D F#m
than a thou - sand else - where, bet - ter one day in your
E A F#m D E
house, O Lord, than a thou - sand else - where.
1.
A E A E
D.C. (rpt. v.1)
Last time
A E A E A
Fine

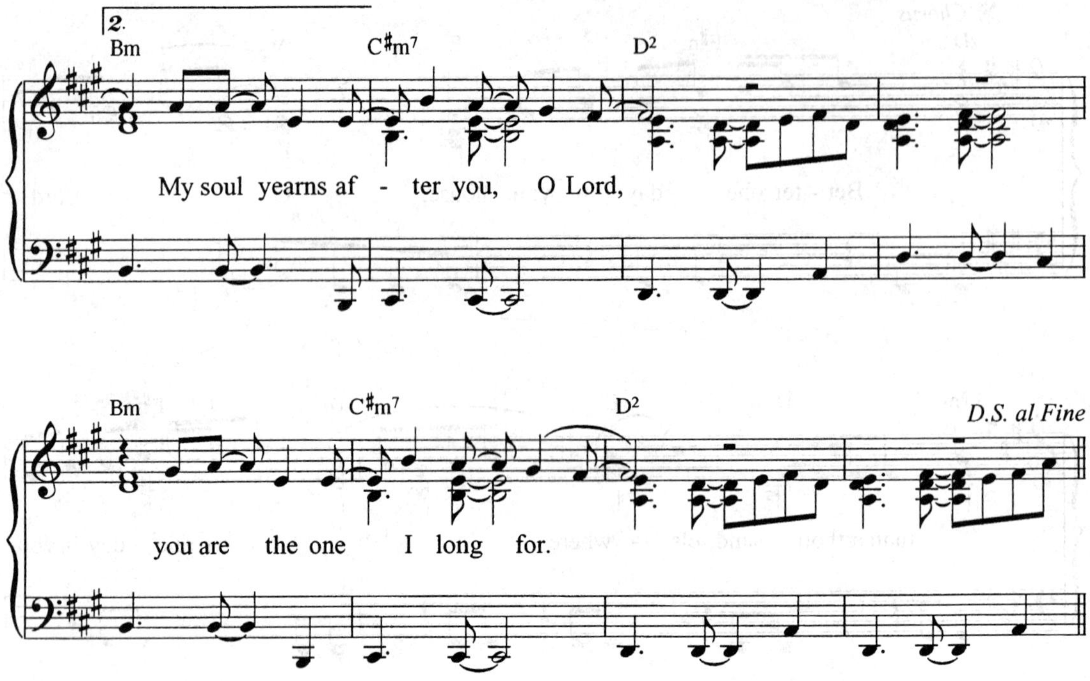
2.
Bm
C#m7
D2
My soul yearns af - ter you, O Lord,
Bm
C#m7
D2
D.S. al Fine
you are the one I long for.

The heavens declare the glory of God;
the skies proclaim the work of his hands.

Psalms 19:1

1301 I love to tell the story

Words: Miss Hankey

Music: W.G. Fischer

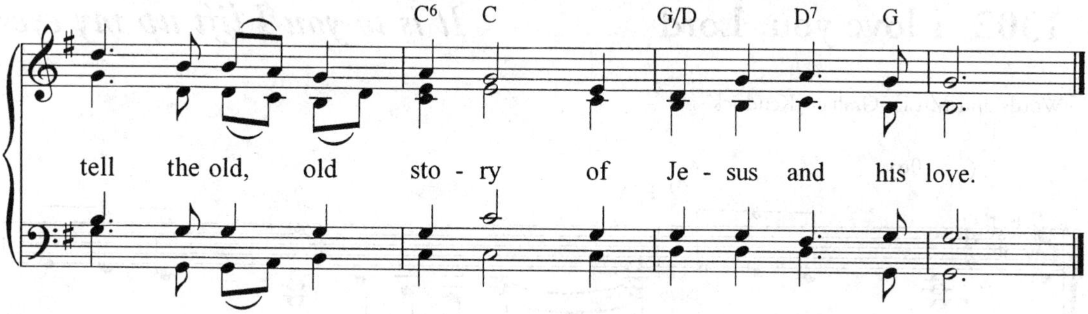

2. I love to tell the story:
more wonderful it seems
than all the golden fancies
of all our golden dreams.
I love to tell the story:
it did so much for me;
and that is just the reason
I tell it now to thee.

3. I love to tell the story:
'tis pleasant to repeat
what seems, each time I tell it,
more wonderfully sweet.
I love to tell the story,
for some have never heard
the message of salvation
from God's own holy word.

4. I love to tell the story,
for those who know it best
seem hungering and thirsting
to hear it, like the rest.
And when, in scenes of glory,
I sing the new, new song,
'twill be the old, old story
that I have loved so long.

1302 I love you, Lord

Words and Music: Graham Kendrick

D
A
3
voice and ans - wered me.
love that res - cued me.
Am7
Am7/G
Though the fears of death sur-round me
I'll com - plete all I have pro - mised
G
D/F#
A2
I won't be a - fraid if you are there.
in the pre - sence of your peo - ple here,
C
Em
When I call your name you hear me,
call - ing on your name for e - ver,
C
Em
A
when I am brought low I find you near.
liv - ing al - ways in your house of prayer.

Esus4 E A/F♯
It is to you
F♯m7/E Bm7 C♯m7 Bm7 D/E
I lift up my eyes, on - ly
1. A A/G D/F♯ Dm/F
you.
2. Esus4 E A/F♯ F♯m7/E Bm7
It is to you I lift up
C♯m7 Bm7 D/E A
my eyes, on - ly you.
A/G D/F♯ Dm6/F A

1303 I love you, Lord

Joy

Words and Music: Jon Ellis

With a driving rhythm
D
A
D
A
Chorus
G2
D
G2
D
G2
D
G
C
D
1. I love you, Lord, I wor-ship you, I love you, Lord, al - ways. So thank - ful, Lord, you saved my life, you saved my life to - day.
2. And Lord, I love to bring to you the hon - our due your name; just look at what you've done for me, I'll ne - ver be the same.
Let me be a shin - ing light for you, let me be a joy to you al - ways, let me be a shin-ing light for you, let me be a joy to you al-ways.

1304 I'm amazed

I'll never stop

Words and Music: Martyn Layzell

2. Swept away by the force
of your Spirit's burning flame;
like a wave bound for shore
that will never cease to break.
Mercies new every morning;
Jesus, I give you glory.

3. You are love, you are grace,
your compassions never fade.
You are joy in my pain,
you're the King of endless days.
Mercies new every morning;
Jesus, I give you glory.

Shout for joy to the Lord, all the earth.
Worship the Lord with gladness;
come before him with joyful songs.
Know that the Lord is God.
It is he who made us, and we are his;
we are his people, the sheep of his pasture.

Enter his gates with thanksgiving
and his courts with praise;
give thanks to him and praise his name.
For the Lord is good and his love endures for ever;
his faithfulness continues through all generations.

Psalm 100

1305 I'm calling out to you *Passion for Jesus*

Words and Music: Brian Houston

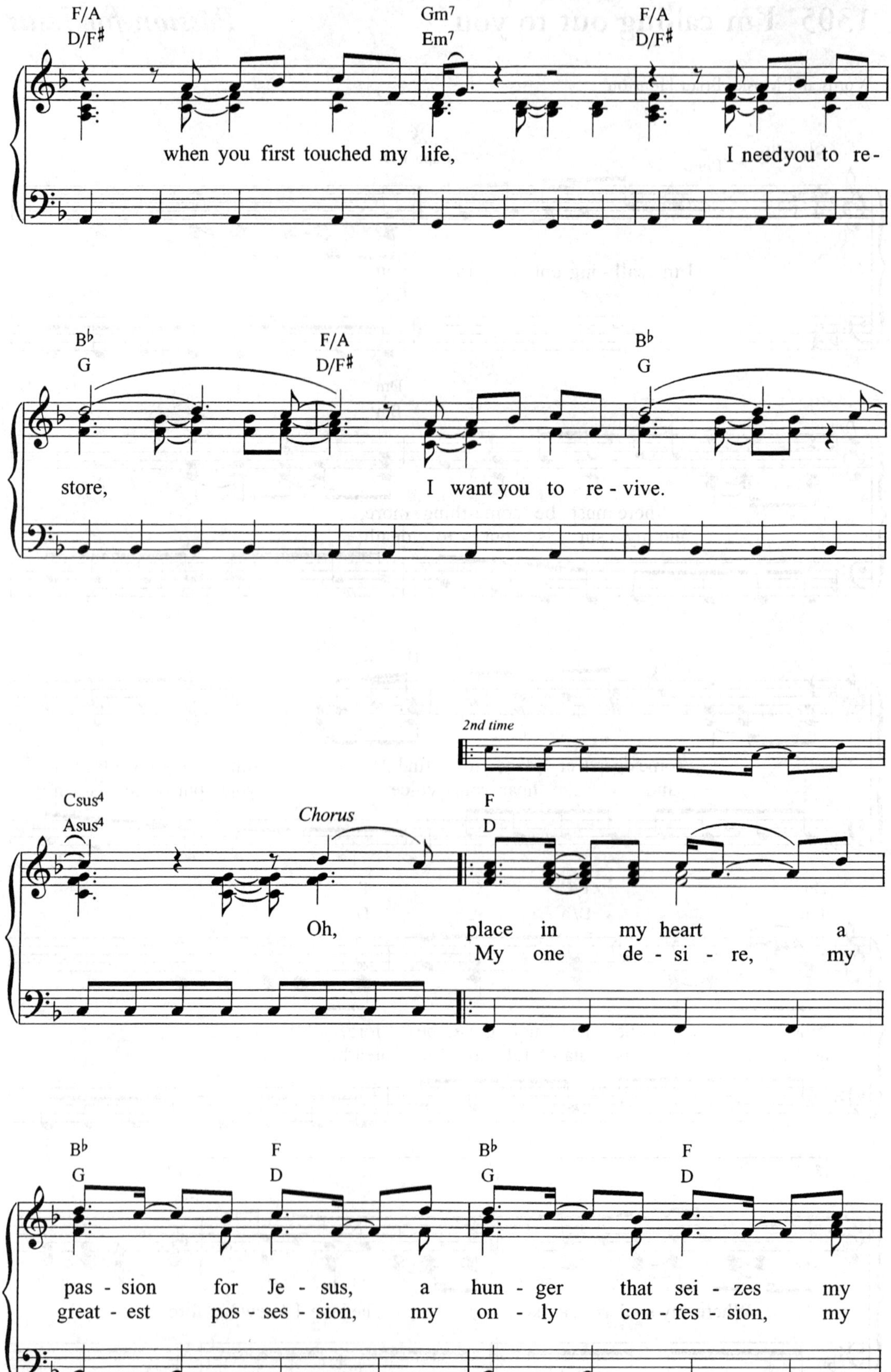
F/A D/F#
Gm7 Em7
F/A D/F#
when you first touched my life,
I need you to re-
B♭ G
F/A D/F#
B♭ G
store,
I want you to re - vive.
2nd time
Csus4 Asus4
Chorus
F D
Oh,
place in my heart a
My one de - si - re, my
B♭ G
F D
B♭ G
F D
pas - sion for Je - sus, a hun - ger that sei - zes my
great - est pos - ses - sion, my on - ly con - fes - sion, my

1.
B♭
G
Csus4
Asus4
C
A
2.
C
A
B♭sus2
Gsus2
pas - sion for you.
pas - sion for you.
3.
C
A
F
D
D.S.
I'm call - ing out to pas - sion for you.

1306 I'm coming back to you, my Father

Words and Music: Tim Lomax

back to your arms of grace.

You ran for miles to meet this child

re - turn - ing from the wil - der-ness.

Your o - pen arms will hold me now

to wel-come home the one you lost.

No-thing I do can make you love me more

E
B
Chorus
and you will ne-ver love me a-ny less. Fa-ther, when you
E
A2
draw me close I see a vis-ion of the cross, your
E
B
lov - ing arms out-stretched for me, for-giv-ing
E
E/G♯
A
words that set me free. Fa - ther, thank you
E
A2
for your grace, it's so much more than I de-serve. Fa-ther, thank
B7
E
you for your grace.

1307 I'm learning to love you *Learning to love you*

Words and Music: Paul Oakley

D
Chorus
C/D
For you are faith-ful in all of your ways,
D
in wis-dom un-search-a - ble, and full of
C/D
D
grace.
Oh, you are
C G C
beau - ti - ful be - yond words.
I'm learn-ing to love

G
Am7
G/B
you.
1, 3.
2.
4.
C
F
D.S.
C
2. So teach me to love
F2
C
We are like sha-dows that change with the day;
F2
and like the flow-ers our beau-ty will

C
Cm/E♭
fade.
But yours is the
F
king-dom and the pow - er;
Cm/E♭
F
for e - ver and e - ver your glo - ry
G
D.S.S. to ad lib. verse
will al - ways re - main.

1308 I'm making melody *Making melody*

Words and Music: Matt Redman

Strong beat
D
C
I'm mak - ing me - lo - dy in my heart to you.
D
C
I'm mak - ing me - lo - dy in my heart to you.
Bm
Bm/A
G
Pour - ing out your praise with ev - 'ry-thing with-in.
Yours will al - ways be the song I love to sing.
1.
D
C
2.
D
How can

G A D
hearts not love your name? How can
G A D
souls not sing your praise?
G G/A G/B
Je - sus, you put mu - sic
G/A D C D.C. D
in my soul. soul.
1. 2.

1309 I'm trading my sorrows

Trading my sorrows

Words and Music: Darrell Evans

I'm trad-ing my sor-rows,
I'm trad-ing my sick-ness,

I'm trad-ing my
I'm trad-ing my

shame,
pain,

I'm lay-ing them down for the joy of the
I'm lay-ing them down for the joy of the

Last time to Coda

Lord.
Lord.

Yes, Lord, yes, Lord,

yes, yes, Lord; yes, Lord, yes, Lord, yes, yes, Lord;

G C Em D G C
yes, Lord, yes, Lord, yes, yes, Lord, a - men.
Em D G C Em D
I'm pressed but not crushed, per-se-cut-ed, not a-ban-doned,
G C Em D/F♯ G C
struck down, but not des-troyed; I'm blessed be-yond the curse, for his
Em D G C Em D
pro-mise will en-dure, that his joy's gon-na be my strength.

Dsus4 D F
Though the sor-row may last for a night, his joy comes with the morn-
CODA
C D.C. al Coda Em D G C
- ing. La, la, la, la, la, la, la,
Em D G C Em D/F#
la, la, la, la, la, la, la, la, la, la, la, la, la, la, la, la,
G C Em D G C
la, la, la, la, la, la, la, la, la, la, a - men.

Em D G C Em D
La, la, la, la, la, la, la, la, la, la, la, la,
G C Em D/F♯ G C
la, la, la, la, la, la, la, la, la, la, la, la, la, la, la, la, la,
Em D C G/B Am7 D7 G
la, la, la, la, a - men.

1310 In and out of season

Simply believe

Words and Music: James Wright

C D G
great-er is he that is in us
Chorus
D C G Am7
than he with-in the world. Simp-ly be-lieve in his pro-mi-ses to
D C G Am7 D C G
you, keep on hold - ing to his words of truth, don't give up
F C D
but keep on trust - ing and he will see you through.
C G Am7 D C G
Simp-ly be-lieve in his pro-mi-ses to you, keep on hold-
Am7 D C G F C
- ing to his words of truth, don't give up but keep on trust-

D
- ing and we will see the high - est moun - tain re-moved.
G Am7 D C G Am7 D B D.C.
1.
2.
D C G Am7 D C
Simp-ly be-lieve
G Am7 D C G Am7
in his pro-mi-ses to you, keep on hold - ing to his words of truth,
D C G Am7 D C
don't give up on his pro-mi-ses to you, just simp-ly be-lieve.
G Am7 D C G

Therefore God exalted him to the highest place
and gave him the name that is above every name,
that at the name of Jesus every knee should bow,
in heaven and on earth and under the earth,
and every tongue confess that Jesus Christ is Lord,
to the glory of God the Father.

Philippians 2:9-11

1311 In Christ alone

Words: Stuart Townend

Music: Keith Getty

2. In Christ alone! – who took on flesh,
fullness of God in helpless babe!
This gift of love and righteousness,
scorned by the ones he came to save:
till on that cross as Jesus died,
the wrath of God was satisfied
for ev'ry sin on him was laid:
here in the death of Christ I live.

3. There in the ground his body lay,
Light of the world by darkness slain:
then bursting forth in glorious day
up from the grave he rose again!
And as he stands in victory
sin's curse has lost its grip on me,
for I am his and he is mine –
bought with the precious blood of Christ.

4. No guilt in life, no fear in death,
this is the pow'r of Christ in me;
from life's first cry to final breath,
Jesus commands my destiny.
No pow'r of hell, no scheme of man,
can ever pluck me from his hand;
till he returns or calls me home,
here in the pow'r of Christ I'll stand!

For where two or three come together in my name,
there am I with them.

Matthew 18:20

1312 I need thee every hour

Words: Annie Sherwood Hawks — Music: Robert Lowry

1. I need thee ev-'ry hour, most gra - cious Lord; no
ten - der voice like thine can peace af - ford.
Chorus
I need thee, oh, I need thee! Ev - 'ry hour I need thee! Oh,
bless me now, my Sa - viour! I come to thee.

2. I need thee ev'ry hour,
stay thou near by;
temptations lose their pow'r
when thou art nigh.

3. I need thee ev'ry hour,
in joy or pain;
come quickly and abide,
or life is vain.

4. I need thee ev'ry hour:
teach me thy will;
and thy rich promises
in me fulfil.

5. I need thee ev'ry hour,
most holy One;
Oh, make me thine indeed,
thou blessèd Son!

1313 I need you here

Need you here

Words and Music: Reuben Morgan

Esus4 E Bm7 A
I only want to be where you are.
Esus4 E Chorus E/A A E/G#
Holy, holy is the Lord,
D A/E E Asus4 A
King of glory for ever,
E6/G# E/G# 1. Bm7 E D.C.
Saviour of the world.
2. G D/F# A/E A

1314 I never knew

Sweeter name

Words and Music: Tim Hughes

1315 In every day that dawns *I know you love me*

Words and Music: Kate Simmonds and Stuart Townend

Bsus4 B Chorus E E2/D♯
I'm grate - ful for the air
C♯m7 E/B F♯/A♯ F♯
I breathe, I'm so thank - ful for this life
B7sus4 E E2/D♯
I live, for the mer - cies that you pour
C♯m7 E/B F♯/A♯ F♯
on me, and the bles - sings that meet ev -
B7sus4 F♯m7 E/A
- 'ry need. And the grace that is chang-ing me

B F#m7 E/A
from a hope-less case to a child that's free,
B F#m7 E/A B
free to give you praise, for in ev-'ry-thing I know you love
E D2(6) A2/C#
me.
B E D2(6)
I know you love me.
A2/C# B D.C. E

1316 In him we live and move

Words and Music: Randy Speir

With energy

In him we live and move and have our

being, in him we live and move and

have our being. being.

Make a joy - ful noise, sing un-to the Lord, tell him of your love,

G A Bm Cm A G
dance be - fore him. Make a joy - ful noise, sing un-to the Lord,
A G A D.S.
tell him of your love: hal - le - lu - jah! In him we

1317 In the beauty of holiness

Words and Music: Robin Mark

In the beau-ty of
ho-li-ness we see you, Son of Right-eous-ness,
I could bring, was there e-ver a song to sing
so we bring all that we pos-sess to lay at your
that could e-ver ex-press, my King, the work that you've
feet; in the place where your glo-ry shines,
done; could I e-ver con-ceive of this,

G♯m
C♯m7
Je - sus, lov - er of all man - kind,
all the depths and the height and breadth
A
E
you have drawn us with love di - vine
of the rich - es I now pos - sess
A
E
Chorus
to make us com - plete.
be-cause of your love.
So I pause at your
A
E
B
gates once more as my heart and my spi - rit soar,

A E
and I wish I could love you more,
A E
1.
my God and my King.
Is there tri-bute that
2.

1318 In the presence of holiness

Your blood says everything

Words and Music: Billy Somerville

In the pre-sence of ho - li - ness when I can-not speak

your blood says ev - 'ry-thing.

In the pre-sence of per-

- fect love I am too weak,

E
B
A
your blood says ev - 'ry - thing,
E
B
your blood says ev - 'ry - thing.
A
Chorus
E
Hear
E/D♯
C♯m7
Aadd9
the word
spo - ken
E
E/D♯
C♯m7
from
the tree;

Aadd9
E
E/D#
C#m7
hea-ven bro - ken o - pen.
Aadd9
E
B
Your blood says ev - 'ry - thing,
A
E
your blood
B
A
E
says ev - 'ry-thing.

The Lord is my rock, my fortress and my deliverer;
my God is my rock, in whom I take refuge.
He is my shield and the horn of my salvation, my stronghold.

The Lord lives! Praise be to my Rock!
Exalted be God my Saviour!

Psalm 18:2, 46

1319 In the presence of your people *Celebration song*

Words and Music: Brent Chambers

2. Lai, lai, lai-lai-lai-lai-lai-lai *(etc.)*

1320 In this place

Words and Music: Michael Neale

(♩= 66)
E
B/D♯
C♯m
A²
F♯m⁷
In this place I will praise the one who died to take

Bsus⁴
B
E
B/D♯
C♯m
A²
my place. I will bring my of - fer - ing and bow

F♯m⁷
Bsus⁴
B
F♯m⁷
E/G♯
be-fore the King of kings. Fears are now e - rased

A²
F♯m⁷
E/G♯
A²
in this sweet em - brace for the

F#m7
E/G#
A
B
B7sus4
1.
E
glo - ry of the Lord is in this place.
A2
2.
E

1321 Into the centre

Words and Music: Bruce Ellis and Dan Wilt

2, 3, 4.
B♭ F Gm E♭
G D Em C
ev - 'ry pray'r, you know the bro - ken - ness we
ev - 'ry pray'r, you know we're ask - ing, Fa - ther,
B♭ F Gm E♭
G D Em Chorus C
have to bear. You know the hun - ger of our
are you there?
B♭ F Gm E♭
G D Em C
ge - ne - ra - tion, you know the lies that we've been
B♭ F Gm E♭
G D Em C
cap - tive of: you know we're long - ing for a

B♭ G F D Gm Em E♭ C
re - ve - la - tion, you know.
B♭ G F D Gm Em E♭ C
(You know.)
B♭ G F D Gm Em E♭ C
To repeat
Last time
B♭ G F D
1st time D.C.
2nd time D.S. (v.3)
B♭ G Fomit3 Domit3
(And you)

Praise the Lord, O my soul;
all my inmost being, praise his holy name.
Praise the Lord, O my soul,
and forget not all his benefits –
who forgives all your sins
and heals all your diseases . . .

Psalm 103:1-3

1322 Into your hands *With all I am*

Words and Music: Reuben Morgan

1. In - to your hands I com-mit a-gain all I am for you, Lord. You hold my world in the palm of your hand and I am yours for e - ver.

2. I'll walk with you wher-e - ver you go; through tears and joy I'll trust in you and I will live in all of your ways and your pro-mi - ses for e - ver.

Chorus
Je-sus, I be-lieve in you, Je-sus, I be-long

F/A C/A B♭ Gm
to you; you're the rea-son that I live, the rea-son that I sing
1.
Csus4 C F F/C C
with all I am.
Last time
2.
F Fine F F2 Gm9
am. am.
Csus4 C Bridge Fsus4 F C/E Gm
I will wor - ship you, I will wor - ship you,
Csus4 C Fsus4 F C/E
I will wor - ship you, I will wor -
To repeat Bridge
To continue
B♭/D Csus4 C Csus4 C D.S. al Fine
- ship you. I will wor- Je-sus, I be-lieve

1323 Into your presence we come

Words and Music: Tom Lane

In - to your pre-sence we come,

in - to your pre-sence we come, Lord Je - sus,

to wor - - ship you,

to wor -

A/C# Bm Bm/G# F#m
- ship you, to wor -
D E
- ship you.
Chorus
A E Bm7
With-out ble - mish, with-out stain, you are the Lamb that bore
F#m A E
all our pain, we give to you the sa - cri-fice of praise.
Bm7 A
With-out hon - our,

E
Bm7
with - out fame, you walked the way of suf -
F#m
A
E
- f'ring and shame. We give to you the sa - cri-fice of praise,
Bm7
A
we give to you the sa -
E
F#m
E/F#
F#m
- cri-fice of praise.

This righteousness from God
comes through faith in Jesus Christ
to all who believe.
There is no difference,
for all have sinned
and fall short of the glory of God,
and are justified freely by his grace
through the redemption that came by Christ Jesus.

Romans 3:22-24

1324 In your presence

In your presence, O God

Words and Music: Lynn DeShazo

C Am7 Bm7 G C2 D
- vers can-not o - ver-flow me, where my feet are on a rock;
of e - vil can-not reach me, where I'm co-vered by your blood;
Em7 C Am7 Bm7
I want to hide where the bla - zing fi - re can - not burn me,
I want to be where the schemes of dark-ness can - not touch me,
1. D.S. 2.
G C Dsus4 D Dsus4 D Chorus
in your pre-sence, O God. In your In your
G D Em7 C C/D G D
pre - sence, that's where I am strong, in your pre - sence, O
Em7 C C/D G D Em7 C
Lord, my God; in your pre - sence, that's where I be-long,

Em7 Bm7 Em7 Bm7 C Bm7
seek-ing your face, touch-ing your grace, in the cleft of the rock
Am7 G/B C G/D D G F C
in your pre-sence,O God. You are my firm
F C Em D C
foun - da - tion, I trust in you all day long;
F C F C
I am your child and your ser - vant, and
Em7 D C Dsus4 D
D.S.
you are my strength and my song, you're my song. In your

Who may ascend the hill of the Lord?
Who may stand in his holy place?
He who has clean hands and a pure heart.

Psalm 24:3, 4a

1325 In your presence *God is here*

Words and Music: Lara Martin (Abundant Life Ministries, Bradford, England)

Simply
Amaj7
Dmaj7
1. In your pre - sence there is full - ness of life,
2. In your pre - sence there is per - fect peace;
and heal - ing flow - ing for bo - dy, soul and mind.
in the still - ness, I be - hold your de - i - ty.
God of mi - ra - cles, God of the im - pos - si - ble is
God of won - der, God of pow - er is
here, God is here.
here, God is here.
Asus2
A
Chorus
God is here,

A2 D2 A2
let the bro - ken-heart-ed re - joice. (Lift up your head.)
D2
God is here, let the sick say I am well.
E A2
(All-suf-fi - cient one.) God is here, let the
D2 A2
weak say I am strong. (Let the weak say I am strong.) God is here,
F#m7 E 1. D2
his won-ders to per-form.

2.
D
E
Oh, his won-ders, yes, his won-ders, his
D2
won-ders to per-form. Oh, his won-ders, yes, his won-ders,
E
1.
2.
A2
his won-ders to per-form. won-ders to per-form.

1326 In you we live

Words and Music: Graham Kendrick

In you we live, Jesus, in you we move.

In you we breathe, Jesus,

in you we love and we are your bo - dy here,

we are your bo - dy here.

E
Your touch: our hands, your words: our voice,
You give: we share, you lead: we go,
your way: our feet, your tears in our eyes,
you send: we serve, you build and we grow,
A
E
your Spi-rit is here.
your Spi-rit is here.
A
E
1. A-cross the world, you're mov-ing; the sound of prayer
2. You are the light that's dawn-ing, you are the hope
A
is grow-ing strong-er
trans-form-ing all things;

E
from ev - 'ry tribe and na - tion join - ing in one
free - ing the whole cre - a - tion to join in one
1.
A
1st time repeat v.1 only
2nd time sing both verses
2.
A
sal - va - tion song.
sal - va - tion song,
E
B
E
one song.
1.
D.C.
2.
A/B
E
(One song.)
In you we live,
In you we breathe,
B
E
A/B
E
Je - sus, in you we move.
Je - sus, in you we love.
(One song.)

1327 I rejoiced when they said to me

Let us go to the house of the Lord

Words and Music: Steve James

A7
peo - ple now the place, a liv - ing tem - ple built to
grace and peace with - in; re-flect the beau - ty of the
Am7 Dsus4 D C
praise you. These gates by Christ
Sa - viour! Where ev - 'ry na -
Em
held o - pen wide; his sac - ri - fice, the way pre-scribed,
- tion, tribe and tongue will ga - ther round your throne, as one,
A7 Am7 Dsus4 D Bridge
we en - ter in, his prai - ses sing - ing. The
in u - ni - ty, his prai - ses sing - ing. From

C/D
D2
walls have now been bro - ken; brought near by Je - sus' blood.
glo - ry in - to glo - ry, in heav'n we take our place,
The tem - ple he is build - ing shall
we cast our crowns be - fore him in
stand for e - ver - more.
won - der, love and praise.
CODA
Chorus D.S.
D
I re- Re-joice in the
G2
C
Em
G
Lord, re-joice in the Lord.

When Jesus spoke again to the people,
he said, 'I am the light of the world.
Whoever follows me will never walk in darkness,
but will have the light of life.'

John 8:12

1328 I see the Lord

Words and Music: John Chisum and Don Moen

I see the Lord, I see the Lord ex-al-ted

high up-on the wor-ship of the peo-ple of the earth; I see the

Lord, I see the Lord, my eyes have seen the King,

2nd time to Coda

the Lamb up-on the throne who reigns for

Asus4 A G/A D Dsus4/A D
Verse
e - ver - more. The train of his
A/C# G/B Bm D/A G2 G
robe fills the tem - ple, a cloud of heav'n - ly
Asus4 A Bm Asus4 A G
wor - ship - pers sur - round - ing his throne; we join with them
A Bsus4/C# F#/A# Bm Bm/A Em7 Dmaj7/F# Gmaj7/B Asus4
now cry - ing, 'Ho - ly, ho - ly is the Lamb, the Lamb a - lone.'
D.S. al Coda
CODA
G/A A Asus4 A G/A D
Chorus
I see the e - ver - more.

1329 I see the Lord

Words and Music: Paul Oakley

Smoothly
Capo 3 D
F D C A F D
1. I see the Lord, and he is high and lift - ed up, and his
2. I see your ho - li-ness, and light sur-rounds your throne; who am
B♭ G C7sus4 A7sus4
train fills the tem - ple.
I to come be-fore you?
F D C A F D
2nd time to
I see you, Lord, and you are high and lift - ed up, and your
But now my guilt is gone, my sins are washed a-way, through your
B♭ G Csus4 Asus4 C A B♭ G F D
Chorus
train fills the tem - ple. And I cry ho - ly,

Bb F Bb F Csus4 C
G D G D Asus4 A
ho-ly is the Lord, ho-ly is the Lord most high. And I cry
Last time to Coda
Bb F Bb F Bb F
G D G D G D
ho - ly, ho-ly is the Lord, ho-ly is the Lord most
2nd time
Csus4 C Bb Csus4 C
Asus4 A G Asus4 A
high. blood I come.
Bb C Dm7
G A Bm7
Who am I that I should gain the Fa - ther's love?

B♭ G
Csus4 Asus4
C A
Now my eyes have seen the King.
B♭ G
C A
Dm7 Bm7
Touch my lips that I may tell of all you've done:
Gm7 Em7
C7sus4 A7sus4
fill my heart I cry, be glo - ri - fied!
CODA
D.C. al Coda
Csus4 Asus4
C A
F D
high.

Praise him with the sounding of the trumpet,
praise him with the harp and lyre,
praise him with tambourine and dancing,
praise him with the strings and flute,
praise him with the clash of cymbals,
praise him with resounding cymbals.

Psalm 150:3-5

1330 I stand amazed

Words and Music: Paul Oakley

Slow 4
Verse
A D/A A E/A
I stand a-mazed when I re - a - lise your
D E A D E A
love for me is be - yond all mea - sure. Lord, I
D E D E A A/C♯ Chorus
can't de - ny your love for me is great. It's as
D Dmaj7 D6 A
high, high as the hea-vens a - bove,
E A/C♯ Bm7 D E
such is the depth of your love to - ward those who

A D E D Dmaj7 D6
fear you. O Lord, far as the east is from
A F♯m Bm7
west, you have re-moved my trans - gres-sions. You
D A/C♯ D E D E Bm7 E
make my life brand new: Fa - ther, I love
A (Fine) 1. D/A A E 2. D/A
you. I stand a-mazed
D D/E
Your love is high - er, high as the hea -

A D E D
- vens. Your love is deep - er,
D/E A D E
deep - er than the deep-est o - cean.
Bm7 D/E
Your love is strong - er, strong - er than the pow'rs of dark -
A D E D/E
- ness. Your love is sweet - er,
A D E D.S. al Fine
sweet-er than wine. It's as

Create in me a pure heart, O God,
and renew a steadfast spirit within me.

Psalm 51:10

1331 It's amazing

Words and Music: Geraldine Latty

Exuberantly

It's a-maz - ing, a-stound-ing, ex - tra - va - gant grace. It's a-maz-

- ing, a-stound - ing, ex - tra - va - gant grace. It's a-maz-

- ing, a-stound - ing, ex - tra - va - gant grace. Lord, to you
(Lord, to you

After v.2 chorus, to Bridge ⊕ | *To repeat chorus only* ‖ *Last time*

I lift my praise. It's a-maz-
we lift our praise.)

(vs. 2&3)
To verses
G
D
G
1. In all my griev - ing and
2. In all my pain and
3. In all my days of
C
G
D
G
in all my weep - ing your grace still flows, your
through all my dark - ness your grace still flows, your
qui - et re - stor - ing your grace still flows, your
D
G
D
G
grace still flows. In all my seek - ing and
grace still flows. In my in - dif - fer-ence and
grace still flows. And when I walk with
C
G
C
C/D
Chorus
D.S.
on my re - turn - ing your grace still flows to me.
through all my hard - ness your grace still flows to me. It's a-maz-
joy o - ver-flow - ing your grace still flows to me.

Bridge
G
D
G
Thank you for your kind - ness that
D
G
D
G
leads me to re - pen - tance, thank you for your pow'r that
Am
G/B
C
G/B
D
G
saves me, Je - sus! Thank you for your name that
D
G
C
lifts me to the Fa - ther. What an a - maz - ing, ex -
D
Chorus
D.S.
tra - va - gant grace! It's a - maz-

Let us acknowledge the Lord;
let us press on to acknowledge him.
As surely as the sun rises,
he will appear;
he will come to us like the winter rains,
like the spring rains that water the earth.

Hosea 6:3

1332 It's me, it's me, O Lord

Words and Music: Spiritual

STANDING IN THE NEED 13 7 13 7 and Refrain

2. Not the preacher, not the deacon,
but it's me, O Lord,
standin' in the need of prayer;
not the preacher, not the deacon,
but it's me, O Lord,
standin' in the need of prayer.

3. Not my father, not my mother,
but it's me, O Lord,
standin' in the need of prayer;
not my father, not my mother,
but it's me, O Lord,
standin' in the need of prayer.

4. Not the stranger, not my neighbour,
but it's me, O Lord,
standin' in the need of prayer;
not the stranger, not my neighbour,
but it's me, O Lord,
standin' in the need of prayer.

1333 I've had questions *When the tears fall*

Words and Music: Tim Hughes

Capo 3
F D
F/G D/E
Am7 F#m7
1. I've had ques - tions with-out ans - wers,
But there's one thing that I'll cling to;
2. In the lone hour of my sor - row,
you sur-round me and sus-tain me;
F D
Am7 F#m7
Gsus4 Esus4
I've known sor - row, I have known pain.
you are faith - ful, Je - sus, you're true.
through the dark - est night of my soul,
my de - fen - der, for e - ver - more.
F D
Chorus
C/E A/C#
Gsus4 Esus4
G E
When hope is lost, I'll call you Sa - viour.
F D
C/E A/C#
Gsus4 Esus4
When pain sur-rounds, I'll call you heal - er.

1.
F D
Am7 F#m7
F/G D/E
F D
When si-lence falls, you'll be the song with-in my heart.
D.C. (v.2)
2.
F D
F/G D/E
heart.
Bridge
F D
F/G D/E
C/E A/C#
F D
I will praise you, I will praise you, when the tears fall,
G E
C/E A/C#
F D
still I will sing to you. I will praise you,

F/G D/E C/E A/C♯ F D
Je - sus, praise you, through the suf - f'ring
G E C/E A/C♯ F D
Final Chorus
still I will sing. When hope is lost,
C/E A/C♯ Gsus4 Esus4 G E F D
I'll call you Sa - viour. When pain sur- rounds,
Dm7 Bm7 F D
I'll call you heal - er. When si - lence falls,
Am7 F♯m7 F/G D/E F D
you'll be the song with- in my heart.

The Spirit of the Sovereign Lord is on me,
because the Lord has anointed me
to preach good news to the poor.
He has sent me to bind up the broken-hearted,
to proclaim freedom for the captives
and release from darkness for the prisoners,
to proclaim the year of the Lord's favour
and the day of vengeance of our God,
to comfort all who mourn,
and provide for those who grieve in Zion –
to bestow on them a crown of beauty instead of ashes,
the oil of gladness instead of mourning,
and a garment of praise instead of a spirit of despair.

Isaiah 61:1-3a

1334 I've thrown it all away

Take the world but give me Jesus

Words and Music: Matt Redman

E♭ C F/A D/F♯ E♭2 C2
pare; you've won my heart, now this will be my
care; you've won my heart, now this will be my
F D E♭ C B♭ G E♭ C
Chorus
pray - er. 'Take the world but
pray - er. Last time only: Now I've seen you
Gm Em
Repeat Chorus 4th time only
give me Je - sus!' You're the trea - sure in this life.
as the Sa - viour, I will leave the rest be - hind:
1, 3, 4.
C7/E A/C♯ E♭2 C2 B♭2 G2
'Take the world but give me Je - sus!' is my cry.
2.
B♭2 G2
D.S.
5.
B♭2 G2
is my cry. 2. In - is my cry.

1335 I want to be holy

Words and Music: Wendy Rayner and Andrew Rayner

(♩ = 110)
Esus2 Bsus2 C#m7
1. I want to be ho - ly and live my life for you;
want to be ho - ly and live what I be - lieve;
Asus2 C#m7 Bsus4
in all that I say and all that I do, Lord, make me
the things that I do be on - ly for you, Lord, make me
Esus2 C#m7 Bsus2 Esus2
ho - ly. I want to be ho -
ho - ly. I want to be ho -
Bsus2 C#m7 Asus2
- ly but things get in the way. The cry of my heart
- ly, your touch up - on my life. I'm down on my knees

© Copyright 2001 Kevin Mayhew Ltd.

C♯m7
Bsus4
Esus2
is 'Set me a - part', Lord, make me ho - ly.
and ask - ing you, please, Lord, make me ho - ly.
C♯m7
Bsus2
Chorus
E/G♯
Asus2
So send the fire, come and
C♯m7
Bsus4
E/G♯
burn up all my sin. Breathe through me now
Asus2
C♯m7
Bsus4
and stir the pas - sion deep with - in. The
Amaj7
F♯m7
world's rich - est trea - sures are the voi - ces that call; their

Asus2
C♯m7
beau - ty and plea - sures, I'll give them all,
Bsus2
I'll give them all to be
Esus2/G♯
Asus2
Bsus4
ho - ly.
Esus2/G♯
Asus2
Bsus4
1.
D.S.
2.
Esus2
2. I

1336 I want to be more like you

Words and Music: Clint Brown

1337 I want to give you more *High above*

Words and Music: Brian Platt

Dm7
G7
ho - - ly.
Chorus
C
C/E
F
C/E
Dm7
Je - sus, you are God, high a - bove all
G7
C
C/E
F
C/E
else, mak - er of the u - ni-verse, high a -
Dm7
G7
Last time
C
Fine
bove all else.
C
Am
Mak - er of the u - ni - verse, you're ho - ly,
Dm7
G7
2nd time D.S. al Fine
high a - bove the hea - vens you are ho - ly.

1338 I want to hear you say

My reward

Words and Music: Paul Baloche

I want to hear you say the words to me, 'Well

done'; I want to hear you say,

'Good and faith - ful ser - vant'; I want to hear

you say, 'I've pre-pared a place for you';

Bm9
let all the trea - sures of this world
Dmaj7
fade a-way.
Chorus
A
Je - sus,
Je - sus,
Esus4 E Esus4 E6
you are my re - ward; to hear your voice on that
you are my re - ward; to see your face on that
Dmaj7
Last time to Coda
A
To repeat Chorus
day is all I'm liv - ing for.
day is all I'm liv - ing for.
To repeat verse
D.S.
To Bridge
Fmaj7
Bridge
I want to hear
In the twink -

G
- ling of an eye
we'll all be changed.
Fmaj7
G
We'll meet you in the sky,
we will see
A
A/G
you face to face.
CODA
Dmaj7
D.S.S. al Coda
A
A/G
Dmaj7
A
Je - sus,
all I'm liv - ing for.

Therefore, if anyone is in Christ,
he is a new creation;
the old has gone, the new has come!

2 Corinthians 5:17

1339 I was glad

Words and Music: Gerrit Gustafson and Don Moen

Verse
Dm Bm C A Dm Bm
Here we are, in your courts we stand with our
B♭ G F/A D/F♯ Gm9 Em9 C A F D Dm Bm
hearts and hands up - raised; here we are,
C A Dm Bm B♭ G F/A D/F♯
by the blood of the Lamb, by your grace we come and
Gm7 Em7 F/A D/F♯ Gm7/B♭ Em7/G Gm7 Em7 B♭/C G/A C A
D.S.
by your grace we stand. I was glad

God, who has called you into fellowship
with his Son Jesus Christ our Lord, is faithful.

1 Corinthians 1:9

1340 I was made to praise you

Words and Music: Chris Christensen

G Am7 Dsus2 D
1. I was made to praise you, I was made to
2. I will al-ways praise you, I will al-ways
C/G G B7 Em G/A Am
glo - ri - fy your name, in ev-'ry cir - cum - stance to
glo - ri - fy your name, in ev-'ry cir - cum - stance I'll
C/D D Am7 Bm7 Cmaj7 C/D G
find a chance to thank you. I was made to
find a chance to thank you. I will al-ways
Am7 Dsus2 D C/G G B7
love you, I was made to wor - ship at your
love you, I will al-ways wor - ship at your
Em G/A A C/D D6 G
feet, and to o - bey you, Lord, I was made for you.
feet, and I'll o - bey you, Lord, I was made for you.

1341 I was sinking deep in sin *Love lifted me*

Words: James Rowe Music: Howard E. Smith

SAFETY Irregular

Capo 3 G
B♭
F7
D7
1. I was sink - ing deep in sin, far from the peace - ful shore,
B♭
G
ve - ry deep - ly stained with - in, sink - ing to rise no more;
E♭
C
but the Mas - ter of the sea heard my des - pair - ing cry,
E♭m B♭ B♭maj7 C7 B♭ F7 B♭
Cm G Gmaj7 A7 G D7 G
from the wa - ters lift - ed me: now safe am I.

Bb F7 Bb Eb Cm Eb F7 Bb
G D7 G C Am G D7 G
Chorus Love lift - ed me! Love lift - ed me!
Love lift - ed e - ven me! Love lift - ed e - ven me! When no - thing
1. 2.
C7 F F7 Bb F7 Bb
A7 D D7 G D7 G
else could help, love lift - ed me! love lift-ed me!

2. All my heart to him I give;
ever to him I'll cling,
in his blessed presence live,
ever his praises sing.
Love so mighty and so true
merits my soul's best songs;
faithful, loving service, too,
to him belongs.

3. Souls in danger, look above;
Jesus completely saves;
he will lift you by his love
out of the angry waves.
He's the Master of the sea,
billows his will obey;
he your Saviour wants to be –
be saved today.

1342 I will be a living sacrifice

Sacrifice

Words and Music: Craig Wallis

(♩ = 120)
F
Fmaj7
B♭2/F
Capo 3 D
Dmaj7
G2/D
F
D
F/A
D/F♯
1. I will be a liv-ing sac - ri - fice,
2. I will hold to all that's true
B♭2
G2
B♭2/F
G2/D
F
D
pure and
and give it
F/A
D/F♯
B♭2
G2
B♭2/F
G2/D
ho - ly in your eyes,
all to fol - low you.

F/G
D/E
B♭2
G2
I will fol - low where you lead;
You give strength when I am weak;
F/G
D/E
I'm fall - ing deep - er in - to
you are ev - 'ry - thing I
1.
B♭2
G2
deep.
2.
B♭maj7
Gmaj7
need.
Chorus
B♭/C
G/A
Cm
Am
F
D
F/A
D/F♯
Ho - ly, ho - ly, ho - ly are you,
Ho - ly, ho - ly, ho - ly are you,

B♭2 G2
B♭/C G/A
Cm Am
F D
Lord. I'm set a - part for the One
Lord. You paid the price that I
F/A D/F♯
1.
B♭maj7 Gmaj7
B♭/C G/A
Cm Am
that I a - dore.
could not af -
2.
B♭2 G2
B♭/C G/A
Cm Am
1st time D.S. (repeat v.1)
F D
ford.
Fmaj7 Dmaj7
B♭2/F G2/D
F2 D2

The Son is the radiance of God's glory
and the exact representation of his being,
sustaining all things by his powerful word.

Hebrews 1:3a

1343 I will bless the Lord for ever *Made me glad*

Words and Music: Miriam Webster

Capo 3
E♭2 C2
B♭2 G2
1. I will bless the Lord for e - ver,
He has de - liv - ered me from all fear,
2. Whom have I in hea - ven but you?
1.
I will trust him at all times.
he has
There's none
2, 3.
set my feet up - on a
I de - sire be-sides
rock.
you.
E♭ C
I will not be moved,
You have made me glad,

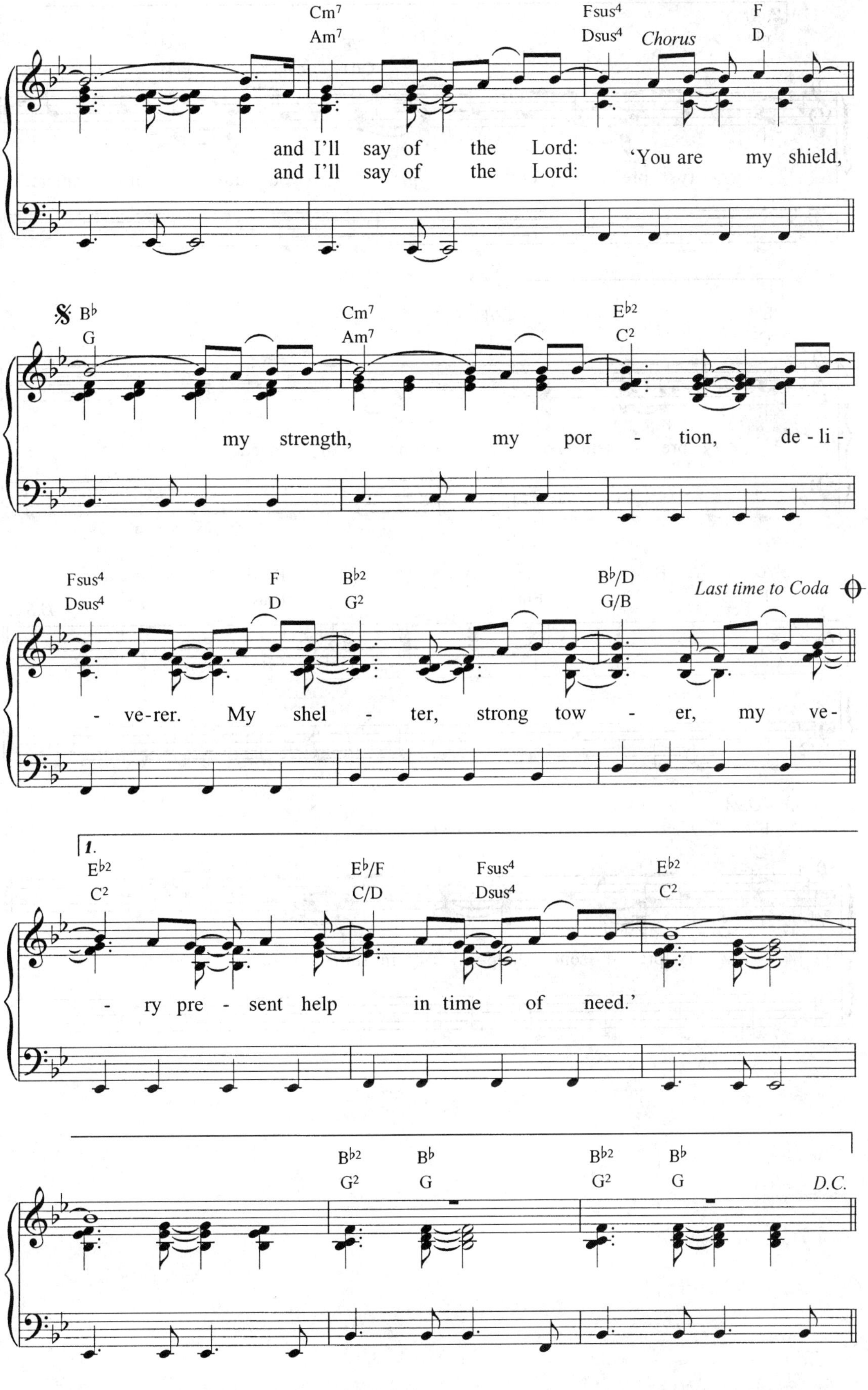
Cm7 Am7 Fsus4 Dsus4 Chorus F D
and I'll say of the Lord: 'You are my shield,
and I'll say of the Lord:
Bb G Cm7 Am7 Eb2 C2
my strength, my portion, de-li-
Fsus4 Dsus4 F D Bb2 G2 Bb/D G/B Last time to Coda
-verer. My shelter, strong tower, my ve-
1.
Eb2 C2 Eb/F C/D Fsus4 Dsus4 Eb2 C2
-ry present help in time of need.'
Bb2 G2 Bb G Bb2 G2 Bb G D.C.

2, 4.
Eb2 C2
Eb/F C/D
Chorus
Fsus4 Dsus4
D.S.
- ry pre - sent help, you are my shield,
3.
Eb2 C2
Eb/F C/D
Cm7 Am7
- ry pre - sent help in time of need.'
Bb/D G/B
Gm Em
Fsus4 Dsus4
D.S.S.
CODA
Eb2 C2
Eb/F C/D
Bb G
- ry pre - sent help in time of need.'

1344 I will dance, I will sing

Words and Music: James Wright

(♩ = 140)
Chorus
Capo 3
F D
B♭2 G2
F D
I will dance, I will sing, and with all my heart I'll
C A
F D
B♭2 G2
praise you, for the joy that you bring caus - es my heart
F D
C A
F D
to o - ver - flow. I will shout to the King,
B♭2 G2
F D
C A
to my hope and my sal - va - tion,

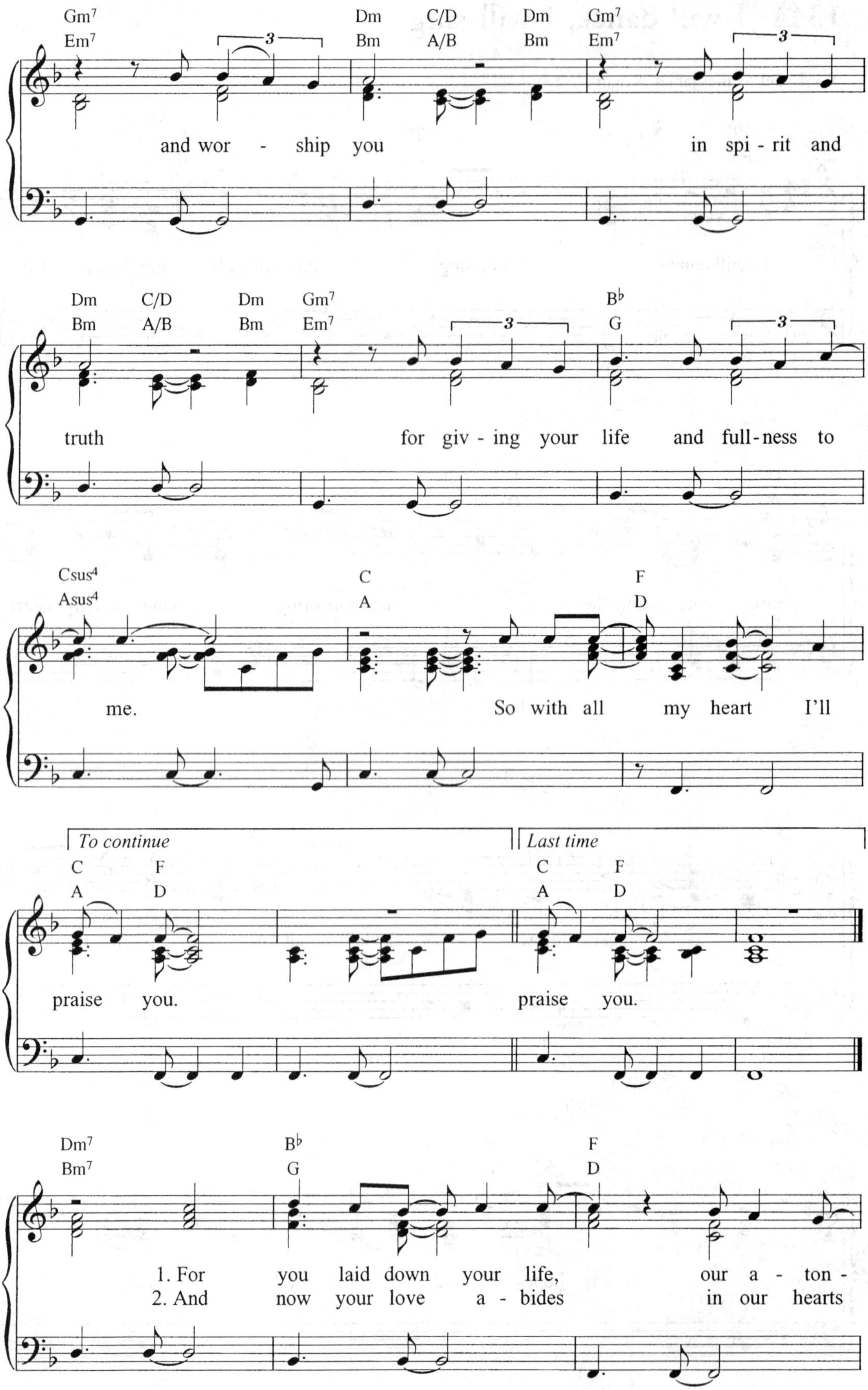
Gm7 Dm C/D Dm Gm7
Em7 Bm A/B Bm Em7
and wor - ship you in spi - rit and
Dm C/D Dm Gm7 B♭
Bm A/B Bm Em7 G
truth for giv - ing your life and full - ness to
Csus4 C F
Asus4 A D
me. So with all my heart I'll
To continue
Last time
C F C F
A D A D
praise you. praise you.
Dm7 B♭ F
Bm7 G D
1. For you laid down your life, our a - ton -
2. And now your love a - bides in our hearts

C Dm7
A Bm7
- ing sac - ri - fice, re -
and in our lives, u -
B♭ F Csus4 C
G D Asus4 A
leased the chains that held us in cap - ti - vi - ty.
ni - ting us in love, in truth and des - ti - ny.
Dm7 B♭ F
Bm7 G D
You rolled the stone a - way when you rose
No long - er held by sin for it's Christ
C Dm7 B♭
A Bm7 G
on the third day, and now you reign ex - alt -
who lives with - in; our right - eous - ness, our wis -
F Csus4 C
D Asus4 A
Chorus
D.S.
- ed o - ver all. I will dance,
- dom and our strength.

1345 I will enter your house *Blessed to be a blessing*

Words and Music: Lara Martin (Abundant Life Ministries)

Very rhythmic
D C G/B D
I will en - ter your house with thanks-giv - ing, I will sing of your
C G/B G A
good-ness to me. For my heart is e - ter - nal - ly grate - ful,
G Em7
I am blessed a - bun - dant-ly. You have giv - en me
Bm7 A G A Bm
life in all its full-ness, and joy no words can des-cribe.
Em7 Bm7 A G
But I know it's for more than me, it's for those,

A
those you sent me to reach. I am
D G Em7
blessed, blessed to be a bles - sing, I am blessed, I
A D G
live un-der an o - pen hea-ven, blessed, that all may see it's
Em7 1. A 2. A
Christ, Christ in me. I am
D C G/B C D F

1346 I will lift my voice and sing *You are great*

Words and Music: Jared Anderson

(♩ = 136)
Capo 3
Verse
Gm Em
E♭ C
Gm Em
E♭ C
I will lift my voice and sing, great is the Lord;
to the giv-er of good things, great is the Lord;
no be-gin-ning and no end, great is the Lord;
I will sing a-gain, great is the Lord;
B♭/F G/D
Cm9 Am9
all the earth re - sounds with praise, the o -

B♭/D G/B B♭/F G/D Gm Em
- ceans break their waves; my heart will join their song;
Cm9 Am9 Fsus4 Dsus4 B♭ G
I will say that you are great.
Chorus 1
All the u -
Gm7 Em7
- ni - verse dis - plays all the won - ders of your ways,
your pow - ers known; you are God and God a - lone;
E♭ C Cm7 Am7 Fsus4 Dsus4
and my heart can - not con - tain but to say that you are great.
let the peo - ple praise you now and say that you are great.
1, 3. 2.
B♭ G Gm Em E♭ C Gm Em
You make

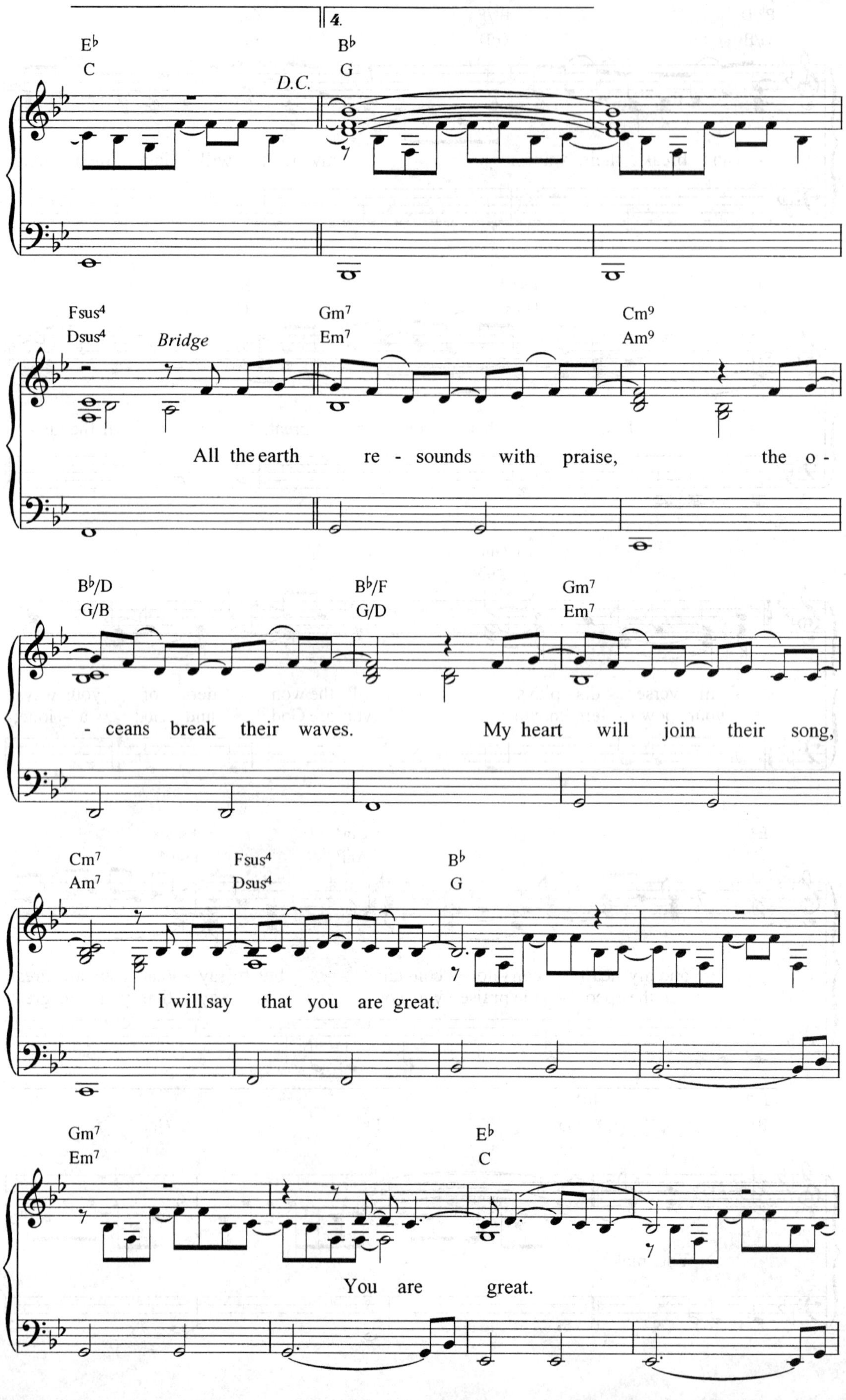

4.
E♭ C
D.C.
B♭ G
Fsus4 Dsus4
Bridge
Gm7 Em7
Cm9 Am9
All the earth re - sounds with praise, the o -
B♭/D G/B
B♭/F G/D
Gm7 Em7
- ceans break their waves. My heart will join their song,
Cm7 Am7
Fsus4 Dsus4
B♭ G
I will say that you are great.
Gm7 Em7
E♭ C
You are great.

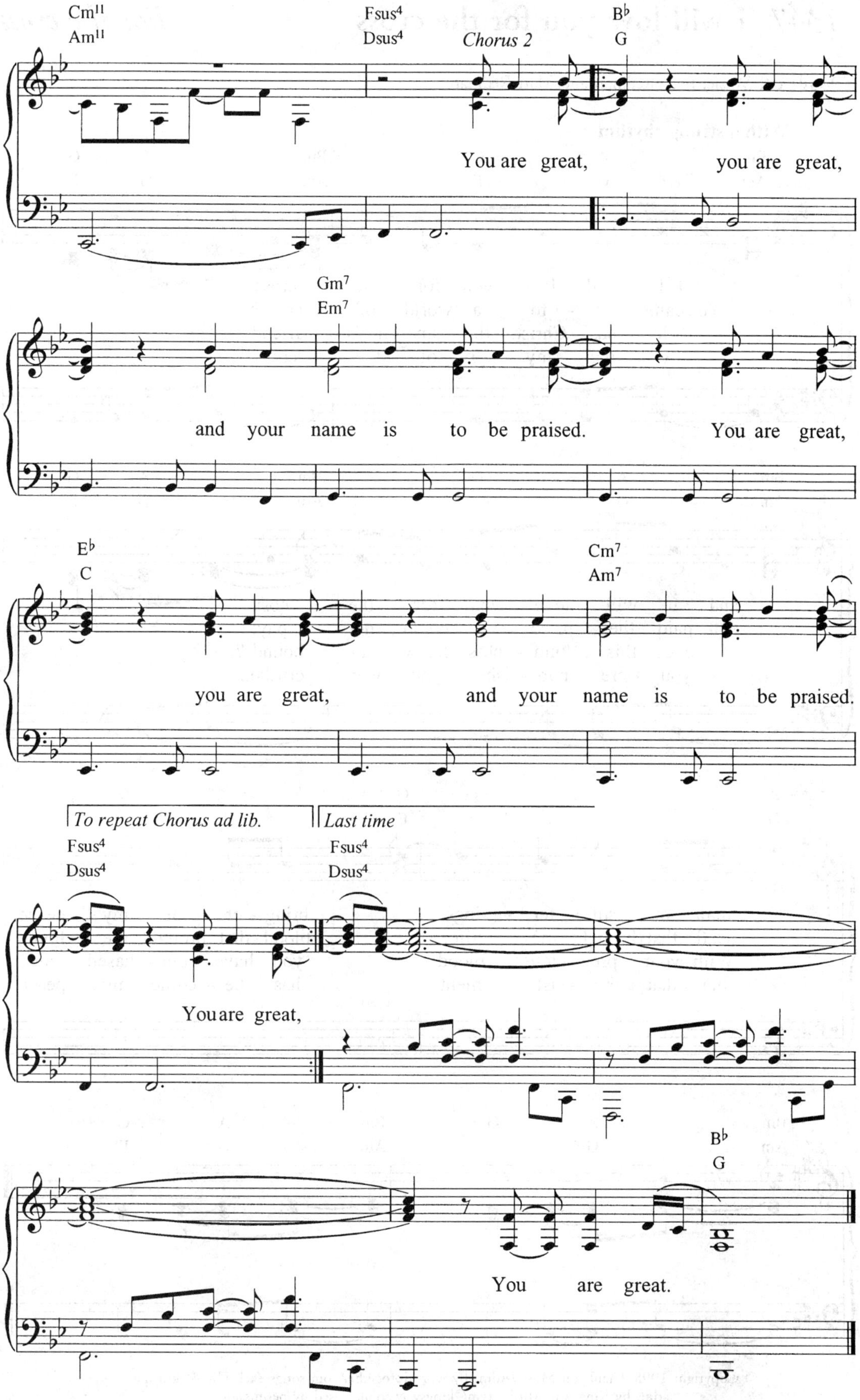

Cm11
Am11
Fsus4
Dsus4
Chorus 2
B♭
G
You are great, you are great,
Gm7
Em7
and your name is to be praised. You are great,
E♭
C
Cm7
Am7
you are great, and your name is to be praised.
To repeat Chorus ad lib.
Last time
Fsus4
Dsus4
Fsus4
Dsus4
You are great,
B♭
G
You are great.

1347 I will love you for the cross *For the cross*

Words and Music: Beth Redman and Matt Redman

With a strong rhythm
Bm A G Bm A G
Capo 2 Am G F Am G F
1. I will love you for the cross,
You came in - to a world of shame,
2. Je - sus Christ, the sin - ner's friend;
O the my - st'ry of the cross,
Bm A G Bm A G
Am G F Am G F
and I will love you for the cost:
and paid the price we could not pay:
does this kind - ness know no bounds?
you were pun - ished, you were crushed;
A G
G F
man of suf - fer - ings, bring - er of my peace.
death that brought me life, blood that brought me home.
With your pre - cious blood you have pur - chased me.
but that pun - ish - ment has be - come my peace.
Bm A G Bm A G
Am G F Am G F

A G
G F
Death that brought me life, blood that brought me home.
Yes, that pun - ish - ment has be - come my peace.
D C
F♯m7 Em7
Chorus
Bm Am
And I love you for the cross,
G F
A G
I'm o - ver - whelmed by the mys -
G F
Bm Am
G F
- te - ry. I love you for the cost
A G
G F
Bm Am
that, Je - sus, you would do this for me. When you were bro - ken, you
G F
A G
G F
were bea - ten, you were pun - ished, I go free. When you

Bm Am G F A G
were wound - ed and re - jec - ted, in your mer - cy,
Gmaj7 Fmaj7
Last time to Coda
I am healed.
1. Bm Am A G G F Bm Am A G G F
Bm Am A G G F Bm Am A G G F
D.C.
2. Bm Am
G F F♯m7 Em7 G F
D.S. al Coda
And I love
CODA
Bm Am G F F♯m7 Em7 G F

'Father, glorify your name!'
Then a voice came from heaven,
'I have glorified it, and will glorify it again.'

John 12:28

1348 I will magnify you

Words and Music: Chris O'Brien

E
B
I will mag - ni - fy you,
C#m
A
E
I will glo-ri - fy you, I will lift my hands
B
A/C#
B/D#
and wor - ship my King.
E
B
So take your right - ful place, Lord,
C#m
A
E
Je - sus, you're my Sa - viour, and I will mag - ni - fy

B A E/G# F#m E Fine
you and glo - ri - fy your name.
C#m B/D# E A6/E E
Je - sus, you are my Lord and I crown you
Death could not hold you down, by your blood I'm
B/D# C#m B/D# E 1.
King, the Re-deem-er of all, your
free. All cre - a - tion re-joice
D Bsus4 B 2.
life an of-fer-ing. and pro -
D Bsus4 B D.C. al Fine
claim his vic-to-ry.

1349 I will never be the same

Words and Music: Ian Hannah

A D/A A Bm7 E/G#
I will ne - ver be the same now my eyes are o - pen wide.
A D/A E/A A D/A A
I have been for - e - ver changed through the
Bm7 Esus4 E A A/C# D
pow-er of his blood. I will tri - umph in the cross
- er fear the grave,
A C#m7 D
that my Sa - viour bore for me. I will stand
I'm a child of his grace. I no long -

1.
E F#m
A/E
E A/C#
in con - fi - dence be-cause of Je - sus. I no long-
- er feel a - shamed, be-cause of Je -
2.
E
D/F#
E/G#
A
sus.

1350 I will not be afraid

Words and Music: Bob Fitts

D
A/D
D
Gmaj7
I will not be a-fraid,
I will not be a-fraid,
D
A/D
D
I will not be a-fraid,
O Lord,
Gmaj7
Em7
G/A
A7
for your love
wash-es a-way my fears,
D
Dmaj7
D
Em7
G/A
A7
for your love
wash-es a-way my fears.
D
Last time
Fine
G
Your love o-ver-whelms

D G D
me, com-plete-ly sur-rounds me.
G D Asus4 A Asus4
And you go be-fore me, you make a way.
A D/F♯ G D
And you are my strength,
G D G
my cou-rage, my fort - ress and I will not be a-fraid,
Bm Gmaj7 Asus4 A Asus4 A
D.C. al Fine
your love melts my fear a-way.

I will proclaim the name of the Lord.
Oh, praise the greatness of our God!
He is the Rock, his works are perfect,
and all his ways are just.
A faithful God who does no wrong,
upright and just is he.

Deuteronomy 32:3-4

1351 I will praise him

Words and Music: Margaret J. Harris, alt.

Steadily
C F/C C F/C C
I will praise him, I will praise him,
C/E F Gsus4 G
praise the Lamb for sin - ners slain.
C Dm7 Em7 F2
Give him glo - ry, all you peo - ple, for his
C/E F C/G G G7 Am F2
blood has washed a - way each stain, for his
C/E F C/G G G7 C
blood has washed a - way each stain.

1352 I will praise you

Words and Music: Sam Lane

G Verse
C
I will praise you, O Lord, with all my heart.
G
C
I will tell of your won - der - ful deeds,
G
C
I will sing with joy, be - cause of you.
G
C
G Chorus
I will praise you, the Al - migh-ty God.
I will re - joice

C F C
in you, be-cause you love me,
G C F
I will re - joice in you, be-cause
C F G
Fine
you saved me. You are King for e - ver,
F G F
you rule with right - eous - ness. You are my
G F G
D.C. al Fine
de - liv - 'rer, in you, Lord, I can trust.

1353 I will praise you, my God and King

Words and Music: Tim Lomax

(♩ = 76)
F#m/E E F#m/E E
1. I will praise you, my God and King. I'll bless your
A B F#m/E E F#m/E
name now and al - ways. Great Je - ho - vah! Wor - thy of
E E/G# E/A B Chorus
praise. No one can grasp how great you are. Your king - dom
E A E E/G# E/A
reigns for e - ver - more, your grace and mer - cy will en - dure.

2. I will speak of your majesty.
I'll meditate on all you've done.
I will tell of your awesome pow'r –
I will proclaim how great you are!

3. We will sing of your righteousness.
All you have made will praise your name.
Saints exalt you with kingdom praise.
We will proclaim how great you are!

1354 I will rejoice

Words and Music: Brent Chambers

I will re-joice, I will re-joice,

I will re-joice for I've made my choice

to re-joice in the Lord. to re-joice in the Lord.

to re-joice in the Lord. 1. The

2. It doesn't depend on the circumstance,
the strength of my arm or my voice,
it doesn't depend on the way I feel,
I've made up my mind and I'm gonna rejoice.

1355 I will sing of your love for ever *To the King*

Words and Music: Nick Baty

G/B
C Am7 Gsus4 F
Chorus
Hal-le-lu - jah
C Am7 Gsus4 F
to the King who is to come,
C Am7 Gsus4 F
1.
C Am7
we raise our voi - ces
and de - clare your migh-
Gsus4 F
2.
C Am7 Gsus4
- ty name.
and de-clare your migh - ty name.
F
C

In him the whole building is joined together
and rises to become a holy temple in the Lord.
And in him you too are being built together
to become a dwelling in which God lives by his Spirit.

Ephesians 2:21-22

1356 I worship you

Words and Music: Steve Merkel

(♩ = 60)
D F♯sus/C♯ F♯7 Bm7 Am7 D7 Em7 E7
I wor - ship you, Je - sus, wor - ship you,
A7sus7 A7 Bm7 Em7 D/F♯ G D/F♯
for you a - lone are ho - ly;
Em7 D/F♯ Asus4 A Em7 D/F♯
you a - lone are God. You a - lone are
G A Bm7 D/A
1. Em7 A7sus4 A7
wor - thy of the long - ing of my heart.
2. Em7 A7sus4 A7 D
heart.

1357 I worship you

This is what I live to do

Words and Music: Steve Thompson and Velveta Thompson

Steadily
Chorus
G/F F Csus4 C C/E G/F F Csus4 C C/E
I worship you, I honour you: pour-ing out my
F G Am C/E F G Am C/E
love to you, lay-ing down my all for you, sur-ren-der-ing my
F G Am C/E F G C
life to you; this is what I live to do.
G C C/E F C G G/B C C/E
1. On the al - tar of the Lord, we of - fer up our
2. When I think of your great love, the scars you bore for

F G/B C C/E F C G
lives; in wor - ship to the most high God we
me: on the cross you took my shame, and
1.
G/F C/E F
D.S.
bring our sac - ri - fice. I
2.
G C C/E F Gsus4 G Gsus4 G
gave me free - dom through your name. I
G/F F Csus4 C C/E G/F F Csus4 C C/E
wor - ship you, I hon - our you, I
G/F F Csus4 C C/E G/F F C
wor - ship you, I hon - our you.

1358 Jesus Christ

All my love

Words and Music: Noel Richards

2. I am safe
upon the ocean of your mercy.
I am loved
with all the passion of eternity.
It is deeper than the deepest sea;
like a tidal wave it carries me.
All your love . . .

3. So I stand
upon your promise of eternal grace.
I believe
that I will one day see you face to face.
I will worship you forever more
in ways I never have before.
All my love . . .

1359 Jesus Christ is Lord

Words and Music: Ramon Pink

(♩ = 126)

Chorus Gm
Capo 3 Em

Je - sus Christ is Lord, Je - sus Christ is Lord,

E♭maj7 Cm7 Dm7
Cmaj7 Am7 Bm7

Je - sus Christ is Lord, Je - sus Christ is Lord of the

To repeat *To continue / Last time*

Gm Dm7 N.C. Gm
Em Bm7 Em *Fine*

na - tions. na - tions.

Cm7 Am7 Dm7 Bm7
he is en-throned on
Gm Em Cm7 Am7
jus - tice; his blood has
E♭/F C/D F D B♭ G F/A D/F♯ Gm Em Gm2/F Em2/D
o - ver-come the e - ne - my of our souls,
C2/E A2/C♯ C2 A2 D2omit3 B2omit3 N.C.
D.C. al Fine
he is our migh - ty de - li - ve-rer.

1360 Jesus Christ is waiting

Words: John L. Bell and Graham Maule

Music: Traditional French melody

NOEL NOUVELET 11 11 10 11

Em A Em D C D Em
1. Je - sus Christ is wait - ing, wait - ing in the streets;
A Em D C D Em
no one is his neigh - bour, all a - lone he eats.
B7 Em Bsus4 B7
Lis - ten, Lord Je - sus, I am lone - ly too.
Em A Em D C D Em
Make me, friend or stran - ger, fit to wait on you.

2. Jesus Christ is raging,
raging in the streets,
where injustice spirals
and real hope retreats.
Listen, Lord Jesus,
I am angry too.
In the kingdom's causes
let me rage with you.

3. Jesus Christ is healing,
healing in the streets;
curing those who suffer,
touching those he greets.
Listen, Lord Jesus,
I have pity too.
Let my care be active,
healing, just like you.

4. Jesus Christ is dancing,
dancing in the streets,
where each sign of hatred
he, with love, defeats.
Listen, Lord Jesus,
I should triumph too.
Where good conquers evil,
let me dance with you.

5. Jesus Christ is calling,
calling in the streets,
'Who will join my journey?
I will guide their feet.'
Listen, Lord Jesus,
let my fears be few.
Walk one step before me,
I will follow you.

1361 Jesus, come, come reveal whose I am *My Redeemer*

Words and Music: Brian Doerksen

C2
Chorus
G
D
So I come with con - fi-dence in -
G/B
Dsus4
D
G
to my Fa - ther's house; I be-lieve you
D
G/B
C
are the Lamb the pro - phets spoke a-bout.
Am
G/B
D2
On the cross you pur - chased me; my life's no long - er mine.

Em D C
I'm yours, my Re -
Gsus4 G
deem - er.
1.
2. Je - sus, come,
2.
D/G C
I'm yours,
Am Gsus4 G D/G C
my Re - deem - er. I'm yours,
Am Gsus G D/G C2/G G
my Re - deem - er.

For to us a child is born,
to us a son is given,
and the government will be on his shoulders.
And he will be called
Wonderful Counsellor, Mighty God,
Everlasting Father, Prince of Peace.

Isaiah 9:6

1362 Jesus, draw me ever nearer

May this journey

Words and Music: Margaret Becker and Keith Getty

1. Je - sus, draw me e - ver near - er, as I

la - bour through the storm. You have called me to this

pas - sage, and I'll fol - low, though I'm worn. May this

jour - ney bring a bles - sing, may I rise on wings of

2. Jesus, guide me through the tempest,
keep my spirit staid and sure.
When the midnight meets the morning,
let me love you even more.

3. Let the treasures of the trial
form within me as I go.
And at the end of this long passage,
let me leave them at your throne.

1363 Jesus, hope of the nations *Hope of the nations*

Words and Music: Brian Doerksen

D
E
you are the rock in whom we trust.
our Prince of Peace, draw-ing us near.
A
F#m
You are the light, shin-ing for all
Je-sus, our hope, liv-ing for all
D
E
1.
D/E
the world to see. You rose from the dead,
who will re-ceive,
2.
D
A
D/A
Lord, we be-lieve.
A
D/A
D.C.
Last time
A

1364 Jesus! I am resting

Words: Jean S. Pigott

Music: James Mountain

TRANQUILLITY 87 85 87 85

1. Jesus! I am rest-ing, rest-ing in the joy of what thou art;

I am find-ing out the great-ness of thy lov-ing heart.

Thou hast bid me gaze up-on thee, and thy beau-ty fills my soul,

for, by thy trans-form-ing pow-er, thou hast made me whole.

2. O how great thy loving-kindness,
vaster, broader than the sea!
O how marvellous thy goodness,
lavished all on me!
Yes, I rest in thee, Beloved,
know what wealth of grace is thine,
know thy certainty of promise,
and have made it mine.

3. Simply trusting thee, Lord Jesus,
I behold thee as thou art,
and thy love so pure, so changeless,
satisfies my heart;
satisfies its deepest longings,
meets, supplies its every need,
compasseth me round with blessings;
thine is love indeed!

4. Ever lift thy face upon me
as I work and wait for thee;
resting 'neath thy smile, Lord Jesus,
earth's dark shadows flee.
Brightness of my Father's glory,
sunshine of my Father's face,
keep me ever trusting, resting,
fill me with thy grace.

1365 Jesus, I could sing *If I have not love*

Words and Music: Matt Redman

1. Je - sus, I could sing in the tongues of men and an - gels, but
if I have not love I am just a clang - ing cym - bal, an emp - ty
sound. just a clang - ing cym - bal, an emp - ty
sound. This is a love
song, this is a love song, Je - sus, a love

2. And Jesus, I could pray
 with a faith that moves a mountain,
 but if I have not love
 it is just a noise resounding, an empty sound.

3. It's the overflow of hearts,
 as we gaze upon your beauty,
 a reflection of your worth,
 for we've seen a glimpse of you in your glory, Lord.

1366 Jesus is exalted

Words and Music: Alan Rose

With energy
E B/D♯ A/C♯ E
1. Jesus is exalted to the highest place,
2. throne of God will last for all eternity, we will
3. let us throw aside all that would hinder us, and
A E Bsus4 B
seated at the right hand of our God. He
reign with him as those he has redeemed. For we
run as those who run to win the prize. For
A E A E
reigns in pow'r and glory, he is God's appointed heir, he is
are a chosen people, we will be the bride of Christ, he has
we will see his glory, we will see him face to face, we will
A E Bsus4 B E/G♯ Chorus
righteous, he is holy, he is Lord!
chosen us to ever be with him! Halle-
join him as his glory fills the skies!

A E B C#m7
lu - jah! He is King of kings. Hal - le -
A E B E/G#
lu - jah! He is the Lord. Hal - le -
A E B G#/B# C#m7
lu - jah! He is Je - sus Christ, reign-ing for
Last time to Coda
A E Bsus4 1. B D.C.
e - ver-more, e - ver - more. 2. The
2. B D Bridge A/C# E
The day is com - ing when he will ap-pear,

G D Asus4
his glo - ry shin - ing like the sun;
A C G D
and ev - 'ry na - tion then will see and fear
C G Bsus4
the migh-ty and ex-alt - ed one.
CODA
B D.C. al Coda Bsus4 B E
3. So more.

Give thanks to the Lord, call on his name;
make known among the nations what he has done,
and proclaim that his name is exalted.
Sing to the Lord, for he has done glorious things;
let this be known to all the world.

Isaiah 12:4-5

1367 Jesus is Lord

Words and Music: Keith Getty and Stuart Townend

1. 'Je - sus is Lord' – the cry that e - choes through cre -

a - tion: re - splen - dent pow'r, e - ter - nal

Word, our Rock. The Son of God, the King whose

glo - ry fills the hea - vens, yet bids us come to taste this

2. Jesus is Lord – whose voice sustains the stars and planets,
yet in his wisdom laid aside his crown.
Jesus the Man, who washed our feet, who bore our suffering,
became a curse to bring salvation's plan.

3. Jesus is Lord – the tomb is gloriously empty!
Not even death could crush this King of love!
The price is paid, the chains are loosed, and we're forgiven,
and we can run into the arms of God.

4. 'Jesus is Lord' – a shout of joy, a cry of anquish,
as he returns, and every knee bows low.
Then every eye and every heart will see his glory,
the Judge of all will take his children home.

1368 Jesus, I've come to worship *The heart of my King*

Words and Music: Barry Hart

D
A/C♯
F♯m
E
D/E
so much more than the songs that I sing; for what
Last time to Coda
A
D
E
F♯m
plea - ses you is look-ing at the things your child - ren do, that's
D
A/C♯
E
wor - ship that touch - es the heart of my King,
To verse
D2
A
E/A
D2
the heart of my King.
To Bridge
A
E/A
D2
D.C.
A2

Bridge
Cmaj7 Bm7 A2
Je - sus, I have heard your call to fol-low, and
Cmaj7 Bm7 A2
when I take my cross up I will see it's
Cmaj7 Bm7 F#m7 Bsus4
in the sac - ri - fice of my sur-ren - dered life I will
D.S. al Coda
G D/F# Esus4 E D/E
Chorus
know the truth and the truth will set me free. Je - sus,

CODA
D
A/C#
D
A/C#
wor-ship that touch - es, that's wor-ship that touch - es, that's
D
A/C#
E
wor - ship that touch - es the heart of my King.
D2
A
E/A
The heart of my King,
D2
A
E/A
the heart of my King,
D2
A
the heart of my King.

1369 Jesus, Jesus, Jesus, Jesus *Jesus, we celebrate your fame*

Words and Music: Tommy Walker

D/A Em7 A7 Bm7 A/C# D G
na-tions sing your song. E-ven now there's mil-lions far and wide lift-ing
his-to-ry pro-claims the earth has ne-ver been the same since you
ev-'ry knee will bow; we'll crown you Lord and King of kings and then
D/A A7 Dsus4 D
Chorus
G Em7 Bm7 A
up your name on high.
showed the world your grace. Hal-le-lu - jah, hal-le-lu-jah, hal-le-lu-
all the world will sing.
G E/G# A D G A#dim7 Bm7 Bm7/A
- jah to the King. Hal-le-lu - jah to our Sa - viour, it's of
To repeat Chorus
G Asus4 G/A D
his great fame we sing. Hal-le-lu-
To next verse (D.S.) or Last time
G Asus4 G/A D
his great fame we sing.

1370 Jesus, King of the ages *Prophet, Priest and King*

Words and Music: Faith Forster and David Lyle Morris

Jesus, King of the a - ges, plead-ing our

cause be - fore the throne of God.

Jesus, the liv - ing Word of God, our

Pro-phet, Priest and King, our Pro-phet, Priest and King.

(last time)

C♯m7 A B E C♯m7 A B
1. From the start you were there, Word of God, an - cient
2. At the cross you poured out cost - ly blood, per - fect
E C♯m7 A F♯m B
pro - mi - ses you came to ful - fil;
sa - cri - fice, a - ton - ing for sin,
G♯m A F♯m F♯m/E
you came re - veal - ing the Fa - ther's heart, his fa - vour, his pur - pose, his
so we may en - ter the ho - ly place to meet you, our faith - ful High
B/D♯ C♯m D
will: shar - ing his good news with the poor, de -
Priest; as we come to the mer - cy - seat we
Bridge
F♯m B D.C. C♯m
clar - ing God's king - dom is here. Je - sus shall reign at the
find grace in our time of need.

D F#m7 F#m7/E B/D#
Fa-ther's hand till all of his e - ne-mies cease:
C#m D F#m7
hell and de-struc - tion, dis - ease and death are un - der his glo - ri-ous
B Amaj7
feet. We will reign with Christ (we will reign with Christ), we will
C#m F#m7
reign with Christ (we will reign with Christ), we will reign with Christ (we will
Bsus4 B D.C. al Fine
reign with Christ) for e - ver. With

Praise the Lord.
How good it is to sing praises to our God,
how pleasant and fitting to praise him!

Psalm 147:1

1371 Jesus, my Friend

Words and Music: Stuart Barbour

A2 B C#m7 E/G# F#m B7sus4
My soul is long - ing for you, my Je - sus.
1.
E Esus4 E Esus4
2.
E

The Lord will surely comfort Zion
and will look with compassion on all her ruins;
he will make her deserts like Eden,
her wastelands like the garden of the Lord.
Joy and gladness will be found in her,
thanksgiving and the sound of singing.

Isaiah 51:3

1372 Jesus, my Lord *Now I belong to Jesus*

Words and Music: Norman J. Clayton

ELLSWORTH 10 10 9 6 and Refrain

G Gmaj7 G6 Am D6 D7 G Gmaj7 G6
1. Je - sus, my Lord, will love me for e - ver, from him no pow'r of
Am D6 D7 B Em A D Em A6 A7
e - vil can se - ver, he gave his life to ran - som my soul, now I be-long to
D Chorus G G6 Am7 D7 Gmaj7 F#/D G
him; now I be-long to Je - sus, Je - sus be-longs to me,
G7 E E7 Am Am7 Edim G A D7 G
not for the years of time a - lone, but for e - ter - ni - ty.

2. Once I was lost in sin's degradation,
Jesus came down to bring me salvation,
lifted me up from sorrow and shame,
now I belong to him;

3. Joy floods my soul, for Jesus has saved me,
freed me from sin that long had enslaved me,
his precious blood he gave to redeem,
now I belong to him;

1373 Jesus, my passion in life *Above all else*

Words and Music: Vicky Beeching

1. Je - sus, my pas - sion in life is to know
2. Je - sus, you've shower-ed your good - ness on

you. May all o - ther goals bow down to this
me, you've gi - ven your gifts so free - ly. But

jour - ney of lov - ing you more.
there's one thing I'm long - ing for.

Hear my heart's cry and my prayer for this life.

Asus4
A
D/G
Chorus
D/F♯
A-bove all else,
Em2
A
D/G
a-bove all else,
a-bove all else,
D/F♯
Em
Asus4
D
give me your-self.
D.C.
Last time

1374 Jesus, my Saviour, to Bethlehem came

Seeking for me!

Words: A.N. Music: E.E. Hasty

Capo 3
F B♭ F C7 F B♭6 B♭ F C7 F
D G D A7 D G6 G D A7 D
1. Je - sus, my Sa - viour, to Beth - le - hem came, born in a man - ger to
C7 F C F B♭ F C7 F B♭6 B♭
A7 D A D G D A7 D G6 G
sor - row and shame; oh, it was won - der - ful: blest be his name!
F C7 F C
D A7 D A
Chorus
Seek - ing for me, for me! Seek - ing for me! For
F C C7 F
D A A7 D
me! For me!
Seek - ing for me! Seek - ing for me! Seek - ing for me!

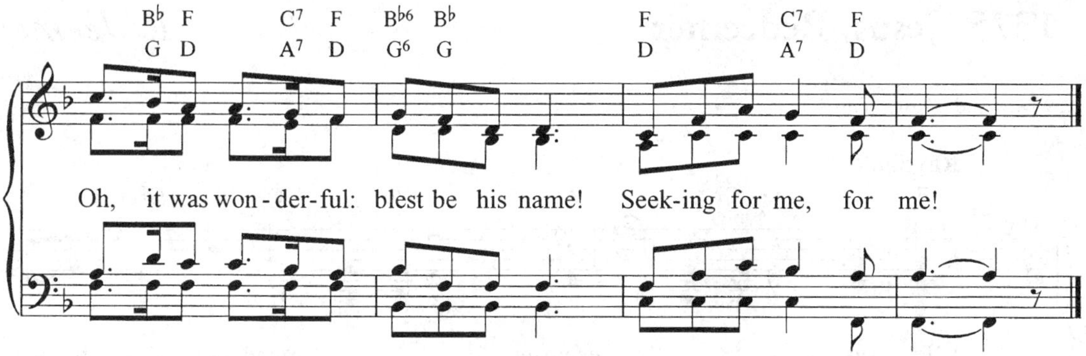
B♭ F C7 F B♭6 B♭ F C7 F
G D A7 D G6 G D A7 D
Oh, it was won - der- ful: blest be his name! Seek-ing for me, for me!

2. Jesus, my Saviour, on Calvary's tree,
paid the great debt, and my soul he set free;
oh, it was wonderful - how could it be?
Dying for me, for me!

Dying for me! Dying for me!
Dying for me! Dying for me!
Oh, it was wonderful: how could it be?
Dying for me, for me!

3. Jesus, my Saviour, the same as of old,
while I was wandr'ing afar from the fold;
gently and long did he plead with my soul,
calling for me, for me!

Calling for me! Calling for me!
Calling for me! Calling for me!
Gently and long did he plead with my soul,
calling for me, for me!

4. Jesus, my Saviour, shall come from on high -
sweet is the promise as weary years fly;
oh, I shall see him descend from the sky,
coming for me, for me!

Coming for me! Coming for me!
Coming for me! Coming for me!
Oh, I shall see him descend from the sky,
coming for me, for me!

1375 Jesus, Redeemer

Redeemer

Words and Music: Tim Hughes

E
E2/G#
you a-lone are won-der-ful, you a-lone are Coun-sel-lor,
A
E2/G#
A
A/B
e-ver-last-ing Fa-ther, migh-ty in the hea-vens.
E
E2/G#
Ne-ver to for-get the love you dis-played up-on a cross,
A
E2/G#
A
A/B
Son of God I thank you, Prince of Peace, I love your
E
E2/G#
A
A/B
E
name.

Will you not revive us again,
that your people may rejoice in you?
Show us your unfailing love, O Lord,
and grant us your salvation.

Psalm 85:6-7

1376 Jesus shall reign where'er the sun

Words: Isaac Watts

Music: Melody attributed to John Hatton

DUKE STREET LM

2. Peoples and realms of ev'ry tongue
dwell on his love with sweetest song;
and infant voices shall proclaim
their early blessings on his name.

3. To him shall endless prayer be made,
and endless praises crown his head;
his name like sweet perfume shall rise
with every morning sacrifice.

4. Then all the earth shall rise and bring
peculiar honours to its King;
angels descend with songs again,
and earth repeat the loud amen.

1377 Jesus, the Holy One

Words and Music: Susie Hare

1. Je - sus, the Ho - ly One, the pre - cious gift of

God's own Son. Je - sus, the Ho - ly One, we

bow be - fore you now. We bow down, we

bow down, we bow down be - fore you. We

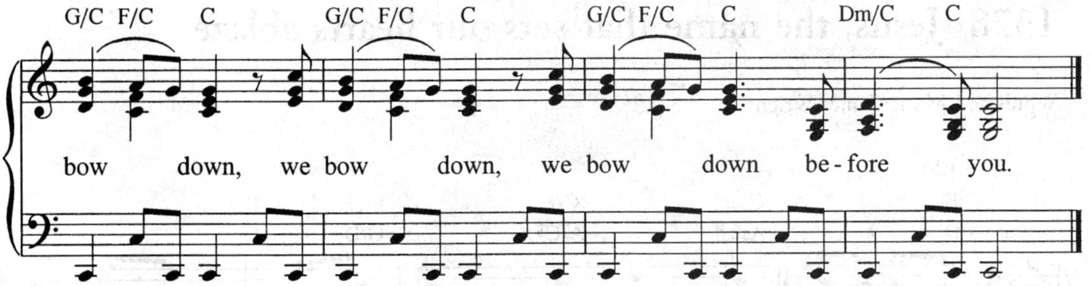

2. Jesus, the Holy Lamb,
the sacrifice of God for man.
Jesus, the Holy Lamb,
we bow before you now.

3. Jesus, the holy name
that takes our sin, that bears our shame.
Jesus, the holy name,
we bow before you now.

1378 Jesus, the name that sets our hearts ablaze

Words and Music: James Wright

F D7b9 Gm7 F/A Gm/Bb
D B7b9 Em7 D/F# Em/G
you, Je - sus, name a - bove
F/C Bb/C 1. F Bb F/A Gm7 F
D/A G/A D G D/F# Em7 D
all names we wor - ship you. 2. Je - sus, the
2. F D7b9 Gm7 F/A Gm/Bb
D B7b9 Em7 D/F# Em/G
you. Je - sus, name a - bove
F/C Bb/C F Bb F/A Gm7 F
D/A G/A D G D/F# Em7 D
all names, we wor - ship you.

1379 Jesus, the source of all our joy

Words and Music: Graham Kendrick

2. Our God who none has ever seen,
you have brought so near
the beating heart of love divine,
close enough to hear.
And in your words we hear a voice
that puts our fear to flight,
the Father singing over us,
songs of pure delight.

3. How can we ever comprehend
all your blood had bought?
Making a way for us to share
the very life of God.
To know the love that burned for you
before the world began,
and by your power to become
God's own children.

4. We hear the passion of your prayer,
that we may be one,
so all the world may believe
you have truly come.
Teach us to love with that same love
that sent you from above.
To know the Father and make known
his amazing love.

1380 Jesus, you alone

Words and Music: Tim Hughes

Driving
Capo 3
B♭ G
E♭ C
1. Je - sus, you a - lone must be my first love, my
2. Day and night I lift my eyes to seek you, to
B♭/F G/D
F D
B♭ G
first love. The se - cret place and high - est praise shall be
seek you. Hun - gry for a glimpse of you in glo -
E♭ C
B♭/F G/D
F D
Bridge
E♭ C
F D
yours, shall be yours. To your throne I'll
- ry, in glo - ry.
Gm Em
F D
E♭ C
F D
Gm Em
F D
bring de - vo - tion, may it be the sweet - est sound:

E♭ F Gm F E♭
C D Em D C
Lord, this heart is reach - ing for you now.
B♭ B♭/A B♭/G B♭/F
G G/F♯ G/E G/D
Chorus
So I'll set my sights up - on you,
You a - lone will be my pas - sion,
B♭/E♭ B♭/D B♭/C F B♭ B♭/A
G/C G/B G/A D G G/F♯
set my life up - on your praise; ne - ver look - ing to
Je - sus, you will be my song: you will find me long -
1.
B♭/G B♭/F E♭ Fsus4
G/E G/D C Dsus4
a - no - ther way.
2.
B♭/G B♭/F E♭ Fsus4 E♭2
G/E G/D C Dsus4 C2
D.C.
(last time D.S. al Fine)
Fine
- ing af - ter you.

1381 Jesus, you are

Words and Music: Rita Baloche

(♩ = 67)
G
Chorus
Je - sus, you are,

C2
Dsus4
Em7
Dsus4
you are ev - 'ry-thing I'm not, and

C2
F2
G
ev - 'ry-thing that I want to be; Je - sus, you are,

C2
Dsus4
Em7
Dsus4
you are the ma - ker of my heart;

To repeat
Last time
To continue
Verse
C2 F2 G G C2 G2 C2 Gsus2 G
fi-nish what you start-ed in me. Je-sus, you are,
This is the hope I have, it's some-thing I can - not see; you wil-ling-ly gave your life, wil-ling to die for me; now I

Em7
F2
be - lieve, I be - lieve, I
C2
Dsus4
Chorus
D.S.
be - lieve.
Je - sus, you are,

An angel of the Lord appeared to them,
and the glory of the Lord shone around them,
and they were terrified.
But the angel said to them, 'Do not be afraid.
I bring you good news of great joy
that will be for all the people.
Today in the town of David
a Saviour has been born to you;
he is Christ the Lord.
This will be a sign to you:
You will find a baby wrapped in cloths
and lying in a manger.'

Suddenly a great company of the heavenly host
appeared with the angel, praising God and saying,
'Glory to God in the highest,
and on earth peace to all on
whom his favour rests.'

Luke 2:9-14

1382 Jesus, you are my King

Words and Music: Tim Lomax

D F#m7 G A D/F#
For I want to be be-side you, to
G9 A2 G9
thank you for your grace. I give my heart
D F#m7 G9 A7 D F#m7
for you to have and hold and I'll
G9 A Bm Em7 A7
sing my love for you, Lord, as my life with you un - folds.
D A7sus4 A7 D

1383 Joy of my desire

Words and Music: Jennifer Randolph

Chorus
E♭maj7 F/E♭ B♭/D B♭ B♭/D Fm7 B♭
Cmaj7 D/C G/B G G/B Dm7 G
I worship you in spirit and in truth.
E♭maj7 F/E♭ Dsus4 D/F♯ Gm Gm/F
Cmaj7 D/C Bsus4 B/D♯ Em Em/D
I worship you in spirit and in truth. There will
E♭maj7 B♭/D Cm7 E♭/F B♭
Cmaj7 G/B Am7 C/D G
never be a friend as dear to me as you.

He has taken me to the banquet hall,
and his banner over me is love.

Song of Solomon 2:4

1384 Joyous light of heavenly glory

Words and Music: Marty Haugen

2. In the stars that grace the darkness,
in the blazing sun of dawn,
in the light of peace and wisdom,
we can hear your quiet song.
Love that fills the night with wonder,
love that warms the weary soul,
love that bursts all chains asunder,
set us free and make us whole.

3. You who made the heaven's splendour,
ev'ry dancing star of night,
make us shine with gentle justice,
let us each reflect your light.
Mighty God of all creation,
gentle Christ who lights our way,
loving Spirit of salvation,
lead us on to endless day.

1385 Just got to be with you

Beautiful, lovely Jesus

Words and Music: Jami Smith

Em D
look at all the love you pour'd
A D A Em
out for me; look at all the love,
D A
the blood and tears that flood down for me.
D A E D
Beau - ti-ful, love-ly
1. 2.
E D D Last time to Coda
Je - sus. - sus.

E/G♯ A²/C♯ D E/G♯ A²/C♯ D
What-e - ver is true and no - ble, what-e - ver is right;
E/G♯ A²/C♯ D E/G♯ A²/C♯
what-e - ver is ad-m'ra-ble, what-e - ver is
D F♯m
right; if a - ny - thing is
D F♯m
ex - cel - lent, if a - ny - thing is
D F♯m
wor - thy of praise; if a - ny - thing is

D
E
pure and love - ly, think on these things,
D
E
think on me.
Think on these things,
D
E
D
E
D.S. al Coda
think on me,
think on me.
CODA
Em
D
Look at all the love pour'd
A
D
A
out for me.

1386 King Jesus, I believe

Words and Music: Martyn Layzell

Dm
Bm
E♭
C
- tice flow up - on this earth, a ne - ver-fail - ing stream.
- rit of the Sov - 'reign Lord em-pow'r us once a - gain.
F
D
Chorus
B♭
G
B♭/A
G/F♯
I'm thir - sty, long-ing just
Gm
Em
E♭
C
B♭
G
to see your king - dom come. Pray - ing that to - day
F/A
D/F♯
Gm
Em
E♭
C
your love is shown. I'm
B♭
G
B♭/A
G/F♯
Gm
Em
thir - sty for the will of God to be

E♭ C
B♭ G
F/A D/F♯
Last time to Coda
made known, pray - ing for the day of your re - turn.
Gm Em
E♭ C
D.C.
Cm Am
We pray,
A♭maj7 Fmaj7
B♭ G
Gm Em
we pray, we pray, we seek your face.
Cm Am
A♭maj7 Fmaj7
F D
We pray, we pray.
1.
2.
D.S.
CODA
Gm Em
E♭maj7 Cmaj7
I'm

Sovereign Lord,
you have made the heavens and the earth
by your great power and outstretched arm.
Nothing is too hard for you.
O great and powerful God,
whose name is the Lord Almighty,
great are your purposes and mighty are your deeds.

Jeremiah 32:17, 18b, 19a

1387 King of love

Words and Music: Doug Horley

F C F Dm7
King of love, praise you, King of love,
B♭ F C F
wor - ship you, King of love, thank you, I'm
1. 2.
Dm B♭ Dm B♭
trea - sure in your eyes. trea - sure in your eyes.
F C Dm
I know my heart will love you for e - ver, I know your word, I'll
B♭ F C
al - ways be your child. I know my soul is safe for e - ter - ni - ty, 'cos

Dm7
B♭
1.
D.C.
2.
you hold me close
in your arms.
in your arms.
G
D
Em
C
Gon-na give you all the praise I can,
gon-na give you all the thanks I can,
in your arms I will be,
King of love hold - ing me.
Gon-na give you all the love I can,
gon-na give you all the praise I can,
in your arms I will be,
King of love hold - ing me.

G
D
Gon - na give you all the praise I can, gon - na give you all the thanks I can,
Em
C
G
King of love, King of love, I wor- ship you. King of love,
Gsus2
G
Em
C
praise you, King of love, wor - ship you,
G
Gsus2
G
Em
King of love, thank you, I'm trea - sure in your eyes.
C

1388 King of my life *Lead me to Calvary*

Words: Jennie E. Hussey Music: William James Kirkpatrick

DUNCANNON 86 86 and Refrain

D A7 D G D A7 D A
1. King of my life, I crown thee now, thine shall the glo - ry be;
D A D G D G6 D A7 D
lest I for-get thy thorn-crowned brow, lead me to Cal - va - ry.
Chorus A D A7 D A A7 F#m A7 D
Lest I for-get Geth - se - ma-ne; lest I for-get thine a - go-ny;
Bm F#7 G Bdim D G6 D A7 D
lest I for-get thy love for me, lead me to Cal - va - ry.

2. Show me the tomb where thou wast laid,
tenderly mourned and wept;
angels in robes of light arrayed,
guarded thee whilst thou slept.

3. Let me like Mary, thro' the gloom,
come with a gift to thee;
show to me now the empty tomb,
lead me to Calvary.

4. May I be willing, Lord, to bear
daily my cross for thee;
even thy cup of grief to share,
thou hast borne all for me.

1389 King of the ages

Words and Music: Keith Getty and Stuart Townend

2. Your arms of love are reaching out
to every soul that seeks you;
your light will shine in all the earth,
bringing grace and a great salvation.

3. The day will come when you appear,
and every eye shall see you.
Then we shall rise with hearts ablaze,
with a song we will sing for ever.

King of the ages

All you have done

Words and Music: Eoghan Heaslip

verse 2
Capo 1
A♭ G
B♭m Am
1. King of the ages, history's pages point to you.
2. Father to nations, for-ever patient and faithful.
E♭/G D/F♯
Ancient of Days, all of your ways show your wonders.
To each generation you show compassion and mercy.
A♭ G
A♭maj7 Gmaj7
Jehovah Jireh, our awesome provider and healer, the
Jehovah Nissi, our sov-'reign protector and fortress, the

E♭/G D/F♯ A♭ G
au - thor of time, be glo - ri - fied as we wor - ship.
Lord of all life, be glo - ri - fied as we wor - ship.
1st time repeat verse 1
Chorus
B♭m Am B♭m/D Am/C E♭/G D/F♯
All you have done
All you have done
A♭ G E♭/G D/F♯ Fm Em
tells of your great - ness, tells of your worth. The
shows us your good - ness, shows us your a - bun - dance. The
B♭m Am B♭m/D Am/C E♭/G D/F♯
Last time to Coda
works of your hands dis - play your
works of your hands re - veal your
1.
A♭ G
ma - je - sty.

2.
A♭
G
Last time D.S.
(repeat Chorus)
glo - ry.
A♭momit3
Gomit3
D.C.
CODA
A♭
G
glo - ry.

They will be called oaks of righteousness,
a planting of the Lord
for the display of his splendour.

Isaiah 61:3b

1391 Knowing your grace *Child of the King*

Words and Music: Stuart Townend and Terry Virgo

Gently
Bm F♯m7 Em7 A7sus4
1. Know - ing your grace has set me free, Lord, I'm
Bm F♯m7 Em7 Am7 D9
seek - ing your face; I feel your plea - sure, your
Gmaj7 A/G F♯m7 Bm7
joy in the ones you have cho - sen by name. You've
1.
Em7 C♯m7b5 F♯7
lif - ted my bur - dens and cast off my shame.
2, 3.
Em7 A7sus4 Em/D D
Fine
I am a child of the King.

F#m7 Chorus
Bm
Gmaj7
You will fin - ish the work you've be - gun in me,
F#m7
C/D
D
I'm a - dop - ted, a son in your fa - mi - ly!
Gmaj7
F#m7
Em7
F#sus4
F#
You've drawn me with kind - ness and love
Em7
C2(6)
A/C#
D.C.
in - to this ho - ly place.

2. Feeling your touch
gives me such peace, Lord.
I love you so much,
I know you'll lead me.
Wherever I go I'll be under your wing,
for I am a child of the King.

3. What can I say?
Your lavish mercy
turned night into day –
my guilt has gone now.
Forever I'll stand in your presence and sing,
for I am a child of the King.

1392 Lately, I've been thinking about you *Ocean*

Words and Music: Lamont Hiebert

(♩ = 88)
C F2 C F2
(v.2)
1. Late - ly, I've been think - ing 'bout you,
2. I'll sing un - til I sense a smile
C F2 C F2
(v.2)
and late - ly, I've been dream - ing of you.
up - on your great and love - ly face;
C F2 C F2
Late - ly, I can't get you out
and till I know your glo - ries
G F2
of my head, get you
in this place, glo-ries

G
F2
out of my head. Yeah, yeah!
in this place. Yeah, yeah!
C
Csus/D
There's some - thing a - bout the o - cean
There's some - thing a - bout the sun - rise
F2
G
makes me rise up and praise;
re - minds me of your faith - ful - ness;
C
Csus/D
there's some - thing a - bout the hea - vens
there's some - thing a - bout the o - cean
F2
G
makes me stand in awe a - gain.
and I'm lost in love a - gain.

C
F2
G
F2/A
G/B
C
F2
To repeat
G
D.C.
Last time
G
F2/A
G/B
C

To him who loves us
and has freed us from our sins by his blood,
and has made us to be a kingdom and priests
to serve his God and Father –
to him be glory and power for ever and ever!
Amen.

Revelation 1:5b-6

1393 Lead me on, Lord

Words and Music: Dave Bankhead and Mike Burn

(♩ = 84)
E E/G♯ B E/G♯
1. Lead me on, Lord, lead me on.
2. Fill me up, Lord, make me strong.
A E/G♯ B E/G♯
Help me trust in your word.
I'll de - pend on your word.
A B C♯m E/G♯
Let it be as a lamp to my feet,
Let it be a safe - guard for my mind,
A B C♯m E/G♯
and a light for my path. I have
and a shield for my soul. I have

1.
Last time
A E/G♯ F♯m7 B7 E E
Fine
made my choice: I'm fol-low-ing you. you.
set my heart on fol-low-ing
2.
E B Chorus E/G♯ A E/G♯
you. Lead me on, Lord, lead me on.
B E/G♯ A E/G♯
I will trust in you.
B E/G♯ A E/G♯
Fill me up, Lord, make me strong:
B/D♯ E F♯m7 E/G♯ Asus2 B7
D.C. al Fine
I will fol - low you.

Great and marvellous are your deeds,
Lord God Almighty.
Just and true are your ways,
King of the ages.
Who will not fear you, O Lord,
and bring glory to your name?
For you alone are holy.
All nations will come
and worship before you,
for your righteous acts have been revealed.

Revelation 15:3-4

1394 Let earth and heaven combine

Words: Charles Wesley

Music: Supplement to Wesley's *Hymns*

MILLENNIUM 66 66 88

D G C G C Am7 D D7 G
1. Let earth and heav'n com - bine, an - gels and men a - gree, to
D A7 D A7 D
praise in songs di - vine the in - car - nate De - i - ty; our
D7 Bm/D D7 G D7 G
God con - tract - ed to a span, in -
C D7 Em D G C G D D7 G
com - pre - hen - sib - ly made man.

2. He laid his glory by,
he wrapped him in our clay;
unmarked by human eye,
the latent Godhead lay;
infant of days he here became,
and bore the mild Immanuel's name.

3. Unsearchable the love
that hath the Saviour brought;
the grace is far above
mankind's or angel's thought:
suffice for us that God, we know,
our God, is manifest below.

4. He deigns in flesh to appear,
widest extremes to join;
to bring our vileness near,
and make us all divine:
and we the life of God shall know,
for God is manifest below.

5. Made perfect first in love,
and sanctified by grace,
we shall from earth remove,
and see his glorious face:
then shall his love be fully showed,
and man shall then be lost in God.

1395 Let's think about our God

Words and Music: Tommy Walker

E
1. Let's think
F♯m/E E F♯m/E E
a - bout our God, our Sa - viour and our King, the one
a - bout our Fa - ther's heart, so right and true, he's ne -
a - bout our God, the high and lof - ty one, who says
Bsus4 B F♯m7 B7
who gave it all, he gave up ev - 'ry-thing: let's think
- ver giv - en up, giv - en up on me and you; let's think
he's ne - ver far from the bro - ken - hear - ted ones; let's think
F♯m/E E F♯m/E E
a - bout the man who shed his pre - cious blood so we
a - bout our God, of love and mer - cy free, he's washed
a - bout our Lord, who formed the stars a - bove, so we

Bsus4 B F#m7 B7 Chorus
could be his friends, his friends un - til the end.
us white as snow for all e - ter - ni - ty. And give
could have a glimpse of his glo - ry up a - bove.
F#m7 E/G# B7sus4 E
our love and praise to him, he is
1. 2.
F#m7 E/G# B7sus4 E B7sus4
our Sa - viour and our friend. Let's give our friend.
1. Last time
E D.S.
2. Let's think

2.
Bridge
Asus2
We love you, Lord, we love
E/G#
F#m7
you, Lord; just one thought of you and all
1.
2.
B7sus4
B7sus4
B7
D.S.
we can say is, we love we can say is: 3. Let's think

In a loud voice they sang:
'Worthy is the Lamb, who was slain,
to receive power and wealth and
wisdom and strength
and honour and glory and praise!'

Revelation 5:12

1396 Let the earth and heavens rejoice

For the Lord our God reigns

Words and Music: Craig Smith

(♩ = 130)
D
D G/D
1. Let the earth and hea-
2. Ev-'ry heart be filled
D G A Bm G A D
- vens re-joice, for the Lord our God reigns;
with his light, for the Lord our God reigns;
D G/D D
ev - 'ry child of God lift your voice,
all the hope - less dance with de - light,
G A Bm G A D
for the Lord our God reigns.
for the Lord our God reigns.

Chorus
A Bm7 G D A Bm7 G
Je - sus, Em - man - u - el, he has set us free;
A Bm7 G
hope - less souls re - deem'd
D G A Bm
to tell, for the Lord
G A D G A Bm G A D D.C.
our God reigns; for the Lord our God reigns.

1397 Let the exile come

Come, heal this land

Words and Music: Robin Mark

(♩ = 84)
Chorus
C F G Am
Let the ex - ile come, let the
ta - ble waits in your
F G Am F C
stran - ger come, let the wea - ry come find
Fa - ther's house, there the meek can come and
Am F Am
rest; all you home-less sons, all you
eat; there's a place of rest at your
F Am F G
wi - dow'd ones, all you poor and dis - pos -
Fa - ther's breast, where his mer - cy is com -

C
1.
2.
sess'd. For a
plete.
G Am F C G
Am F C G
1. Does a cry ring out
2. Do the tears of one
3. So may this land we love
Am F C G
from a bro - ken na - tion from a peo - ple who have been
who gave all things for us, do they flow from hea - ven still
be a place of safe - ty, be a light for all the na-
Am F C G
brought low? Was pride in our hearts
be - cause of us? For we have tas - ted grace
- tions of the earth. May your streams of love,

Am F C G
and did we grieve your Spi-rit, have we blocked the an - cient
and we have known your mer-cy, but we have not shown this
may they flow here free-ly, here where ev - 'ry stran - ger
Am F G
wells that flowed?
grace to men. Here is our cov - 'nant
finds a home.
Am G
prayer, who call up - on your
Am F
name; we hum - ble our -

C
F
- selves before you, we hum - ble our -
G
Am
G
F
- selves. Come, heal this land;
Am
G
F
come, heal this land.
Last time
D.S.
C

1398 Let the living stones cry out

Words and Music: John Pantry

Chorus
Am G F C/E Dm7 G C F C/E Dm C
Let the liv - ing stones cry out, ev - 'ry son and
See the tem - ple of our God, now is with the
Bdim E Am F C/E F G Am C/E F
daugh - ter praise, ce - le - brate the won - ders of
hearts of men. Hal - le - lu - jah! sing to him and
1.
Last time
Dm Gsus4 G C C
(Last time, rpt. top line)
his a - maz - ing grace. (Yes,) grace.
his a - maz - ing
2.
C Dm/C C G G/F
grace.
1. Grace that gives to
Praise to him who
2. Praise to him who
See the sto - ry

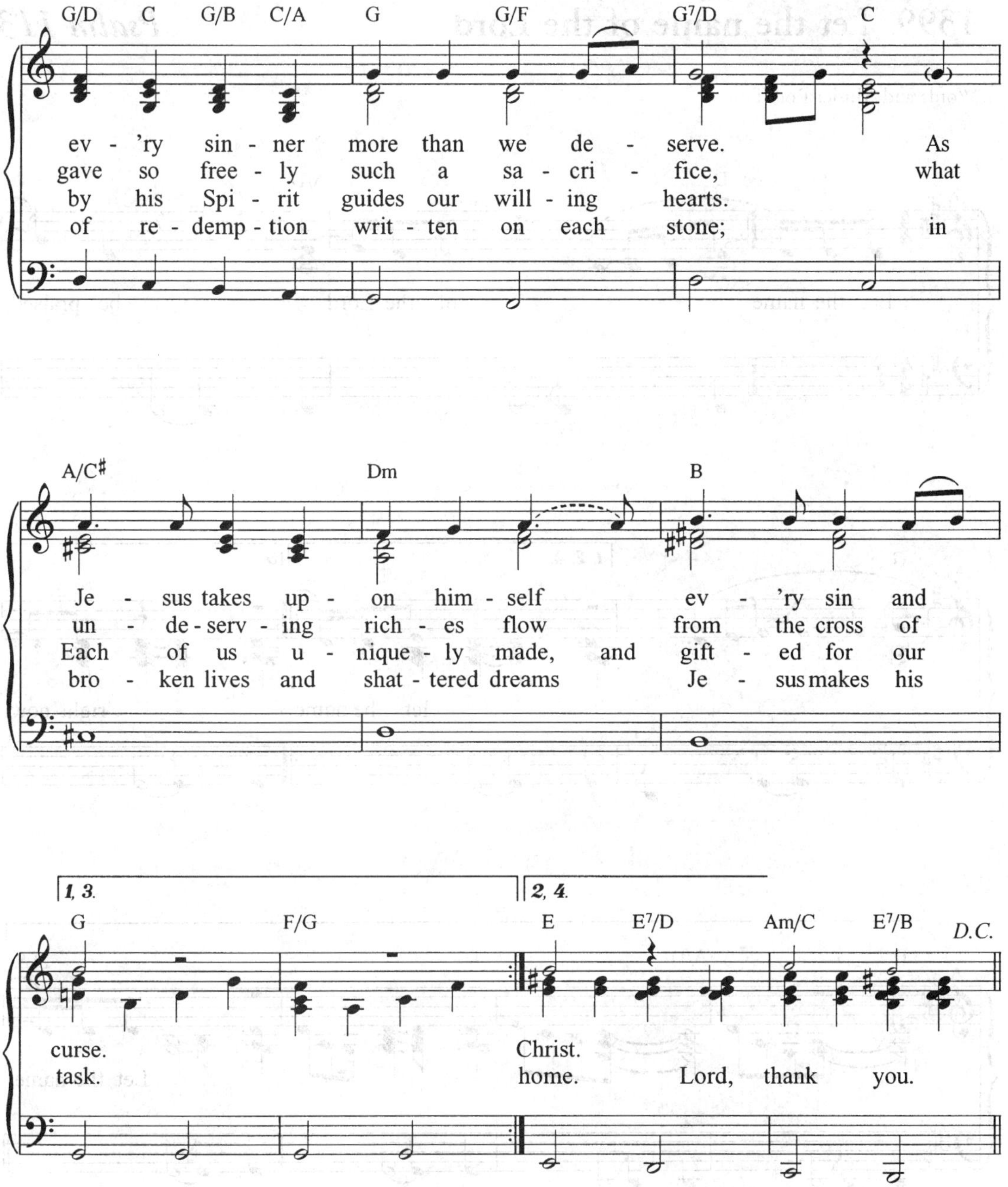
G/D C G/B C/A G G/F G7/D C
ev - 'ry sin - ner more than we de - serve. As
gave so free - ly such a sa - cri - fice, what
by his Spi - rit guides our will - ing hearts.
of re - demp - tion writ - ten on each stone; in
A/C# Dm B
Je - sus takes up - on him - self ev - 'ry sin and
un - de - serv - ing rich - es flow from the cross of
Each of us u - nique - ly made, and gift - ed for our
bro - ken lives and shat - tered dreams Je - sus makes his
1, 3.
2, 4.
G F/G E E7/D Am/C E7/B
D.C.
curse. Christ.
task. home. Lord, thank you.

1399 Let the name of the Lord *Psalm 113*

Words and Music: Rod True

D
A/D
Let the name of the Lord be praised,
G
1, 2, 4.
3.
let the name right now.
D
A/D
G
D.S.
Let the name
5.
G
D
G
right now and for e -

D G D
- ver - more; right now
G D G
and for e - ver - more. From the ris-
A G A
- ing of the sun to the place where it goes down,
G D G
the name of the Lord is to be praised, the name of the Lord
D G D
is to be praised, the name of the Lord is to be praised,

G D G
the name of the Lord is to be praised.
1. 2.
D.S.
D/F♯
Let the name the name of the Lord is to be praised,
G D/A G/B
the name of the Lord is to be praised, the name of the Lord
D/F♯ G D/A
is to be praised, the name of the Lord is to be praised.
G/B G D

He said, 'If you listen carefully
to the voice of the Lord your God
and do what is right in his eyes,
if you pay attention to his commands
and keep all his decrees,
I will not bring on you any of the diseases
I brought on the Egyptians,
for I am the Lord, who heals you.'

Exodus 15:26

1400 Let there be blessing

Words and Music: Heath Jarvis

(♩ = 132)
Chorus C/D
G
F/G
Let there be bles - sing, hon - our,
C/G
Am7
Last time to Coda
C/D
Am/D
bles - sing and hon - our to the Lord of glo - ry.
G
F
C/E
C/D
G
Glo - ry, pow - er, glo - ry and pow - er and praise.
1.
Em7(♭5)
F
2.
Verse
B♭/C
F/C
Let there be
(Leader) And for the great things you have done

G
we wan - na say: (All) we give you glo - ry and hon -
B♭/C
F/C
(Leader)
our for e - ver. And for the way you changed my life,
G N.C.
(Leader)
I want to say: (All) I give you praise. Ain't no
B♭/C
F/C
rock gon - na take my place; ain't gon - na cry out.
D.S. al Coda
E♭maj7
Am/D
C/D
(All) Let all cre - a - tion say. Let there be

CODA
G F G F
Glo - ry, pow - er, glo - ry, pow-
G F
- er, glo - ry, pow - er,
C/E C/D G G/B C
glo - ry and pow - er and praise,
C/E F C/E G
glo - ry and pow - er and praise.

Now the Lord is the Spirit,
and where the Spirit of the Lord is, there is freedom.
And we, who with unveiled faces all reflect the Lord's glory,
are being transformed into his likeness with ever-increasing glory,
which comes from the Lord, who is the Spirit.

2 Corinthians 3:17-18

1401 Let there be glory and honour and praises

Words and Music: James Greenelsh and Elizabeth Greenelsh

(♩ = 69)
D G G/B C Am7 C/D
Let there be glo - ry and hon - our and prai - ses;
G Em7 A9 Dsus4 D
glo - ry and hon - our to Je - sus.
G G/B C Cm/A
Glo - ry and hon - our,
G/D C/D G/D Am/D G/D D7 G C/D D
1.
glo - ry and hon - our to him. Let there be

2.
Am/D G/D D♯dim7 Em A G/D C/D G/D Am/D G/D D♯dim7
hon - our to him. Glo - ry and hon - our to
Em A G/D C/D G/D Am/D G/D D7 C G/B Am7 G
him. Glo - ry and hon - our to him.

1402 Let worship be the fuel

Mission's flame

Words and Music: Matt Redman

Gm
Verse Capo 3 Em
1. Let worship be the fuel for mission's flame, we're
worship be the heart of mission's aim, to
Eb
C
going with a passion for your name, we're
see the nations recognise your fame, 'til
F
D
going for we care about your praise, send us
ev'ry tribe and tongue voices your praise, send us
D
B
Gm
Em
out.
out.
1.
2, 3.
2. Let
Bb
G
Chorus
You should be the praise of ev'ry tongue,
F
D
Eb
C

B♭
G
F
D
you should be the joy of ev - 'ry
E♭
C
D
B
heart, un - til the full - ness of
E♭
C
your king - dom comes, and 'til
D
B
E♭
C
Last time to Coda
that fi - nal re - ve - la - tion dawns,
F
D
Gm
Em
1.
D.S.
send us out. Let

2.
F
D
Bridge
Ev-'ry tribe, ev-'ry tongue,
Ev-'ry note, ev-'ry string,
E♭
C
ev-'ry crea-ture in the heavens and the earth,
ev-'ry me-lo-dy will be for you a-lone.
1.
F
D
ev-'ry heart,
E♭
C
ev-'ry soul will sing your praise, will sing your praise.
2.
Dm7
Bm7
Ev-'ry har-mo-ny that flows from ev-'ry tongue will sing

E♭
C
your praise, will sing your praise, will sing
F
D
D.S.S. al Coda
your praise, will sing your praise.
CODA
F
D
Send us
Gm
Em
out,
E♭
C
send us out,
F
D
send us out,
send us out.
D
B
1.
2.
Gm
Em
Send us

1403 Lift up your heads

Glory to the Lord our God

Words and Music: Steve Merkel

G C F G
al - tars we've built and the works we have done can
2. Who can as - cend to the hill of the Lord?
Verse 1
C F G
ne - ver com - pare to the Sa - viour's love; the
Peo - ple of clean hearts and
Verse 2
F C F
hearts of the hum - ble are tem - ples of
hands. You, who are right - eous and seek - ing his
C G Am F
praise as we wor - ship the An - cient of Days, as we
face, come and wor - ship the An - cient of Days, come and

C G C G
Bridge
wor-ship the An - cient of Days. Glo - ry to the
wor-ship the An - cient of Days.
F C F C Am7 G
Lord our God; glo - ry to the Lamb on the throne; we
G F C Am F
o - pen wide the gates of our hearts, with our lips we rise up and
G F G C F G F
D.S.
praise as we wor-ship the An-cient of Days.

Trust in the Lord with all your heart
and lean not on your own understanding.

Proverbs 3:5

1404 Lift up your heads

Worthy of praises

Words and Music: Lynn DeShazo

D
C² Asus⁴
D
C
D
Bm⁷
Asus⁴
1.Lift up your heads, O ye gates; be lift - ed up, an-cient
2. All na-tions come, wor-ship the Lamb; join in the heaven - ly
G²
D
C
D
doors; peo - ple of God, o - pen your hearts, bow
song; for he was slain and with his blood, he
Bm⁷
Asus⁴
G²
G
down and wor - ship the Lord;
has re-deemed us to God;
he is the Lord, strong and

Em7 Asus4 A
migh-ty; he is the head o-ver all.
Asus4 A
Chorus
D
Ho - ly, Al-migh-ty, Yah-weh is
F C F C D
ho - ly, ho - ly; wor - thy,
F C F C
he is ex-al-ted and wor - thy, wor - thy of
Last time to Coda
1.
D C2 A7sus4 D Am7
prai - ses.

2.
Bridge
D
B♭
C
D
Wor-thy the Lamb who was slain;
B♭
C
Asus4
A
D.S. al Coda
wor-thy of pow-er and rich-es and hon-our and praise.
CODA
C2
A7sus4
D
Am7
D

Not to us, Lord, not to us
but to your name be the glory,
because of your love and faithfulness.

Psalm 115:1

1405 Light of my life

Words and Music: Chris Bowater

Gm2
D2
3
D2/C♯
Bm7
Bm7/A
in ev - 'ry-thing,
be
G2
Gm2
D2
3
Lord
in ev - 'ry-thing.

1406 Light of the world *Here I am to worship*

Words and Music: Tim Hughes

With feeling

1. Light of the world, you stepped down into darkness,
 o-pened my eyes, let me see beau-ty that made this
 heart a-dore you, hope of a life spent with you.

2. King of all days oh so high-ly ex-al-ted,
 glo-rious in hea-ven a-bove. Hum-bly you came to the
 earth you cre-a-ted, all for love's sake be-came poor.

Chorus

So here I am to wor-ship, here I am to bow down, here I am to
say that you're my God, and you're al-to-ge-ther

E
B/D♯
lovely, altogether worthy, altogether
E/G♯
1, 3.
A
A2
wonderful to me.
Last time
A
A2
E
Fine
2.
A
Bridge
And I'll ne-
B/D♯
E/G♯
A
B/D♯
E/G♯
-ver know how much it cost to see my sin upon
1.
A
Bsus4/A
2.
A
Bsus4/A
Asus2
D.S. al Fine
B7sus4
that cross. And I'll ne-
that cross.
So here I am to

1407 Like a fragrant oil

Fragrant

Words and Music: Paul Oakley

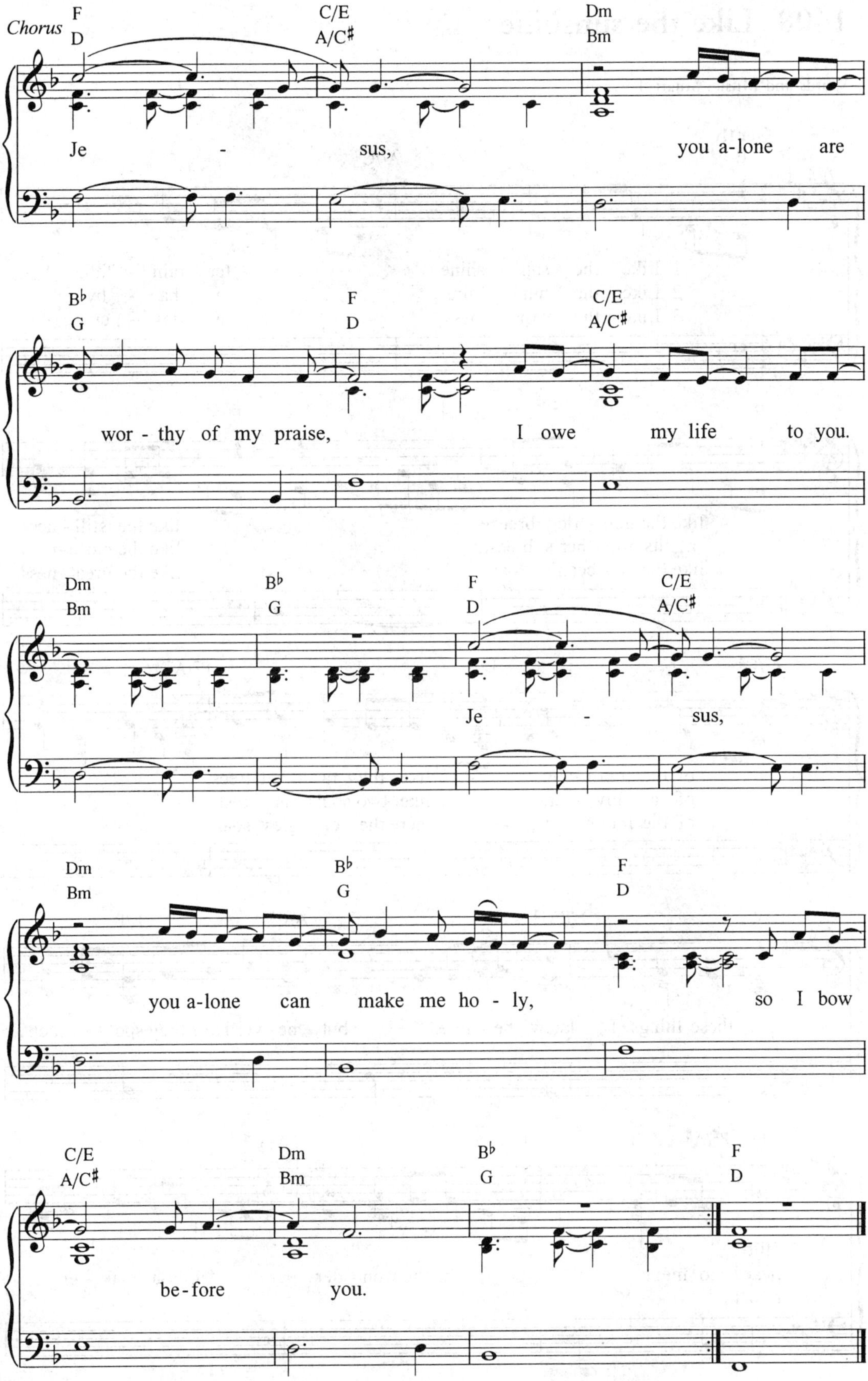
Chorus
F D C/E A/C♯ Dm Bm
Je - sus, you a-lone are
B♭ G F D C/E A/C♯
wor - thy of my praise, I owe my life to you.
Dm Bm B♭ G F D C/E A/C♯
Je - sus,
Dm Bm B♭ G F D
you a-lone can make me ho - ly, so I bow
C/E A/C♯ Dm Bm B♭ G F D
be-fore you.

1408 Like the sunshine

Words and Music: Stuart Townend

E/B A C#m7 Bsus4 B E
whose heart de - lights in me.
A2/C# E A2/C#
Last time
E
Fine
Bm7
Chorus
A E
The heav'ns de - clare his mag - ni - fi - cence,
Bm7 A E
the earth re - sounds with his praise;
Bm7 A E F#m7
be still, my soul, and be sa - tis - fied to wor - ship him,
B7sus4 B
D.C.
to wor - ship him.

1409 Longing for light

Christ, be our light!

Words and Music: Bernadette Farrell

2. Longing for peace, our world is troubled.
Longing for hope, many despair.
Your word alone has power to save us.
Make us your living voice.

3. Longing for food, many are hungry.
Longing for water, many still thirst.
Make us your bread, broken for others,
shared until all are fed.

4. Longing for shelter, many are homeless.
Longing for warmth, many are cold.
Make us your building, sheltering others,
walls made of living stone.

5. Many the gifts, many the people,
many the hearts that yearn to belong.
Let us be servants to one another,
making your kingdom come.

1410 Look away to the cross *Room at the cross*

Words: Frances Jane van Alstyne (Fanny J. Crosby) Music: Ira D. Sankey

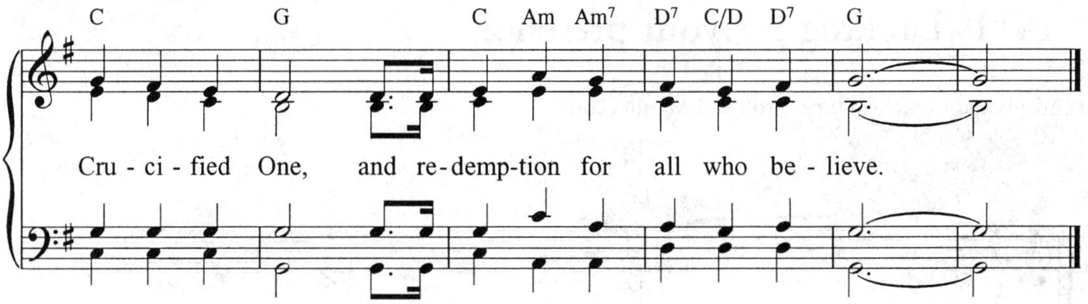
C G C Am Am7 D7 C/D D7 G
Cru - ci - fied One, and re-demp-tion for all who be - lieve.

2. Look away to the cross of the Crucified One,
to the cross where he suffer'd and bled;
and today he invites you to come if you will,
and be cleansed in the blood that he shed.

3. Look away to the cross of the Crucified One,
where the winepress alone he hath trod;
where he cried in his anguish, ''Tis finish'd, 'tis done!'
And commended his Spirit to God.

4. There is life at the cross of the Crucified One,
and its hope is abiding and sure;
for the rapture that flows from the love he bestows
shall for ever and ever endure.

1411 Looking for your presence

Words and Music: Godfrey Birtill and Martin Scott

Dsus4 D G D/F♯ Em
pray Car-ry-ing you, car-ry-ing you, in-to the ci-
C D G D/F♯
-ty streets and homes. Car-ry-ing you, car-ry-ing you,
Em C Dsus4
we hear the foot-steps of the Lord.
D Em C
Can your hea-vy glo-ry, can your
Em C Em
hea-vy glo-ry, can your hea-vy
C G Gsus2(4) G
glo-ry rest on me?

1412 Looks like tonight

Rain down

Words and Music: Martin Smith and Stuart Garrard

F♯m
A/E
D
for hea-ven's rain.
this bar - ren land,
It's gon-na rain,
hope in my hands,
A
yeah.
yeah.
Chorus
D2
D
'Cos it's liv - ing wa - ter we de - sire so flood
Dmaj7
D
A
our hearts with ho - ly fire. Rain down,
D
all a-round the world we're sing-ing. Rain down,

A
can you hear the earth is sing-ing? Rain down, my
D
heart is dry but still I'm sing-ing. Rain down,
1.
2. Back to the start,
2.
F♯m
D
down on me. rain it down.
G D/F♯ A E/G♯
Do not shut, do not shut,
C G/B D
do not shut the hea-vens, but
G D/F♯ A E/G♯
o - pen up, o - pen up,

C G/B D
o - pen up our hearts.
A
Rain down, all a-round the world we're sing-ing.
D
Rain down.
A
Give me strength to cross this wa-ter, keep my heart up - on
D
your al - tar, rain down.
A
Give me strength to cross this wa-ter, keep my feet, don't let

D
me fal - ter, rain down.
F#m A/E D
Do not shut the hea - vens,
F#m 1. A/E
but o - pen up our hearts, o -
D 2. A/E
- pen up our hearts. o -
D
- pen up our hearts.

One thing I ask of the Lord,
this is what I seek:
that I may dwell in the house of the Lord
all the days of my life,
to gaze upon the beauty of the Lord
and to seek him in his temple.

Psalm 27:4

1413 Lord, I am not my own *What I have vowed*

Words and Music: Matt Redman

F C Am Am²/G
day I live is for you, is for you, is for
Fmaj⁷ Am Am²/G Fmaj⁷
you, is for you, is for you, is for you.

2. Now taking up the cross,
walking on your paths,
holding out your truth,
running in this race,
bowing every day,
all for you, my Lord.

3. Earth has nothing I desire
that lives outside of you,
I'm consumed with you.
Treasures have no hold,
nothing else will do,
only you, my Lord.

1414 Lord, I come expectant

Words and Music: Paul Critchley

1. Lord, I come ex - pec - tant in your pre - sence and I

know your heart is full of love for me. How can I re - pay the debt of

love I owe as I bow in wor-ship at your feet?

Ho - ly, ho - ly is the Lord, high and lift - ed up

F
F/G
G
and wor - thy of all praise.
C
G/B
Am7
C/G
Ho - ly, ho - ly is the Lord, lov - er of my
F
F/G
C2
soul and the rul - er of my heart.

2. As I kneel in humble adoration
   and I feel the measure of your glory,
   Lord, I'm reaching out my hands in praise to you;
   come and take this offering I bring.

3. Holy Spirit, come and sanctify me,
   take my life completely as I come to you.
   Purify my heart to honour you, O God,
   as I live to glorify your name.

1415 Lord, I come to you

Words and Music: Andrew Rayner and Wendy Rayner

(♩ = 82)
Cmaj7
Fmaj9
Dm9
1. Lord, I come to you, I come to bow be - fore the
2. Lord, I know I fail to al - ways walk your way, to
Fmaj9/G
Cmaj7
Fmaj9
one whom I a - dore. All that I am, all that I hope
fol - low, come what may. All that I do, all that my fu -
Dm9
Esus4
Chorus
Amaj7
to be is yours. Take my life, O
- ture holds is yours.
Dm9
Esus4
Fmaj7
Esus4
God, my King. Let it be for you a - lone.

Last time to Coda
Amaj7
Dm9
Fmaj7
Em7
Take my all, my ev - 'ry-thing, I give it, Lord, to you.
1.
Dm9
Esus4
Amaj7
Dm9
F/G
D.C.
2.
Dm9
Esus4
D.S. al Coda
CODA
Dm9
Fmaj7
Em7
Dm9
Bm/E
Amaj7
I give it, Lord, to you.

1416 Lord, I stand in the midst of the multitude

Hallelujah to the Lamb

Words and Music: Don Moen and Debbye Graafsma

(♩ = 80)
G
C/G
1. Lord, I stand in the midst of a mul - ti - tude of
2. Lord, we stand by grace in your pre - sence,
G
D/F♯
Em
Em/D
those from ev - 'ry tribe and tongue; we are your
cleansed by the blood of the Lamb; we are your
C
Am7
peo - ple, re - deemed by your blood, pur - chased from
child - ren, called by your name, hum - bly we
C/D
D
C/D
D
3
death by your love. There are no
bow and we pray. Re - lease your
3

G
C/G
words good e-nough to thank you, there are no
pow - er to work in us and through us, 'til we are
G
D/F♯
Em
Em/D
words to ex - press my praise; but I will
changed to be more like you; then all the
C
G²/B
lift up my voice and sing from my heart with
na - tions will see your glo - ry re - vealed and
Am⁷
3
C/D
D
C/D
D
Chorus
all of my strength. Hal - le -
wor - ship you.
3

G G/B C Em D
lu - jah, hal - le - lu - jah, hal - le - lu - jah to the Lamb; hal - le -
G G/B C Cmaj7/D D
lu - jah, hal - le - lu - jah, by the blood of Christ we stand. Ev-'ry
G G/B C Dsus4 D
tongue, ev-'ry tribe, ev-'ry peo - ple, ev-'ry land; giv-ing
Last time to Coda
G G/B C Dsus4 D
glo - ry, giv-ing hon - our, giv-ing praise un - to the Lamb of God.

1.
2.
G
Em
Domit3
Dsus4
Gomit3
E♭
Bridge
B♭2/D
F
Ev-'ry knee shall bow;
ev-'ry tongue con-fess that
Am/D
Bm/D
C/D
D
D.S. al Coda
you are Lord of all.
Hal-le -
CODA
C
praise un - to the Lamb of God.

1417 Lord, I will bow to you

I will bow to you

Words and Music: Pete Episcopo

(♩= 62)
E B/D♯ C♯m7 E/G♯
Lord, I will bow to you, to no o - ther god
A2 Bsus4 B E A/C♯ B/D♯
but you a-lone.
E B/D♯ C♯m7 E/G♯
Lord, I will wor - ship you: no-thing hands have made,
A2 Bsus4 B E
but you a-lone. I will lay
F♯m7 E/G♯
down my i - dols, thrones I have made,

A2 E/G# B7sus4 A2/C# B/D# E B/D#
all that has tak-en my heart; Lord, I will bow to you,
C#m7 E/G# A2 Bsus4 B E A/C# B/D#
to no o - ther god but you a-lone.
E B/D# C#m7 E/G#
Lord, I will bow to you, to no o - ther god
A2 Bsus4 B E B/D#
but you a-lone.
C#m7 E/G# A2 Bsus4 B E

1418 Lord, let your glory fall

Words and Music: Matt Redman

Steadily
D
Dmaj7
G2
1. Lord, let your glo - ry fall
And as a sign to you
D/F#
G2
as on that an - cient day;
that we would love the same,
Bm
Dmaj7/F#
G2
Em7
G
songs of en - dur - ing love,
our hearts will sing that song:
and then your glo - ry
God, let your glo - ry
1.
D
Dsus2
2.
D
(vv.2&3)
Dsus2
Chorus
came.
come.
You are

D/F#
G
good, you are good, and your love en - dures. You are
D/F#
G
good, you are good, and your love en - dures. You are
Bm
Dmaj7/F#
G
good, you are good, and your love en - dures to - day.
Last time
D
G
D.C.
D

2. Voices in unison,
giving you thanks and praise,
joined by the instruments,
and then your glory came.
Your presence like a cloud
upon that ancient day;
the priests were overwhelmed
because your glory came.

3. A sacrifice was made,
and then your fire came;
they knelt upon the ground,
and with one voice they praised.
A sacrifice was made,
and then your fire came;
they knelt upon the ground,
and with one voice they praised.

1419 Lord, the love you give

Let my life be like a love song

Words and Music: Tom Slater and Brenton Brown

(♩= 68)
Em7
C
1. Lord, the love you give, you give so gen - 'rous - ly.
2. So let jus - tice roll like an end - less stream,
D
Am7
You were my sa - cri - fice, you gave your life for me.
flow - ing through my life to the poor and weak.
G
D
And now I want to give, just as I've re - ceived;
Let the things I do and the words I speak
Am7
G/B
C
C/D
to live a life that shines your love for those in need.
re - veal the awe - some love you have shown to me.
G
Chorus
D
(So) Let my life be like a love song, let my life be like a love song,

Am7
G/B
C
D
Last time to Coda
let my life be like a love song to your heart.
Am7
G/B
D
Am7
G/B
1.
D
2.
C
D.C. (v.2)
CODA
G
D
Let my life be like a love song, let my life be like a love song,
Am7
G/B
(Fine)
C
D
Repeat ad lib. al Fine
let my life be like a love song to your heart.

1420 Lord, this heart must sing *Never lose the wonder*

Words and Music: Tim Hughes

Prayerfully
Dm7
F
1. Lord, this heart must sing of all that you have
2. Help me un - der-stand just what it meant for
Bb2
Bbmaj7
Bb2
Bbmaj7
Dm7
done for me: the beau-ty of the cross,
you, Je - sus, the ho - ly King of all
F
Bb2
Bbmaj7
Bb2
Bbmaj7
the great-ness of your loss.
up - on a sin-ner's cross.
So, I'll
Gm7
F/A
Bb2
Bb
Gm7
F/A
thank you for the day when you washed my sin a-

E♭2
Chorus
F6 F Dm7
way. I will ne - ver lose the won-der of the
Fmaj7/A B♭2 F6 F Dm7
blood you shed for me. There could be no great-er love than this through
Fmaj7/A B♭2 Gm7 F/A
all e - ter - ni - ty. So, I'll thank you for the day
B♭2 B♭maj7 Gm7 F/A E♭2
when you washed my sin a - way.

1421 Lord, turn your footsteps

Words and Music: Godfrey Birtill

(♩ = 90)
C2 C/B F2/A C/B
1. Lord, turn your foot - steps to-wards these ru - ins;
2. Lord, turn your foot - steps to-wards these ru - ins;
F/A C/B F/A
we need you here, we need you here.
we need you here, we need you here,
G/B C2 C/B
Our homes are bro - ken, our
in these streets filled with dark - ness, with our
F/A C/B F/A
child - ren are sto - len; we need you here,
child - ren fa - ther-less; we need you here,

G/B
F/A
G2/B
we need you here.
we need you here.
G/B
Chorus
C2
C/B
Our God and King,
An - cient of Days,
yours is the day,
C/A
C/G
F/A
Al - pha, O -me - ga, Je - sus, Sa -
no one is great - er: come, Lord, save
1.
G4/B
- viour, work your de - li - ve- rance in this place.
Yours is the night,
us! Work your de -
2.
Last time
C2
G4/B
1st time D.C.
C
Fine
li - ve- rance in this place.

C2
C2/B
C2/A
C2/B
C2
C2/B
Work your de - li - ve-rance in this place.
C/A
1.
C/B
2.
C/B
D.S.
Work your de - li - ve-rance in this place.
- ve-rance in this place.
(Our God and King),

1422 Lord, we believe when we call

Words and Music: John L. Bell

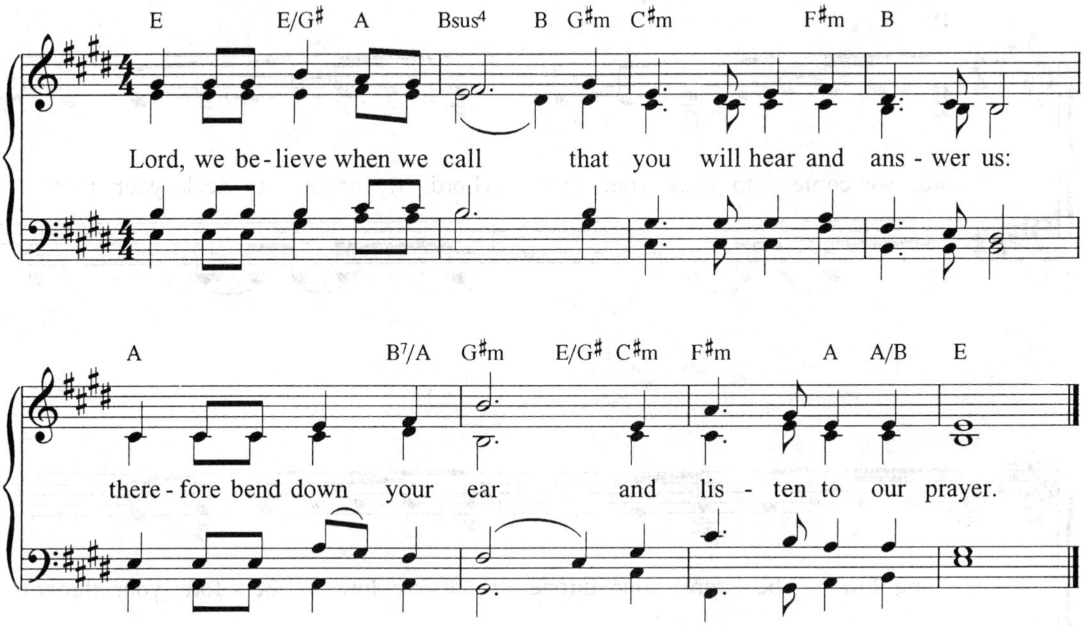
E E/G♯ A Bsus4 B G♯m C♯m F♯m B
Lord, we be - lieve when we call that you will hear and ans - wer us:
A B7/A G♯m E/G♯ C♯m F♯m A A/B E
there - fore bend down your ear and lis - ten to our prayer.

1423 Lord, we come to seek your face

Words and Music: Wes Sutton

(♩ = 106)
D
Lord, we come to seek your face (Lord, we come to seek your face),
A/D
bow - ing low be - fore your throne (bow - ing low be - fore your throne),
G/D
join - ing with the an - gels' songs (join - ing with the an - gels' songs),
D
bring - ing praise to you a - lone (bring - ing praise to you a - lone).

C/D
Wor - thy, wor - thy is the Lamb (wor - thy, wor - thy is the Lamb),
D
heav'n and earth raise up the cry (heav'n and earth raise up the cry),
C/D
see him throned in ma - jes - ty (see him throned in ma - jes - ty),
D
King of glo - ry, Lord of life (King of glo - ry, Lord of life).
B♭maj7
Am7
B♭maj7
Ho - ly, ho -

Am7 B♭maj7 Am7
ly, ho - ly is the
Dsus4 D B♭maj7
Lord. Ho -
Am7 B♭maj7 Am7
ly, ho - ly,
B♭maj7 Am7 D
ho - ly is the Lord.

1424 Lord, we wait

Words and Music: Keith Getty and Stuart Townend

Stately
D A Em/G Em7 G D/A A
1. Lord, we wait for the day of your ap - pear - ing;
D A D/F♯ G A7 D Chorus
Lord, we wait for your com-ing in the clouds. With a
A A/G D/F♯ G A A/G D/F♯
shout the trum - pet will sound, and the dead will be
G B7/F♯ Em G D/A A7 D
raised to life, and we shall meet him in the air!

2. In that day
death is swallowed up in victory;
in that day
sin and death shall be no more.

1425 Lord, what a sacrifice I see

The greatest love

Words and Music: Susie Hare

Steadily
Ab2 Db/Ab Cm7 Fm7
Capo 1 G2 C/G Bm7 Em7
1. Lord, what a sac - ri - fice I see as I turn my eyes to
2. Lord, what a pro-mise of your grace as I turn my eyes to
3. Lord, what a pri - vi - lege I own to free - ly come be -
Bbm7 Ebsus4 Eb Ab Eb/G Fm Ab/Eb
Am7 Dsus4 D G D/F# Em G/D
Cal - va - ry; there, my sins nailed to a tree, a King stands
seek your face; clothed in right-eous-ness, I place my sin - ful -
fore your throne; there, to know and to be known, sur - ren - dered
1. 2, 3.
Bbm7 Db/Eb Eb7 Ab2 Db/Ab Ab Db/F Eb/G
Am7 C/D D7 G2 C/G G C/E D/F#
Chorus
in in - stead of me.
ness in your em - brace.
now to you a - lone. The

A♭ A♭/C D♭2 D♭2/E♭
G G/B C2 C2/D
great - est love that I will e - ver know, the
A♭ A♭/C B♭/D C7/E C7
G G/B A/C♯ B7/D♯ B7
on - ly love that ne - ver lets me go, streams
Fm A♭/E♭ D♭ A♭/C
Em G/D C G/B
from a heart that loves so per - fect - ly; the
B♭m A♭/C D♭ E♭7 A♭ D♭2/A♭ A♭ E♭7sus4 A♭
Am G/B C D7 G C2/G G D7sus4 G
1. 2.
D.C.
great-est love of all is yours to me. me.

1426 Lord, you seem so far

I will sing

Words and Music: Don Moen

(♩ = 70)
Am
1. Lord, you seem so far a - way, a
2. Lord, it's hard for me to see
F
C
G
mil - lion miles or more it feels to-day;
all the thoughts and plans you have for me;
C/G
G
but
Am
though I have - n't lost my faith, I
I will put my trust in you,

Verse 2
F
C
G
know - ing that you died to set me free;
must con-fess right now that it's hard for me to pray;
C/G
G
but I
F
C/E
don't know what to say, and I don't know where to start;
F
but as you give the grace with

G
Chorus
C
all that's in my heart; I will sing,
F
I will praise, e - ven
Am
Em
F
in my dark - est hour, through the sor - row and the pain
G
C
I will sing.
1.
2.
G/B
D.C.

1427 Love unfailing

To the ends of the earth

Words and Music: Joel Houston and Marty Sampson

Em C2 G D Em C2
Love un-fail - ing o - ver-tak - ing my heart. You
G D Em C2 G D
take me in. Find-ing peace a-gain, fear is lost in all you
C2 D
are. And I would give the world to tell your sto-
Em C2
- ry, 'cause I know that you've called me, I know that you've called

G
D
me. I've lost my-self for good with-in your pro-
C
Em
C2
-mise, and I won't hide it, I won't hide it.
Chorus
G
D
Je-sus, I be-lieve in you, and I would go to the
Am7
C2
ends of the earth, to the ends of the earth. For you

G
F2
a-lone are the Son of God, and all the world will see that you are
Last time to Coda
1st time D.C.
2nd time repeat Chorus
3rd time continue
Am7
C2
Em
C
God, that you are God.
G
D
Em
C
CODA
G
D
D.S. al Coda
C2
God.

1428 Make a joyful noise *Psalm 100*

Words and Music: Graham Kendrick

C D G D
to be - long to him, so make a joy - ful
G D C D G D
noise.
C D C/E C D
En - ter now in - to his gates with thanks -
C G/B Am7 G C/E
giv - ing. En - ter now his courts with
Am7 D C G/B
prai - ses, give thanks to him, bless his name for the

Am7 Em D C
Lord is good and his stead - fast love will ne - ver end; his
G/B C Am7 D
faith - ful - ness is to all ge - ne - ra - tions.
C
(Last time only) So make a joy - ful noise.
G D C D G D
C D D.C. C2 G

But the fruit of the Spirit is love, joy, peace,
patience, kindness, goodness, faithfulness,
gentleness and self-control.
Against such things there is no law.

Galatians 5:22-23

1429 Man of sorrows

Alleluia! What a Saviour!

Words: Philip P. Bliss, alt.

Music: Barry Hart

G C6 G D G G/B Em C Cmaj7 C D G
Al - le - lu - ia! Al - le - lu - ia! Al - le - lu - ia! What a Sa - viour!

3. Guilty, vile and helpless we;
spotless Lamb of God was he:
full atonement – can it be?
Alleluia! What a Saviour!

4. Lifted up was he to die:
'It is finished!' was his cry;
now in heav'n exalted high:
Alleluia! What a Saviour!

Chorus

5. When he comes, our glorious King,
all his ransomed home to bring,
then anew this song we'll sing:
Alleluia! What a Saviour!

Chorus

1430 Many are the words we speak *Now to live the life*

Words and Music: Matt Redman

Gmaj7
All we want to do is bring you some - thing real,
1.
D
bring you some - thing true.
A
2.
D.C.
D
(2. We hope that)
A
D.S.
3.
D
A
Help us live the life,
Bm
Dmaj7
Now to go the ex - tra mile, now to turn the o-ther cheek,

Gmaj7
Dmaj7
and to serve you with a life.
Gmaj7
Dmaj7
Let us share your fel - low-ship, e - ven of your suf - fer - ings;
Gmaj7
F#7sus4
ne-ver let the pas - sion die. Now to live the life,
D
now to live the life,
Bm
now to live the life,
D
A7sus4
D
now to live the life.

Praise be to the God and Father of our Lord Jesus Christ!
In his great mercy he has given us new birth into a living hope
through the resurrection of Jesus Christ from the dead.

1 Peter 1:3

1431 May the words of my mouth

Words and Music: Tim Hughes and Rob Hill

B♭ G
E♭ C
I'm glad to do, it's time to live
Gm Em
Gm/F Em/D
C/E A/C♯
F D
a life of love that plea - ses you. And I will give
B♭ G
E♭ C
my all to you, sur-ren - der ev -
Gm Em
Gm/F Em/D
C/E A/C♯
F D
Last time to Coda
- 'ry-thing I have and fol - low you, I'll fol-low
1.
2.
E♭2 C2
E♭maj7 Cmaj7
E♭2 C2
you. 2. Lord, will you.

1, 2, 3.
Gm
Em
F/A
D/F♯
B♭
G
C
A
Repeat and build
I will fol-low,
I will fol-low you.
4.
B♭
G
C
A
Csus4
Asus4
C
A
E♭2
C2
D.S. al Coda
I will fol-low you.
For this is what
CODA
E♭2
C2
B♭
G
you.

'But what about you?' he asked. 'Who do you say I am?'
Simon Peter answered,
'You are the Christ, the Son of the living God.'

Matthew 16:15-16

1432 May we be a shining light *Song for the nations*

Words and Music: Chris Christensen

(♩ = 73)
Capo 3
1. May we be a shining light to the nations, a shining light to the peoples of the earth; 'til the whole world sees the glory of your name. May your pure light shine through us.
2. May we bring a
To next verse
Last time
come in us.

2. May we bring a word of hope to the nations,
a word of life to the peoples of the earth;
'til the whole world knows there's salvation through your name.
May your mercy flow through us.

3. May we be a healing balm to the nations,
a healing balm to the peoples of the earth;
'til the whole world knows the power of your name.
May your healing flow through us.

4. May we sing a song of joy to the nations,
a song of praise to the peoples of the earth;
'til the whole world rings with the praises of your name.
May your song be sung through us.

5. May your kingdom come to the nations,
your will be done to the peoples of the earth;
'til the whole world knows that Jesus Christ is Lord.
May your kingdom come in us.
May your kingdom come in us.
May your kingdom come on earth.

1433 May we daily drink from your river *We stand*

Words and Music: James Wright

F C/F F
D A/D D
words take root with - in us as in - to your like - ness we
run and not grow wea - ry as we fo - cus our eyes on your
E♭2
C2
grow. May we bear the fruit of your
face, with hope, faith and en -
E♭/B♭ B♭ F B♭/F F
C/G G D G/D D
Spi - rit, Lord, may our lives o - ver - flow.
du - rance, Lord, we will fin - ish the race.
Chorus
B♭ C/B♭ B♭maj7 C7/B♭ F
G A/G Gmaj7 A7/G D
And as we walk in the light of your Spi - rit's com - mand
B♭ C/B♭ B♭maj7 C7/B♭
G A/G Gmaj7 A7/G
one with each o - ther u - ni - ted in Je - sus we

Gm7 C/D Dm Gm7
Em7 A/B Bm Em7
stand on the foun - da - tion of your love through your sal -
C/D Dm E♭maj7 E♭/B♭ B♭
A/B Bm Cmaj7 C/G G
va - tion, and we live in the re - ve - la - tion of all that you
F/C C F B♭/F
D/A A D G/D
1.
are, of all you have done through Je - sus the Son.
C/F B♭/F C C
A/D G/D A A
2. 3.
D.S.
2. May we done. And we done through Je - sus the
F B♭/F C/F B♭/F F
D G/D A/D G/D D
Son.

And the peace of God,
which transcends all understanding,
will guard your hearts and your minds in Christ Jesus.

Philippians 4:7

1434 Mercy flows

Words and Music: Leigh Barnard

(♩ = 80)
G D/F♯ C/E D/F♯ G D/F♯ C/E D/F♯
1. Mer - cy
2. Peace that flows from your throne a - bove giv-ing us
3. Jus - tice

Repeat 1st time only
Em D/F♯ C/E D/F♯ G D/F♯ C/E D/F♯
hope so sure and in - fi - nite grace.

C2 D2/F♯ C2 Dsus4 D
Mer - ci - ful Lord, love is your name.

Chorus
G D/F♯ C/E D/F♯ Em D/F♯ C/E Dsus4 D
Take my life, have it all, I'm liv-ing for you, migh-ty God.

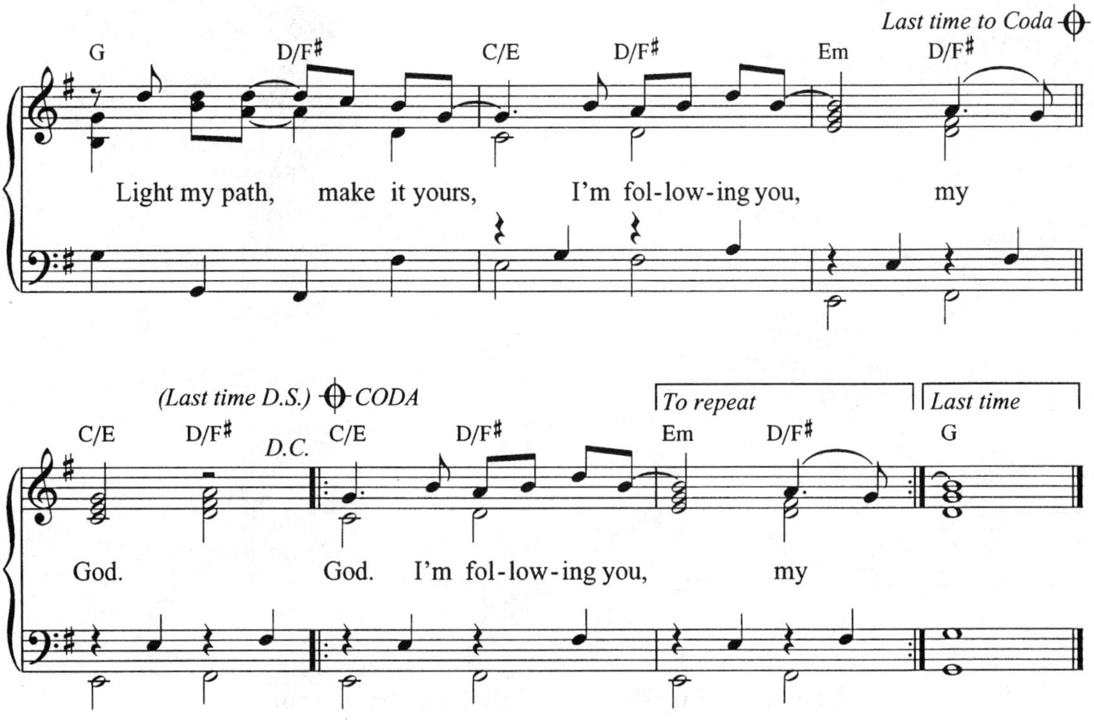
Last time to Coda
G D/F# C/E D/F# Em D/F#
Light my path, make it yours, I'm fol-low-ing you, my
(Last time D.S.) CODA
To repeat
Last time
C/E D/F# D.C. C/E D/F# Em D/F# G
God. God. I'm fol-low-ing you, my

The Lord is my shepherd, I shall not be in want.
He makes me lie down in green pastures,
he leads me beside quiet waters.

Psalm 23:1-2

1435 Mercy in our time of failure

Words: Leith Samuel

Music: Johann Steiner

GOTT WILL'S MACHEN 87 87

G Dsus4 D G Dsus4 D7 G C D7 Em D G Am G D D7
1. Mer - cy in our time of fail - ure, grace to help in time of need:
Bm D7 E7 E Am Am7 D7 D G D7 G C6 D G
this sure pro-mise of our Sa-viour is a word that we may plead.

2. He has passed into the heavens,
he is seated on the throne,
ever for us interceding,
always caring for his own.

3. There is none he will not welcome,
no request he cannot meet;
let us not be slow to ask him,
lay our burdens at his feet.

4. We can never come too often,
never with a need too great,
never with a prayer too simple;
only fear to come too late!

5. Daily on our pilgrim journey
praise him for his matchless grace,
live for his immortal glory
till in heaven we see his face.

1436 Multiply your love

Words and Music: Andy Park

1.
Asus4
Gsus2
through our sim-ple words and deeds
through my sim-ple words and deeds
let us see your har - vest come
let love be mul-ti-plied.
D
2.
Gsus2
2. Mul - ti-ply your
let love be mul-ti-plied.
To Chorus
3.
D
let love be mul - ti-plied.
Chorus
Bm7
G
Let us see your king-dom come
Asus4
Bm7
to the poor and bro-ken ones. Let us see a

G D Asus4
migh-ty flood of jus - tice and mer - cy, O
G2 Asus4 D Dsus4
Je - sus, let love be mul-ti-plied,
D Dsus4
let love be mul-ti-plied.
1. D D.C.
3. Mul - ti-ply your
2. D Dsus4 D
Let love be mul-ti-plied. Let love be mul-ti-plied.
C G D Dsus4
Let love be mul-ti-plied.

D
C
G
Let love be mul-ti-plied.
Let love be mul-ti-plied.
(Voices only)
D
Dsus4
D
(G/D)
(D)
Mul-ti-ply your love through us,
(G/D)
(D)
1.
(G/D)
mul-ti-ply your love.
Mul-ti-ply your
2.
(G/D)
D
G/D
Mul-ti-ply your love through us,
mul-ti-ply your
D
Dsus4
1.
D
G/D
2.
D
G/D
love.
Mul-ti-ply your
Mul-ti-ply your

1.
2.
D
G/D
Dsus4
love.
Mul - ti - ply your love.
Mul - ti - ply your love.

1437 My faith looks up to thee

Words: Ray Palmer

Music: Lowell Mason

HARLAN (OLIVET) 664 6664

2. May thy rich grace impart
strength to my fainting heart,
my zeal inspire;
as thou hast died for me,
O may my love to thee
pure, warm, and changless be,
a living fire.

3. While life's dark maze I tread
and griefs around me spread,
be thou my guide;
bid darkness turn to day,
wipe sorrow's tears away,
nor let me ever stray
from thee aside.

4. When ends life's transient dream,
when death's cold, sullen stream
shall o'er me roll,
blest Saviour, then, in love,
fear and distrust remove;
O bear me safe above,
a ransomed soul.

Be imitators of God, therefore,
as dearly loved children
and live a life of love,
just as Christ loved us
and gave himself up for us
as a fragrant offering and sacrifice to God.

Ephesians 5:1-2

1438 My heart is filled with thankfulness

Words and Music: Keith Getty and Stuart Townend

Thoughtfully
C G/B Am F C/E Am7 F G
1. My heart is filled with thank-ful - ness to him who bore my pain; who
C G/B Am F C/E F G C
plumbed the depths of my dis - grace and gave me life a - gain; who
Am C/G F G Am F C F Gsus4 G
crushed my curse of sin - ful - ness, and clothed me in his light, and
C G/B Am F C/E F G C
wrote his law of right - eous - ness with pow'r up - on my heart.

2. My heart is filled with thankfulness
to him who walks beside;
who floods my weaknesses with strength
and causes fear to fly;
whose ev'ry promise is enough
for ev'ry step I take;
sustaining me with arms of love
and crowning me with grace.

3. My heart is filled with thankfulness
to him who reigns above;
whose wisdom is my perfect peace,
whose ev'ry thought is love.
For ev'ry day I have on earth
is given by the King.
So I will give my life, my all,
to love and follow him.

1439 My hope rests firm

Words and Music: Richard Creighton and Keith Getty

With feeling
D D/F♯ G D
1. My hope rests firm on Je - sus Christ, he
F♯m Bm A G
is my on - ly plea: though all the
A D D/F♯ G Em A
world should point and scorn, his ran - som leaves me
Bm Em A D
free, his ran - som leaves me free.

2. My hope sustains me as I strive
and strain towards the goal;
though I still stumble into sin,
his death paid for it all,
his death paid for it all.

3. My hope provides me with a spur
to help me run this race:
I know my tears will turn to joy
the day I see his face,
the day I see his face.

4. My hope is to be with my Lord,
to know as I am known:
to serve him gladly all my days
in praise before his throne,
in praise before his throne.

1440 My Lord, I come to honour you *My Redeemer lives*

Words and Music: Chris Orange

(♩ = 80)
D G/B G D
My Lord, I come to hon-our you.
D G/B G Asus4 A
Such love, such grace, I find in you.
G D/F# Asus4 A G/B D Asus4 A
Your pre - cious blood poured out for me. Now my
F#m G F#m G
Re-deem - er lives, my Re-deem - er lives,
F#m G A D
my Re-deem - er lives in me.

1441 My Saviour, Redeemer

For all you've done

Words and Music: Reuben Morgan

(♩ = 133)
Verse
E
Esus4
C♯m7
A
B
My Saviour, Redeemer, lifted me from the miry clay.
Almighty, for ever, I will never be the same.
'Cause you came near, from the everlasting to the world we live.
The Father's only Son.

Chorus
E
B/D♯
And you lived, and you died, and you
A/C♯
B
E
rose a-gain on high. And you op - ened the way
B/D♯
A/C♯
B
Last time to Coda
for the world to live a-gain. Hal - le - lu -
A
B
E
- jah, for all you've done.
Esus4
E
Esus4
D.C. al Coda

CODA
C#m7
B
A
- jah,
for all you've done.
B
C#m7
B
Hal - le-hu - jah,
for all you've
(no vocal on repeat)
A
B/A
A
done.
B/A
A/E
B/D#
Hal - le - lu - jah,
for
A/C#
B
Repeat 3 times
E
all you've done.

1442 My soul glorifies the Lord

Words and Music: Adele Kane, Dave Kane and Nic Manders

E
C♯m
My soul glo - ri - fies the Lord, re -
Bsus4
joi - ces in God, he is ho - ly.
E
1.
2.
My
You have lift -
E
A
- ed up the hum - ble, filled the hun - gry with good
I've on - ly dreamed of, set my heart on fire with your
C♯m7
things; his mer - cy frees my soul frees me.
love; your pre - sence takes my breath a - way.

Bsus4
1. B
2. B
You bring joy
Chorus
E
C#m7
Ho - ly, ho - ly is his name,
Bsus4
ho - ly is the Lord, he is ho - ly.
E
1.
Last time
2.
My
A
B
soul glo - ri-fies the Lord, re -
C#m7
Bsus4
B
D.S. al Fine
joi - ces in you, my Sa - viour.

1443 My soul is yearning

You are everything

Words and Music: Brian Doerksen and Steve Mitchinson

Gently (♩ = 60)

G Am F C
My soul is yearn-ing for your liv - ing stream,
G Am F
my heart is ach - ing for you.
G Am F C
All that I long for is found in your heart, you
G F C
are ev - 'ry-thing I need. You are the thirst,
G Am
you are the stream, you are the hun-

F
C
G/B
- ger liv - ing deep in-side of me. You are the food
Am
F
that sa - tis-fies, you are pro-vi-
C/E
F
Gsus4
G
- sion for the jour - ney of our lives.
Am
F
G
You are ev - 'ry - thing, you are.
1, 2.
3.
C
F/C
C

1444 Nations rise and nations fall

Let your kingdom come

Words and Music: Craig Smith

1. Na-tions rise and na - tions fall, lead-ers come and go
Go-vern-ments and dy - nas - ties boast of strength and pow'r
2. Kings and queens leave le - ga - cies of tem-po - ra - ry fame,
but Christ our King rules o - ver all and
but you a - lone reign sov - 'reign - ly and
your throne re-mains e - ter - nal - ly,
you will reign for e - ver.
you will reign for e-
you will reign for e-
1.
2, 3.
- ver, our

C G D G
God reigns for e - ver.
Chorus
D C
Let your king-dom come, let your will be done, let your king-dom come.
G D
Let your king-dom come, let your will be done,
C G
1st time D.C.
Fine
let your king-dom come.
B♭ C F Gm
One God, one Lord, one King, one ma - jes-ty.

B♭ C F Dsus4
One high and lift - ed up, one ho - ly pow'r.
D C G D Em C G
D C G D Em C G D
Our God reigns, our God reigns for e -
1. 2.
C G D Em
- ver. - ver. Our God reigns, our
1. 2.
C G D D
D.S.al Fine
God reigns for e - ver. Our - ver. Let your king-dom come,

1445 No eye has seen

Words and Music: Paul Baloche and Ed Kerr

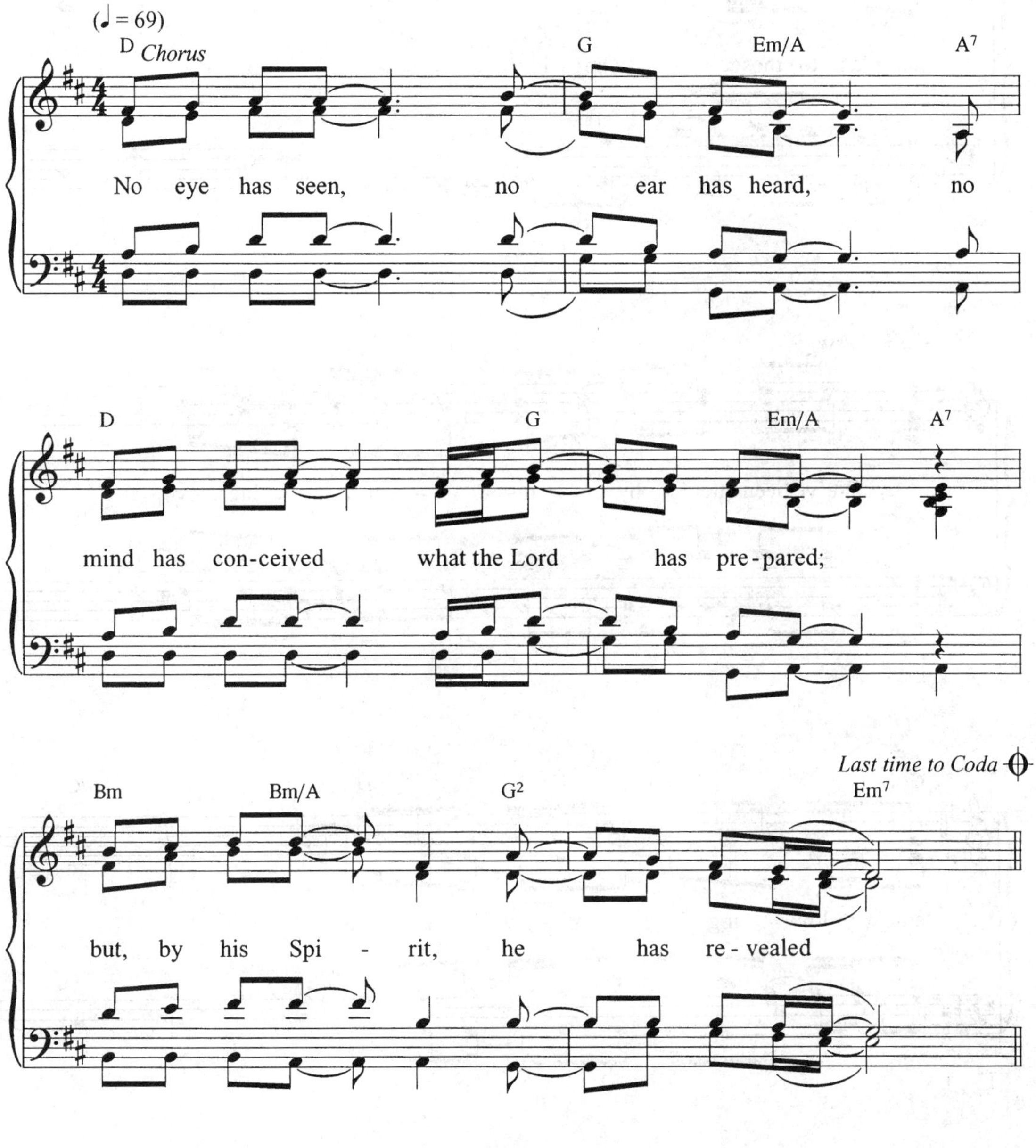
(♩ = 69)
D Chorus
G
Em/A
A7
No eye has seen, no ear has heard, no
D
G
Em/A
A7
mind has con-ceived what the Lord has pre-pared;
Last time to Coda
Bm
Bm/A
G2
Em7
but, by his Spi - rit, he has re-vealed
1.
D/A
Em7/A
his plan to those who love him.

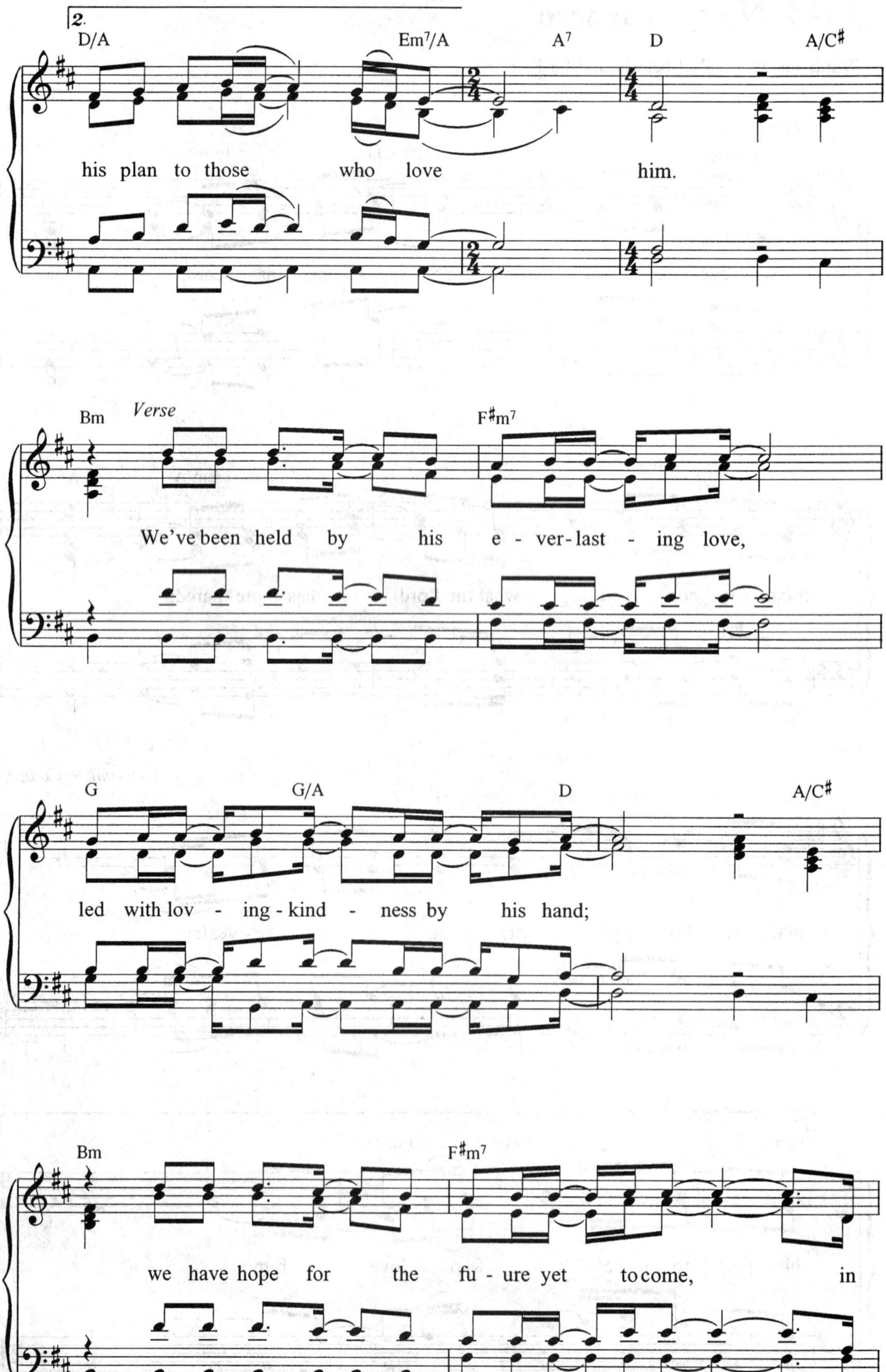
2.
D/A Em7/A A7 D A/C#
his plan to those who love him.
Bm Verse F#m7
We've been held by his e - ver - last - ing love,
G G/A D A/C#
led with lov - ing - kind - ness by his hand;
Bm F#m7
we have hope for the fu - ure yet to come, in

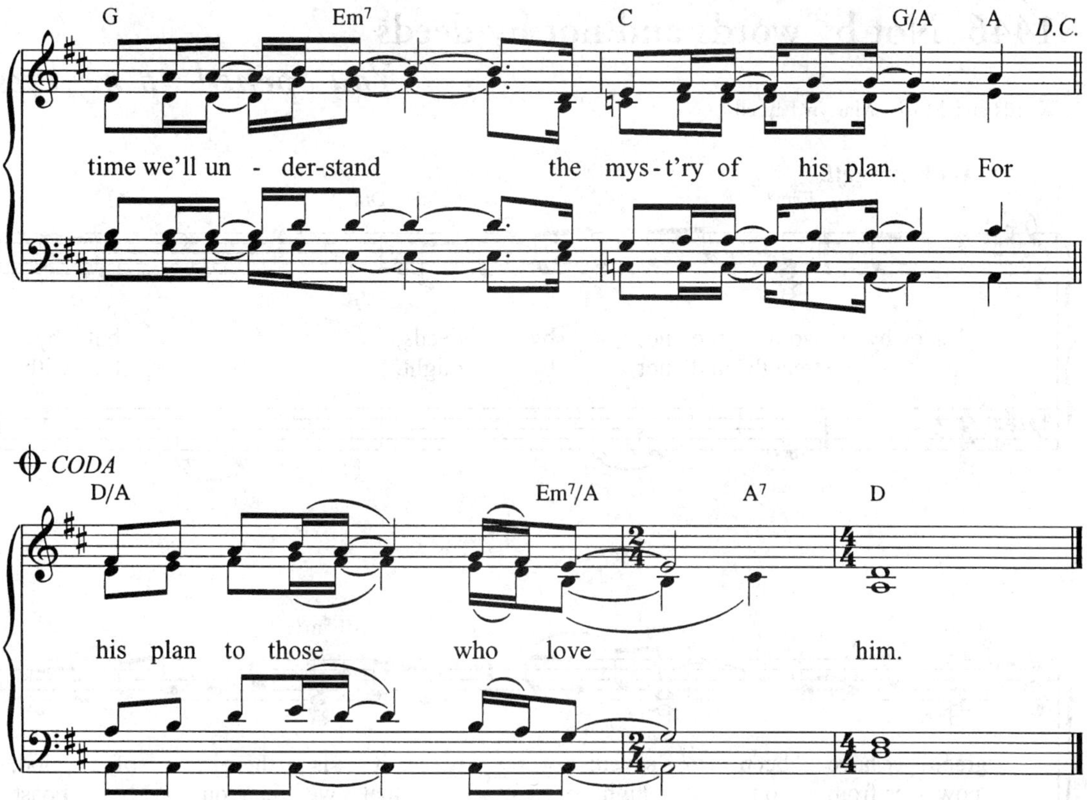

G Em7 C G/A A D.C.
time we'll un - der-stand the mys - t'ry of his plan. For
CODA
D/A Em7/A A7 D
his plan to those who love him.

1446 Not by words and not by deeds

You opened up my eyes

Words and Music: Martyn Layzell

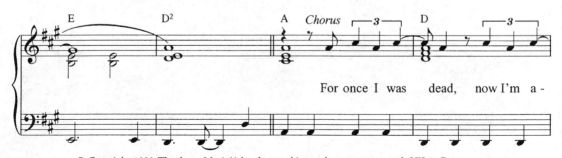

With strength
F♯m9
Dmaj7
1. Not by words and not by deeds, but by
strength and not by might, but with
F♯m9
Dmaj7
F♯m9
grace we have been saved; and it is the gift of God,
pow - er from on high, so that we can on - ly boast,
1.
Dmaj7
E2
Dmaj7
2.
Dmaj7
3
the faith we need. Not by boast in you.
E
D2
A
Chorus
3
D
3
For once I was dead, now I'm a -

E
D
A
3
- live, for free - dom I'm set free; and in your great
D
3
E
D
love, life do I find. You o - pened up my
A
E/G♯
F♯m7
D2
eyes.

2. Not with eloquence or fame,
but in weakness and in shame,
for the power of your strength is then revealed.
And the message of your cross,
seemed such foolishness to some,
but the mercy of your grace is hidden there.

1447 Nothing in this world

Words and Music: Tim Hughes

Tenderly
Capo 1
1. No - thing in this world, no trea - sure man could buy could take the place of draw - ing near to you.
no - thing I want more than to spend my days with you, dwel - ling in your sec - ret place of praise.
There's
Chorus
(And) oh, how I need you.

2. So place within my heart
a fire that burns for you,
that waters cannot quench
nor wash away.
And let that fire blaze
through all eternity,
where one day I shall see you
face to face.

1448 Nothing is too much to ask

Words and Music: Mike Pilavachi and Matt Redman

Gently, building with each section
Gm
Capo 3 Em
F/A
D/F♯
B♭
G
No-thing is too much to ask
now that I have said I'm yours,
C²sus⁴
A²sus⁴
C²
A²
Gm
Em
F/A
D/F♯
Je - sus, take the whole of me
B♭
G
Last time to Coda
Csus⁴
Asus⁴
C²
A²
Gm
Em
3
un - re - serv - ed-ly.
Je - sus, take me deep - er now
F²/A
D²/F♯
B♭
G
C²sus⁴
A²sus⁴
C²
A²
that I might go fur - ther too,

Gm
Em
F2/A
D2/F♯
B♭2
G2
I've re-ceived so much from you
un-de-serv-
Csus4
Asus4
Gm
Em
F2/A
D2/F♯
-ed-ly.
I was made to love you, Lord,
B♭
G
Csus4
Asus4
C
A
Gm
Em
I was saved to wor-ship you.
You will be the fo-cus of
F2/A
D2/F♯
B♭2
G2
1.
Csus4
Asus4
C
A
all e-ter-ni-ty.
2.
Csus4
Asus4
C
A
D.C.
CODA
Csus4
Asus4
-ni-ty.
-ed-ly.

1449 Not I, but Christ

Words: A.A.F. Music: J.H.Burke

D A7 D G D Gmaj7 G6 G G6 D A
1. Not I, but Christ, be hon-oured, loved, ex - alt - ed;
E7 A E7 A E7 A A7
Not I, but Christ, be seen, be known, be heard;
D A7 Bm A D G D
Not I, but Christ, in ev - 'ry look and ac - tion;
A D Bm D A7 D
Not I, but Christ, in ev - 'ry thought and word.

2. Not I, but Christ, to gently soothe in sorrow;
Not I, but Christ, to wipe the falling tear;
Not I, but Christ, to lift the weary burden;
Not I, but Christ, to hush away all fear.

3. Not I, but Christ, in lowly, silent labour;
Not I, but Christ, in humble earnest toil;
Christ, only Christ, no show, no ostentation;
Christ, none but Christ, the gatherer of the spoil.

4. Christ, only Christ, ere long will fill my vision;
glory excelling, soon, full soon, I'll see –
Christ, only Christ, my every wish fulfilling –
Christ, only Christ, my all in all to be.

1450 Now the grave in the tomb is empty

Words and Music: James Wright

(♩ = 157)
Chorus
Capo 3
E♭ B♭/D F
C G/B D
Now the grave in the tomb is emp - ty and the
E♭ B♭ F E♭ B♭/D F
C G D C G/B D
stone has been rolled a - way, and the pow - er of death has been
E♭ B♭ F
C G D
de - feat - ed for Je - sus is a - live to - day. And this
E♭ B♭/D F E♭ B♭ F
C G/B D C G D
is why he came a - mong us, and this is why he had to die
E♭ B♭/D F
C G/B D
that we may know his re - sur - rec - tion pow - er that

E♭ B♭ F A♭7
C G D F7
we may have e - ter - nal life. Death has lost its sting and its
B♭7 B♭/C B♭/F F E♭
G7 G/A G/D D C
power has been de - fea - ted for Christ is ri - sen,
B♭/D E♭ B♭/D B♭/F F A♭7
G/B C G/B G/D D F7
Christ is ri - sen. Tears have turned to joy
B♭7
G7
now that Je - sus Christ is ri - sen from the
C Dm7 C/E 1. C7♯9
A Bm7 A/C♯ A7♯9
D.S.
dead. Now the

2.
B♭/F F B♭/F F B♭/F
G/D D G/D D G/D
Christ is ri - sen, Christ is
F Dm C/E F F/C C Dm/C
D Bm A/C♯ D D/A A Bm/A
ri - sen, Christ is ri - sen,
1.
C F F/C C Gm7 Am7 B♭ B♭/C
A D D/A A Em7 F♯m7 G G/A
Christ is ri - sen, Christ is
2.
F/C C Gm7 Am7 B♭ B♭/C B♭/F F
D/A A Em7 F♯m7 G G/A G/D D
ri - sen, Christ is ri - sen.

1451 O Christ, in thee my soul hath found

None but Christ can satisfy

Words: B.E. Music: James McGranahan

86 86 and Refrain

F F6 F Gm7 F C F
Capo 3 D D6 D Em7 D A D
1. O Christ, in thee my soul hath found, and found in thee a - lone, the
F6 F Gm7 F C G7 C F C7
D6 D Em7 D A E7 A D A7
peace, the joy I sought so long, the bliss till now un - known.
F B♭ F B♭ F C7 F C C7
D G D G D A7 D A A7
Chorus
Now none but Christ can sa - tis-fy, none o - ther name for me, there's
F B♭ F B♭ F C7 F C7 F
D G D G D A7 D A7 D
love, and life, and last - ing joy, Lord Je - sus, found in thee.

2. I sighed for rest and happiness,
I yearned for them, not thee;
but while I passed my Saviour by,
his love laid hold on me.

3. I tried the broken cisterns, Lord,
but ah! the waters failed!
E'en as I stooped to drink they'd fled,
and mocked me as I wailed.

4. The pleasures lost I sadly mourn'd,
but never wept for thee,
till grace the sightless eyes received,
thy loveliness to see.

1452 O for a thousand tongues

Words: Charles Wesley, adapted by Graham Kendrick

Music: Graham Kendrick

(𝅗𝅥 = 80)
C G/B Am7 G/B C
1. O for a thou - sand tongues to sing
2. He breaks the pow'r of can - celled sin,
3. Hear him you deaf, his praise you dumb
F C/E Dm7 G C G/B Am7 G/B
my great Re - deem - er's praise, the glo - ries of my God and
he sets the pris - 'ner free; his blood can make the foul - est
your loos - ened tongues em - ploy. You blind be - hold your Sa - viour
Am Dm7 C/E Dm/F Gsus4 G C G
King, the tri - umphs of his grace! Je - sus the name
clean; his blood a - vailed for me. He speaks, and list -
come and leap, you lame, for joy. My gra - cious Mas -
Am G F C/E Dm7 G
that charms our fears and bids our sor - rows cease;
- 'ning to his voice, new life the dead re - ceive,
- ter and my God as - sist me to pro - claim

Am G F
'tis mu - sic in the sin-ner's ears, 'tis life and
the mourn - ful bro - ken hearts re - joice, the hum - ble
and spread through all the earth a - broad the hon - ours
Dm7 Gsus4 G
Chorus
Am
health and peace.
poor be - lieve. O for a thou-
of your name.
F C G/B F/A C/G F
- sand tongues to sing my great Re -
Dm7 Gsus4 G Am
deem - er's praise, to tell the world the glo - ries of
Last time to Coda
F C G/B F/A C/G F Dm7 Em7
my God and King, the tri-umphs of his

1, 2.
F2
F
G
D.C.
grace!
3.
F2
G
C
G/C
F2/C
grace!
He breaks the pow'r of can - celled sin.
F/C
C
Dm/C
C
G/C
C
G/C
F2/C
He sets the pris - 'ner free. His blood can make the foul -
F/C
C
F/C
Am
G
C
- est clean, his blood a - vailed for me.
D
A/D
D
G
D/F♯
Em
D
A/C♯
D
And list - 'ning to his voice new life the dead re - ceive,

A/D D G D/F# Em7 D
the bro - ken hearts re - joice, the hum - ble poor re -
Asus4 A Am/F F/G
D.S.
ceive. O for a thou - sand tongues to
CODA
F2 Dm7 Em7 F2
grace! The tri - umphs of his grace!
Dm7 F2/G G F2
The tri - umphs of his grace!
Dm7 C

1453 O God of love *How good it is*

Words and Music: Nathan Fellingham and Louise Fellingham

D
A2/C#
ev - 'ry mo - ment you are there, watch -
Hand of mer - cy, hand of love, giv -
D
A2/C#
E
- ing o - ver, you hear my prayer. You
- ing pow - er to o - ver - come. If
Bm7
F#m7
go be - fore me, you're be - hind me,
all be - neath me falls a - way,
D
E
no - thing's hid - den from you.
I know that you are God.
Chorus
A
Bm7
D2
D/E
A
Bm7
How good it is to be loved by you, how good it is.

D2 D/E A Bm7 D2 D/E
How good it is to be loved by you,
A Bm7
how good it is.
1. D2 D/E
Last time D2 D/E A
Fine
2. D2 D/E F#m7 A/C# D F#m7 A/C#
Who can stand a-gainst us? In my weak-ness you are strong.
D F#m7 A/C# D
Your word is e - ver-last - ing, I will
F#m7 A/C# Bm7 A/C# D
D.S. al Fine
praise you, faith - ful one.

1454 O God, you search me

Words and Music: Bernadette Farrell

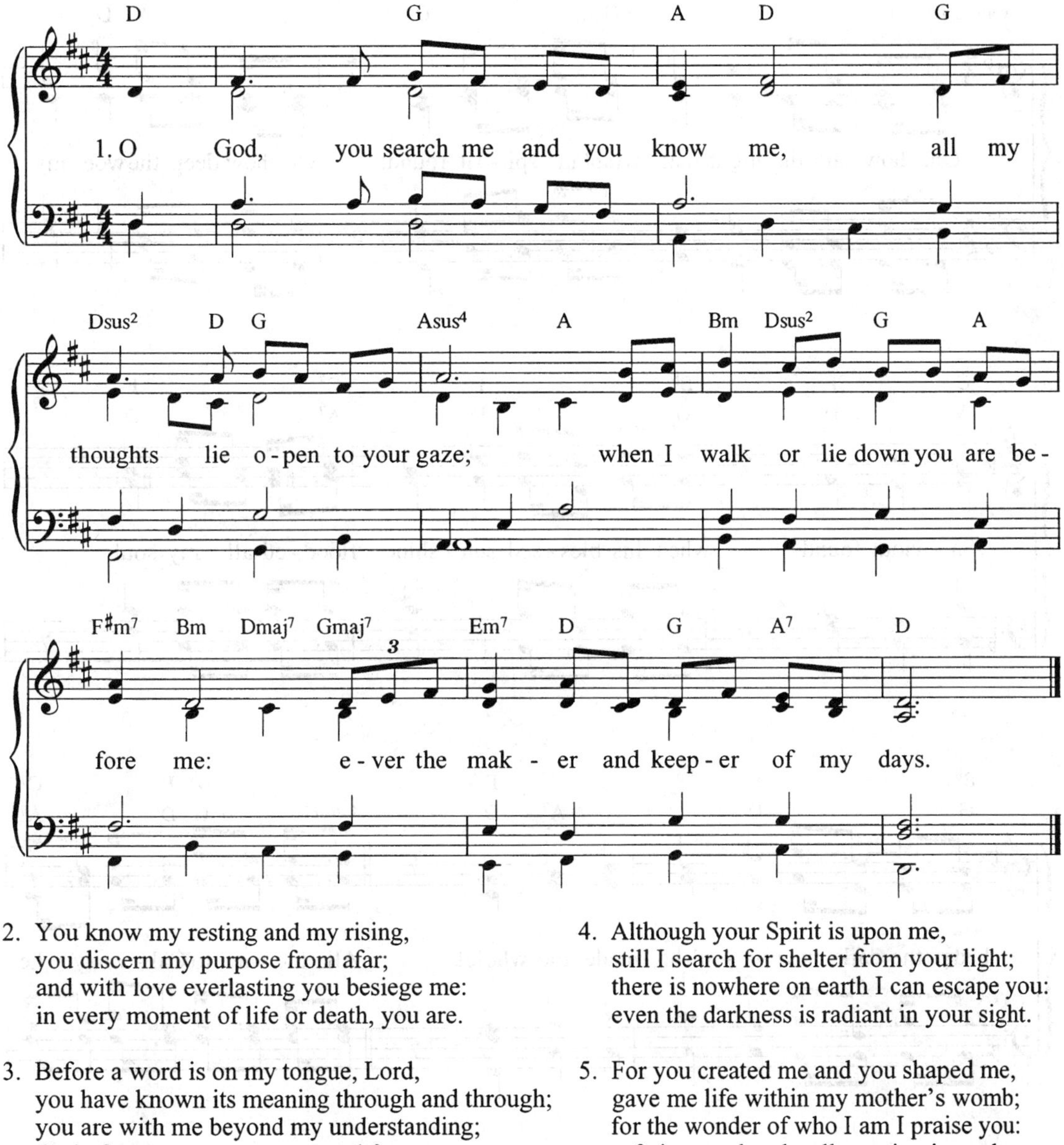
D G A D G
1. O God, you search me and you know me, all my
Dsus2 D G Asus4 A Bm Dsus2 G A
thoughts lie o-pen to your gaze; when I walk or lie down you are be-
F#m7 Bm Dmaj7 Gmaj7 Em7 D G A7 D
3
fore me: e-ver the mak-er and keep-er of my days.

2. You know my resting and my rising,
you discern my purpose from afar;
and with love everlasting you besiege me:
in every moment of life or death, you are.

3. Before a word is on my tongue, Lord,
you have known its meaning through and through;
you are with me beyond my understanding;
God of my present, my past and future, too.

4. Although your Spirit is upon me,
still I search for shelter from your light;
there is nowhere on earth I can escape you:
even the darkness is radiant in your sight.

5. For you created me and you shaped me,
gave me life within my mother's womb;
for the wonder of who I am I praise you:
safe in your hands, all creation is made new.

1455 Oh, how dark the night *All the way to Calvary*

Words: W.G. Moyer

Music: I.H. Meredith

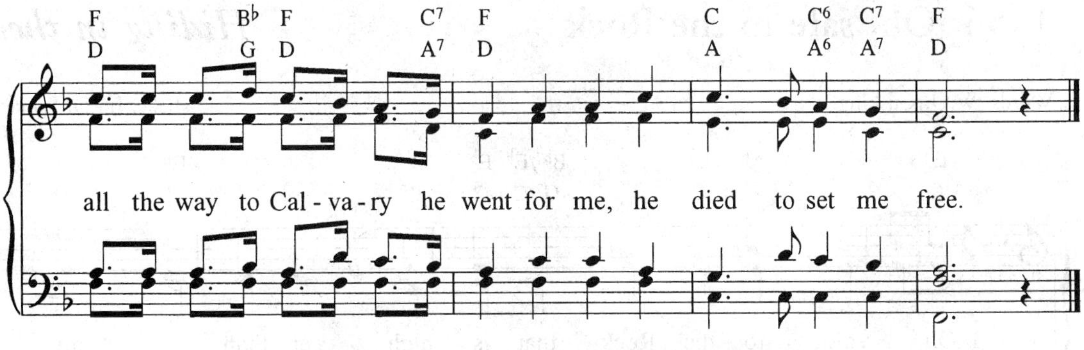
F Bb F C7 F C C6 C7 F
D G D A7 D A A6 A7 D
all the way to Cal - va - ry he went for me, he died to set me free.

2. Tremblingly a sinner bow'd before his face,
naught I knew of pardon – nor his grace;
heard a voice so tender, 'Cease thy wild regret –
I have bought thy pardon, paid thy debt.'

3. Oh, 'twas wondrous love the Saviour show'd for me,
when he left his throne for Calvary,
when he trod the winepress, trod it all alone:
praise his name for ever – make it known!

1456 Oh, safe to the Rock *Hiding in thee*

Words: W.O. Cushing Music: Ira D. Sankey

1. Oh, safe to the Rock that is high-er than I, my soul in its con-flicts and sor-rows would fly; so sin-ful, so wea-ry, thine, thine would I be; thou blest Rock of A-ges, I'm hid-ing in thee.

2. In the calm of the noontide, in sorrow's lone hour,
in times when temptation casts o'er me its power;
in the tempests of life, on its wide, heaving sea,
thou blest Rock of Ages, I'm hiding in thee.

3. How oft in the conflict when press'd by the foe,
I have fled to my Refuge and breathed out my woe;
how often when trails like sea-billows roll,
have I hidden in thee, O thou Rock of my soul.

1457 O Jesus, Son of God

Light of the world

Words and Music: Matt Redman

1.
2, 3.
B7sus4
A/C#
D2
the glo - ry we have seen re - vealed. You shone
who came and walked up - on the earth.
un - der the sha - dow of the cross.
Esus4
Your glo - ry we have seen, the one and
Where through the blood you shed, you have made
on - ly King, and now you're li - ving in our hearts.
peace a - gain, peace for the world that God so loves.
Chorus
D
Light of the world, light of the world,
A
light of the world you shine up - on us, change us,

you heal us, you free us.
D
Light of the world, light of the world, light of the world you
shine up - on us.
A
Last time
D.C.

1458 O Lord, you've searched me

Words and Music: Andrew Grinnell

Gm F/A B♭ F/A Gm F/A
Em D/F♯ G D/F♯ Em D/F♯
- where I can run to, to flee from your pre - sence, or
B♭ F/A Gm F/A B♭ Dm7
G D/F♯ Em D/F♯ G Bm7
hide from your truth. So I wait here for your Spi - rit to
E♭ Csus4 C F B♭maj7
C Asus4 A D Gmaj7
guide me home to you. I re - joice at the cross and bow
F B♭maj7 F B♭maj7
D Gmaj7 D Gmaj7
down at your throne for your sac - ri - ficed Son has made
Dm7 C F B♭maj7
Bm7 A D Gmaj7
my sin his own. This is free - dom I've found, con - dem -

F Bbmaj7 F Bbmaj7
D Gmaj7 D Gmaj7
na - tion has gone, I'm your child, ho - ly King, I will
Dm C F
Bm A D
D.C.
trust you a - lone.
Dm C F
Bm A D

1459 O my soul

Like eagles

Words and Music: Kevin Dukes and Marsha Skidmore

Dm7 Bm7 Gm7 Em7 C A
Chorus
-er he will streng-then, he will guide. And I will soar
F D Dm7 Bm7 Gm7 Em7
on wings like ea-gles; held by the hand
Csus4 Asus4 F/A D/F# Dm7 Bm7
of God, I will run and not grow tired, when
Gm7 Em7 C7sus4 A7sus4 F D
on his name I call; for the Lord is ne-
Dm7 Bm7 Gm7 Em7 Csus4 Asus4
-ver wea-ry, his ways are be-yond my thoughts; I will trust

Dm7 F2/A Gm7 C7sus4 F C/F
Bm7 D2/F♯ Em7 A7sus4 D A/D
1.
in him with all my heart.
B♭ B♭2
G G2
D.C.
Last time
F C/F B♭ B♭2
D A/D G G2
F C/F B♭ B♭2 F
D A/D G G2 D
2.
F B♭2
D G2
And I will rest up - on

his pro - mise, pa - tient-ly I'll wait.
F
D
C/F
A/D
B♭
G
B♭2
G2
F
D
C/F
A/D
B♭
G
B♭2
G2
Chorus
D.S.
And I will soar

1460 O my soul, arise and bless your maker

Words and Music: Stuart Townend

E F#m7 E/G# A E/G# B E F#m7 E/G#
1. O my soul, a - rise and bless your mak - er, for he is your
A E/G# Bsus4 B F#m E/G# Bsus4 B C#m Emaj7/B F#/A# B/A
mas - ter and your friend. Slow to wrath but rich in ten - der mer - cy,
1. 2.
E/G# C#m7 E/G# F#m7 B7 E Fine F#m7 B7 E Chorus
wor - ship the Sa - viour Je - sus. Je - sus. And
C#m Emaj7/B E/G# A F#m E Bsus4 B
I will sing for all my days of hea - ven's love come down. Each

2. King of grace, his love is overwhelming,
bread of life, he's all I'll ever need.
For his blood has purchased me for ever,
bought at the cross of Jesus.

3. When I wake, I know that he is with me,
when I'm weak, I know that he is strong.
Though I fall, his arm is there to lean on,
safe on the rock of Jesus.

4. Stir in me the songs that you are singing,
fill my gaze with things as yet unseen.
Give me faith to move in works of power,
making me more like Jesus.

5. Then one day, I'll see him as he sees me,
face to face, the lover and the loved.
No more words, the longing will be over,
there with my precious Jesus.

1461 On bended knee

Words and Music: Robert Gay

(♩ = 84)
B♭/C F B♭ F B♭
Capo 3 G/A D G D G
1. On bend-ed knee I come, with a hum-ble heart I come,
F Dm7
D Bm7
bow-ing down be-fore your ho-ly throne;
Gm7 C B♭/C F B♭
Em7 A G/A D G
lift-ing ho-ly hands to you, as I
A7sus4 A/C♯ Dm Gm7 C
F♯7sus4 F♯/A♯ Bm Em7 A
pledge my love a-new, I wor-ship you in spi-

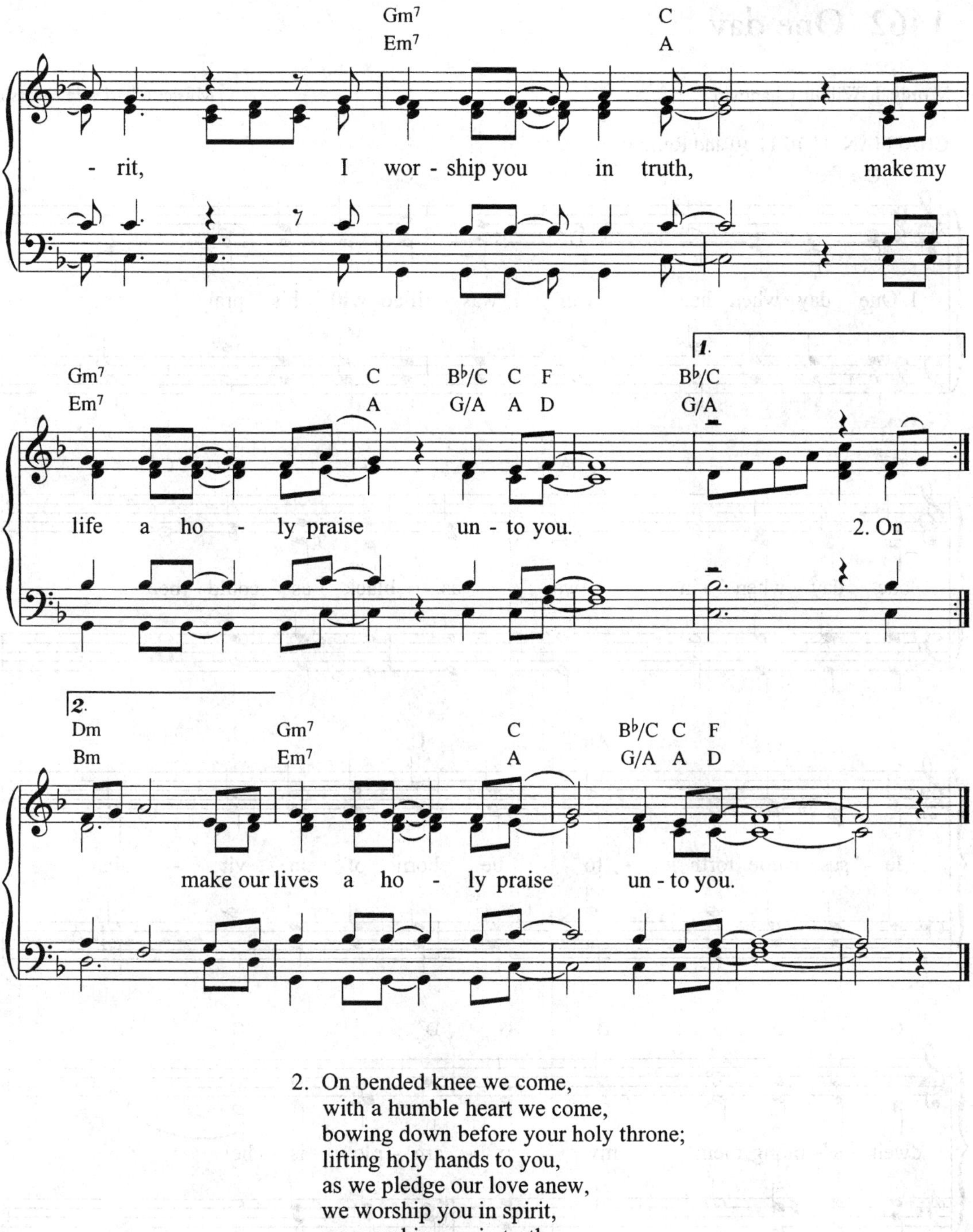

2. On bended knee we come,
with a humble heart we come,
bowing down before your holy throne;
lifting holy hands to you,
as we pledge our love anew,
we worship you in spirit,
we worship you in truth,
make our lives a holy praise unto you,
make our lives a holy praise unto you.

1462 One day

Words: J. Wilbur Chapman

Music: Charles H. Marsh

CHAPMAN 11 10 11 10 and Refrain

1. One day when hea - ven was filled with his prai - ses,

one day when sin was as black as could be,

Je - sus came forth to be born of a vir - gin,

dwelt a - mong men, my ex - am - ple is he!

Chorus

Liv - ing, he loved me; dy - ing, he saved me;

2. One day they led him up Calvary's mountain,
one day they nailed him to die on the tree;
suffering anguish, despised and rejected:
bearing our sins, my Redeemer is he!

3. One day they left him alone in the garden,
one day he rested, from suffering free;
angels came down o'er his tomb to keep vigil;
hope of the hopeless, my Saviour is he!

4. One day the grave could conceal him no longer,
one day the stone rolled away from the door;
then he arose, over death he had conquered;
now is ascended, my Lord evermore!

5. One day the trumpet will sound for his coming,
one day the skies with his glories will shine;
wonderful day, my beloved one bringing;
glorious Saviour, this Jesus is mine!

1463 One God

We believe

Words and Music: Andrew Rayner and Wendy Rayner

A2
C♯m
1. One God, al - migh - ty Fa - ther,
2. Ho - ly Spi - rit of God,
G2
D/F♯
Esus4
mak - er of hea - ven and earth.
Lord and giv - er of life.
A2
C♯m
G2
D/F♯
One Lord Je - sus Christ, through you all things were made.
Fa - ther, Son and Spi - rit, wor-shipped to - ge - ther as one.
Esus4
Dmaj7
You came down from hea - ven by the pow -
We look up to hea - ven through the pow -
F♯m7
Dmaj7
- er of the Ho - ly Spi - rit, God from God and Light from light
- er of the Ho - ly Spi - rit, Je - sus seat - ed with the Fa - ther

F♯m7 Esus4 E Chorus A2 C♯m7
you be-came man. We be-lieve you are the Son of God,
glo - ri - fied.
F♯m7 A2/C♯ Bm7 A/C♯
you came to earth and died for us. Then you rose a-gain and now
D2 Esus4 A2 C♯m7
you reign in hea - ven. We de-clare that you will come a-gain
F♯m7 A/C♯ Bm7 A/C♯
to judge the liv - ing and the dead, O Lord, we will pro-claim your king-
B/D♯ Esus4 A
- dom's rule, for e - ver you will reign.

1464 One offer of salvation *No other name*

Words and Music: Philip P. Bliss

E♭ A♭ E♭ A♭ E♭ A♭ E♭ B♭ B♭7
Capo 1 D G D G D G D A A7
1. One of - fer of sal - va - tion, to all the world made
B♭ E♭ A♭ E♭ A♭ E♭ A♭ E♭ B♭ Fsus4 F7 B♭
A D G D G D G D A Esus4 E7 A
known; the on - ly sure foun - da - tion is Christ, the Cor - ner - stone.
Chorus
E♭ A♭ E♭ A♭ E♭ B♭7 E♭
D G D G D A7 D
No o - ther name is giv - en, no o - ther way is known; 'tis
E♭dim E♭ A♭ A♭dim A♭ Adim E♭ B♭7 E♭
Ddim D G Gdim G G♯dim D A7 D
Je - sus Christ, the first and last: he saves, and he a - lone!

2. One only door of heaven
stands open wide today;
one sacrifice is given
'tis Christ, the Living Way.

3. My only song and story
is Jesus died for me;
my only hope for glory
the Cross of Calvary.

1465 Only a God like you

Words and Music: Tommy Walker

(♩ = 116)
G
D
Em7
On-ly a God like you, on-ly a God like you, on-ly a God like you.
C2
Sing 4 times
G
D
Em7
C2
G
D
For the prai - ses of man I will
Em7
C2
G
ne - ver, ne - ver stand. For the king - doms of this world
D
C2
D
I'll ne - ver give my heart a - way or shout my praise. My al-

G D Em7
le - giance and de-vo - tion, my heart's de - sire and all e-mo-
C2 G D C2
- tion go to serve the Man who died up-on the tree.
D G D Bm7
On-ly a God like you could be wor-
Em7 C G D
- thy of my praise and all my hope and faith. To on-ly a King of all kings
Bm7 Em7 C
1.
do I bow my knee and sing, give my ev-'ry-thing.

2.
Am7 G/B C Em7
my ev-'ry-thing. To on-ly my Mak - er, my Fa - ther, my Sa - viour, Re-
Am7 G/B C Em7 Am7 D
deem-er, Re-stor - er, Re-build - er, Re-ward - er; to on-ly a God like you
Last time to Coda
G Dsus4
do I give my praise.
CODA
Em7 C D.S G
For the
Dsus4 Em7 C2 G

1466 Only you

I will worship

Words and Music: Andy Shaw

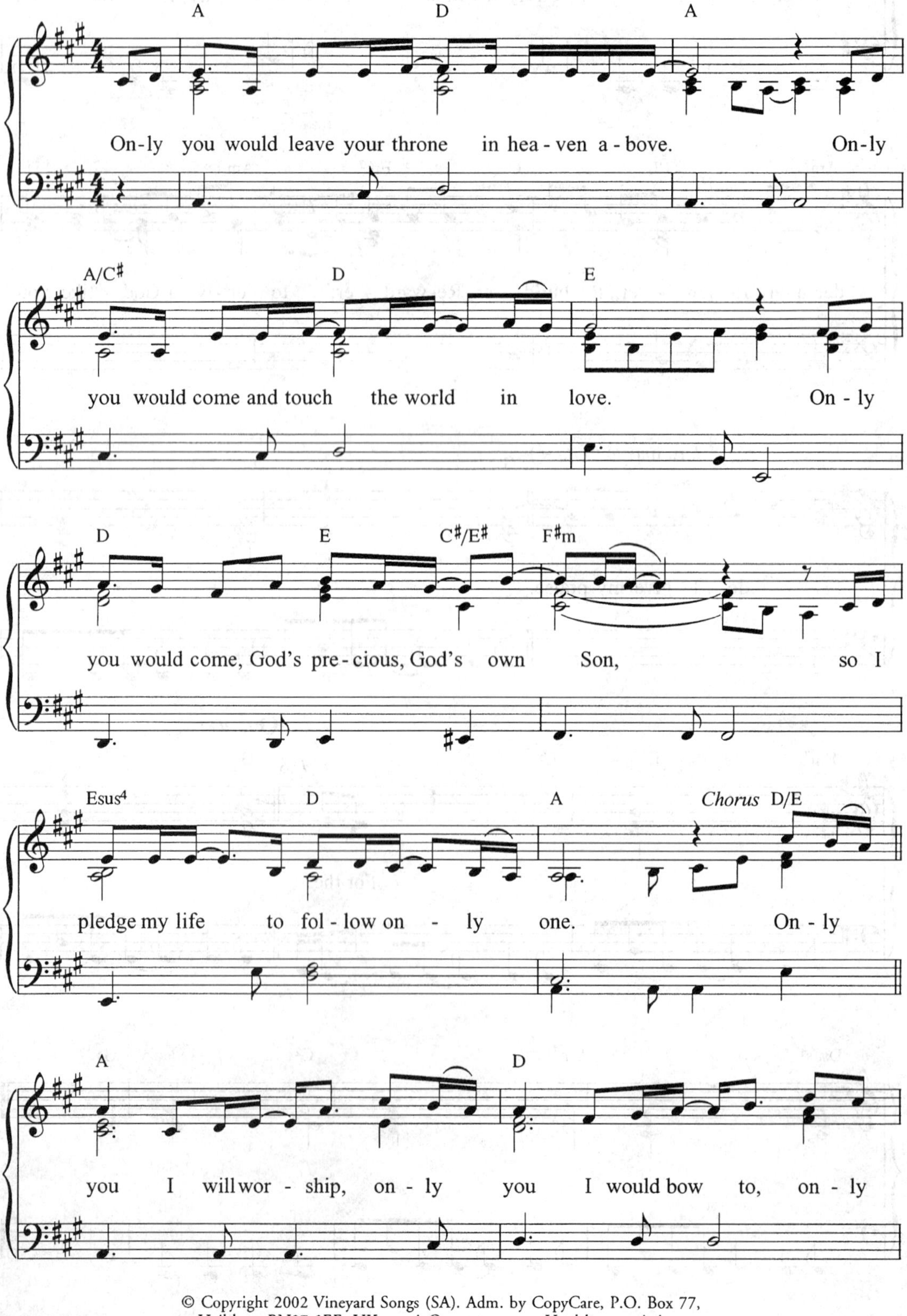
A
D
A
On-ly you would leave your throne in hea - ven a - bove. On-ly
A/C♯
D
E
you would come and touch the world in love. On - ly
D
E
C♯/E♯
F♯m
you would come, God's pre - cious, God's own Son, so I
Esus4
D
A
Chorus
D/E
pledge my life to fol - low on - ly one. On - ly
A
D
you I will wor - ship, on - ly you I would bow to, on - ly

A
Esus4
E
you for whom this song is sung. On - ly
A
D
A
E
you I will live for, on - ly you I will die for, on - ly you, on - ly you, on - ly
D
D/E
A
you.

1467 Open my eyes that I may see

Words and Music: Clara H. Scott

SCOTT 88 98 and Refrain

Capo 1
1. O - pen my eyes that I may see glimp-ses of truth thou hast for me;
place in my hands the won-der-ful key that shall un-clasp and set me free.
Chorus
Si-lent-ly now I wait for thee, rea-dy, my God, thy will to see;
o - pen my eyes, ears, heart, il - lu - mine me, Spi - rit di - vine.

2. Open my ears that I may hear
voices of truth thou sendest clear;
and while the wave-notes fall on my ear,
everything false will disappear.

3. Open my mouth and let me bear
gladly the warm truth everywhere;
open my heart, and let me prepare
love with thy children thus to share.

1468 Open our eyes, Lord

Words and Music: Robert Cull

D G A7 G
O - pen our eyes, Lord, we want to see Je -
D Bm G A7
sus, to reach out and touch him and
G D D♯dim Em
say that we love him; o - pen our ears, Lord,
A7 G D Bm
and help us to lis - ten; O, o - pen our
G A7 G D
eyes, Lord, we want to see Je - sus!

1469 O sacred King

Words and Music: Matt Redman

With awe
G
Verse
C
G
O sac-red King, O ho-ly
O sac-red Friend, O ho-ly
C
Am7
Am/G
D/F#
King, how can I hon-our you right-ly,
Friend, I don't take what you give light-ly,
Am
Am/G
1.
D/F#
hon - our that's right for your name?
friend - ship in - stead of dis -
2.
D/F#
D
Chorus
G
grace. For it's the mys - t'ry of the u - ni - verse,

Am G/B
you're the God of ho - li - ness, yet you wel - come souls like
Cmaj7 C/D G
me. And with the bles - sing of your Fa - ther's heart, you
Am G/B
dis - ci - pline the ones you love, there's kind - ness in your ma - jes - ty.
Cmaj7 Am Am/G D/F#
Je - sus, those who re - cog - nise your pow'r, know
Am Am/G D/F# D G
just how won - der - ful you are, that you draw near.

1470 O soul, are you weary *Turn your eyes upon Jesus*

Words and Music: Helen H. Lemmel

LEMMEL 98 98 and Refrain

F Fdim F B♭ F7 B♭maj7 Gm B♭ F C F
Capo 3 D Ddim D G D7 Gmaj7 Em G D A D
1. O soul, are you wea - ry and trou - bled? No light in the
Am C7 F Fdim F B♭ F
F♯m A7 D Ddim D G D
dark - ness you see? There's light for a look at the
Dm6 C F G7 Cdim C Dm7 G7 C Dm7 C
Bm6 A D E7 Adim A Bm7 E7 A Bm7 A
Sa - viour, and life more a - bun - dant and free!
Chorus
F C Am C7 Dm F7 B♭ B♭maj7 B♭6
D A F♯m A7 Bm D7 G Gmaj7 G6
Turn your eyes up - on Je - sus, look full in his

B♭ B♭6 Dm6 Csus4 C F C7 F Edim
G G6 Bm6 Asus4 A D A7 D C♯dim
won - der - ful face, and the things of earth will grow

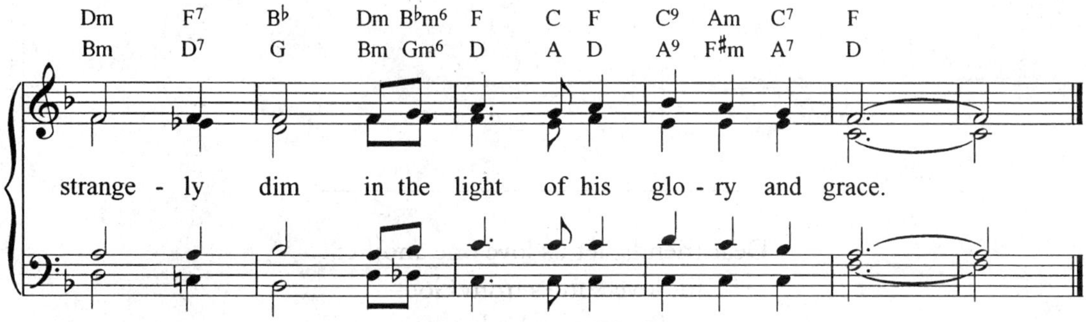
Dm F7 B♭ Dm B♭m6 F C F C9 Am C7 F
Bm D7 G Bm Gm6 D A D A9 F♯m A7 D
strange - ly dim in the light of his glo - ry and grace.

2. Thro' death into life everlasting
he passed, and we follow him there;
over us sin no more hath dominion
for more than conq'rors we are!

3. His word shall not fail you – he promised;
believe him, and all will be well:
then go to a world that is dying,
his perfect salvation to tell!

Dear friends, let us love one another,
for love comes from God.
Everyone who loves
has been born of God and knows God.

Dear friends, since God so loved us,
we also ought to love one another.

1 John 4:7, 11

1471 O the blood of Jesus

Words: vs. 1 & 4 traditional; vs. 2 & 3 Ken Barker

Music: Traditional

O THE BLOOD OF JESUS 66 66

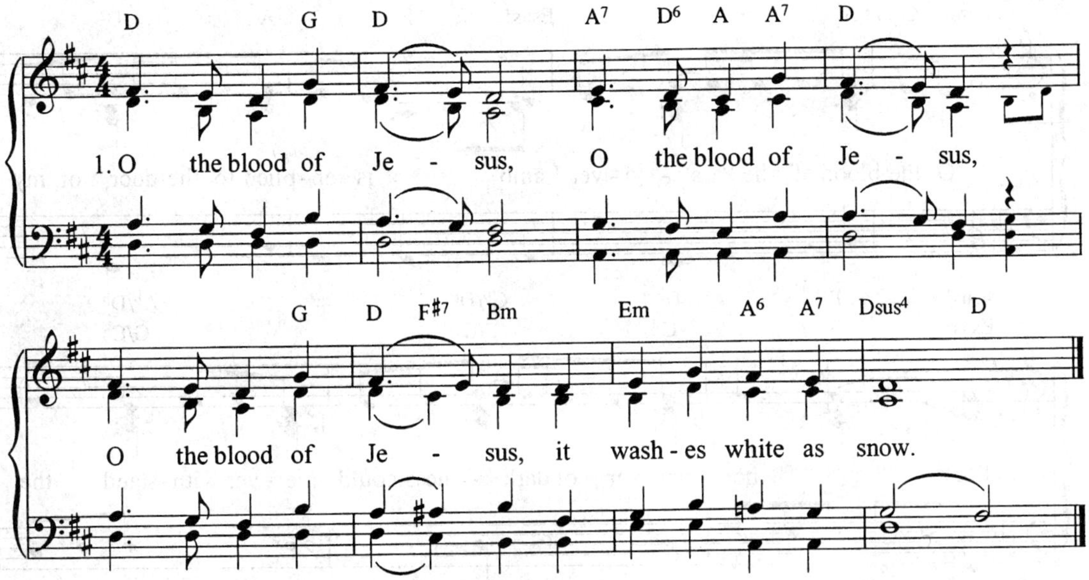

D G D A7 D6 A A7 D
1. O the blood of Je - sus, O the blood of Je - sus,
G D F#7 Bm Em A6 A7 Dsus4 D
O the blood of Je - sus, it wash - es white as snow.

2. O the cross of Jesus,
O the cross of Jesus,
O the cross of Jesus,
his death brings life to me.

3. O the love of Jesus,
O the love of Jesus,
O the love of Jesus,
he freely gives to me,

4. O the blood of Jesus,
O the blood of Jesus,
O the blood of Jesus,
it washes white as snow.

1472 O the blood of the Passover Lamb *Under the blood*

Words and Music: Martin J. Nystrom and Rhonda Gunter Scelsi

(♩. = 60)
Verse
Capo 1
B♭ E♭2 Fsus4 F B♭ E♭2
A D2 Esus4 E A D2
O the blood of the Pass - o - ver Lamb is ap - plied to the door of my
Fsus4 F D♭ G♭/D♭ A♭/D♭
Esus4 E C F/C G/C
life, no pow - er of dark - ness could e - ver with - stand the
G♭/B♭ E♭m7 Fsus4 F B♭ E♭2
F/A Dm7 Esus4 E A D2
force of the blood sac - ri - fice. Though Sa - tan will bring ac - cu -
Fsus4 F B♭ E♭2 Fsus4 F
Esus4 E A D2 Esus4 E
sa - tions, I let him know right where I stand, for
Gm Dm/F E♭2 B♭2/D Cm7 E♭/F F
F♯m C♯m/E D2 A/C♯ Bm7 D/E E
now there is no con - dem - na - tion, I'm un - der the blood of the Lamb.

B♭ E♭/F F B♭ B♭/D E♭ E♭/F F
A D/E E A A/C♯ D D/E E
Chorus
I'm un-der the blood of the Lamb that
B♭ Gm7 Cm7 Fsus4 F Gm Dm
A F♯m7 Bm7 Esus4 E F♯m C♯m
co-vers the guilt of my past, by the
E♭ B♭/D Cm7 A♭maj7 E♭/F F
D A/C♯ Bm7 Gmaj7 D/E E
mer-cy of God, ho-ly and right-eous I stand. I'm
B♭ B♭/D E♭ E♭/F F
A A/C♯ D D/E E
un-der the blood of the Lamb, I'm
B♭ Gm7 Cm7 Fsus4 F Gm Dm
A F♯m7 Bm7 Esus4 E F♯m C♯m
safe and se-cure from the e-ne-my's plan, no wea-pon formed a-
E♭ B♭/D Cm7 E♭/F F B♭
D A/C♯ Bm7 D/E E A
gainst me will stand, I'm un-der the blood of the Lamb.

The Lord reigns,
let the nations tremble;
he sits enthroned between the cherubim,
let the earth shake.
Great is the Lord in Zion;
he is exalted over all the nations.

Psalm 99:1-2

1473 O the King is coming *The King is coming*

Words: Gloria Gaither, William J. Gaither and Charles Millhuff Music: William J. Gaither

KING IS COMING Irregular

Capo 1
E♭7 A♭ A♭7 D♭ B♭7
D7 G G7 C A7
O the King is com-ing, the King is com-ing! I just
E♭ E♭7 A♭ D♭ A♭ E♭7 A♭
D D7 G C G D7 G
heard the trum-pets sound-ing, and now his face I see. O the King is
A♭7 D♭ A♭m B♭7 E♭ D♭/E♭ E♭6 E♭7 A♭
G7 C Gm A7 D C/D D6 D7 G
com-ing, the King is com-ing! Praise God, he's com-ing for me!

1474 O, to see you *Pure light*

Words and Music: Matt Redman and Louie Giglio

D
D/C♯
1. O, to see you as you are, to glimpse the won -
you as you are, to e - ven dare
- ry of your name, how small the voice
of love's pure light, the grace re - flect -
D/C♮
G/B
Gm/B♭
D/F♯
- ders yet un - seen, as - sist my sight, un - veil my eyes to see
to speak or stand, though marked, be - loved to fall as dead when I see
I hum - bly bring, yet with my all I raise a song when I see
- ed in these eyes, the o - ver - flow of those who know they have seen
1.
2.
E
G
Chorus
you. O, to know you. And through grace
you. It is the song you.
Bm7
Dmaj9/F♯
un - told to see you with this heart

Bm7 Dmaj9/F# G A
Last time to Coda
un - veiled to know you, Lord, in your pure light.
3rd time to Tag
1. 2.
Bm7 Dmaj9/F# E D.S. E Bridge
2. How great the glo- We were
C G/B Gm/Bb
dis - graced but you graced us with the warmth of your for -
D/F# C G/B
give - ness. Now you lead us e - ver clo - ser to the
Gm/Bb Asus4 A
Chorus D.S.S.
pure light of your ho - li-ness. And through grace

3rd time
E
Tag
Bm7
Dmaj9/F#
And I'll sing of the won - ders of your grace, sing
G
of the won-ders of your grace, sing of the won-ders of your grace, O
Lord.
And I'll tell of the glo - ry of your name, tell
of the glo - ry of your name, tell of the glo - ry of your name, O
1.
2.
Chorus
D.S.S. al Coda
Lord.
And I'll sing Lord.
And through grace
CODA
D

Therefore, I urge you, brothers,
in view of God's mercy,
to offer your bodies as living sacrifices,
holy and pleasing to God –
this is your spiritual act of worship.

Romans 12:1

1475 Our God is a great big God

Words and Music: Jo Hemming and Nigel Hemming

With a 'Gospel' feel
Chorus
E E7/G# A B7 E E7/G#
Our God is a great big God, our God is a
Last time to Coda
F#7 B7 E E7/G# A
great big God, our God is a great big God and he
F#7 B7 E
1.
2.
holds us in his hands. He's
B A
high - er than a sky - scra - per and he's deep - er than a sub - ma - rine.
E B
He's wid - er than the u - ni - verse and be -

A E C#m
yond my wild-est dreams. And he's known me and he's loved
G#m A E
me since be-fore the world be-gan. How
A E/G# F#m7
won-der-ful to be a part of God's a-maz-ing plan.
Bsus4
D.C.
CODA
A F#7 B7 E
(Fine)
great big God and he holds us in his hands. And he

1476 Our God is strong and mighty

Breaking out

Words and Music: Gary Sadler and Stuart Townend

With energy
F7 B♭/E♭ Cm B♭/E♭ F7 B♭/E♭ Cm
Capo 3 D7 G/C Am G/C D7 G/C Am
B♭/E♭ F7 B♭/E♭
G/C D7 G/C
1. Our God is strong and migh - ty, he's lift - ing up a shout.
2. He's ris - ing in this na - tion, he's com - ing in - to view;
3. Come, do a work with - in me, let me see you as you are;
Cm B♭/E♭ F7 B♭/E♭ Cm B♭/E♭
Am G/C D7 G/C Am G/C
F7 B♭/E♭ Cm B♭/E♭
D7 G/C Am G/C
It's rol - ling down like thun - der: can you
go tell it in the ci - ty what
and make the cause of hea - ven the ob -

F7 B♭/E♭ Cm B♭/E♭ Fm7
D7 G/C Am G/C Dm7
feel it shake the ground?
Je - sus' pow'r can do.
ses - sion of my heart,
B♭7 F7
G7 D7
And ev - 'ry strong - hold trem - bles as we
We're los - ing our re - li - gion: he's e - ven
till ev - 'ry tribe and na - tion bows in
B♭ C
G A
Chorus
hear the li - on roar! He's break - ing out.
grea - ter than we thought! The
wor - ship to the King.
F7 B♭/E♭ Cm B♭/E♭ F7 B♭/E♭
D7 G/C Am G/C D7 G/C
The Lord our God is
Lord our God is break - ing out.

Cm Am
B♭/E♭ G/C
F7 D7
B♭/E♭ G/C
Cm Am
B♭/E♭ G/C
break-ing out. He's break-ing out!
The Lord our God.
F7 D7
B♭/E♭ G/C
C7(♭9) A7(♭9)
Last time
F7 D7
Dm Bm
B♭ G
F D
O God of mer-cy, God of love, come show us the glo-
C/E A/C♯
Dm Bm
-ry of your name. We're touched by the pas-
B♭ G
F D
C/E A/C♯
-sion of your heart, and no-thing will e-ver be the same,

B♭ C B♭/D
G A G/B
no-thing will e - ver be the same, don't let me e -
C/E E♭2 B♭2/D
A/C♯ C2 G2/B
D.C.
- ver be the same.

1477 Our God reigns

Words and Music: Tim Light

(♩ = 109)
Am
F
1. Our God reigns, he is robed in ma - jes - ty,
and feet of glow - ing bronze,
a - dorns the house of God;
C
Am
armed with strength he's from all
the Lord is high and seat -
who can match the splen -
F
C
e - ter - ni - ty,
- ed on his throne. Cre -
- dour of his worth?
Dm
G
Am
migh-tier than the waves, stron-ger than the brea -
a - tion looks to you, the hea-vens ne - ver cease
An - cient of Days, we will ne - ver cease

1.
F
C
-kers of the sea.
2. Eyes of fire
to praise his name.
to be a-mazed.
2, 3.
C
C/B
Am
F
So
C
C/B
Am
come, let us bow down in wor-ship of our God.
F2
C
C/B
Come, let us kneel be-fore the mak-
Am
F2
G
-er of our hearts and praise

Am
F
his awe - some-ness and his ma - jes - ty and
G
Am
F
praise for end - less days, for
1.
G
C
F/C
C
Je-sus our God reigns.
2.
G
C
D.S.
3. Ho - li - ness Je - sus our God reigns.
C/B
Am
F
C
Je-sus our God reigns.

Who is a God like you,
who pardons sin
and forgives the transgression
of the remnant of his inheritance?
You do not stay angry for ever
but delight to show mercy.

Micah 7:18

1478 O what a wonderful, wonderful day

Heaven came down

Words and Music: John W. Peterson

HEAVEN CAME DOWN Irregular

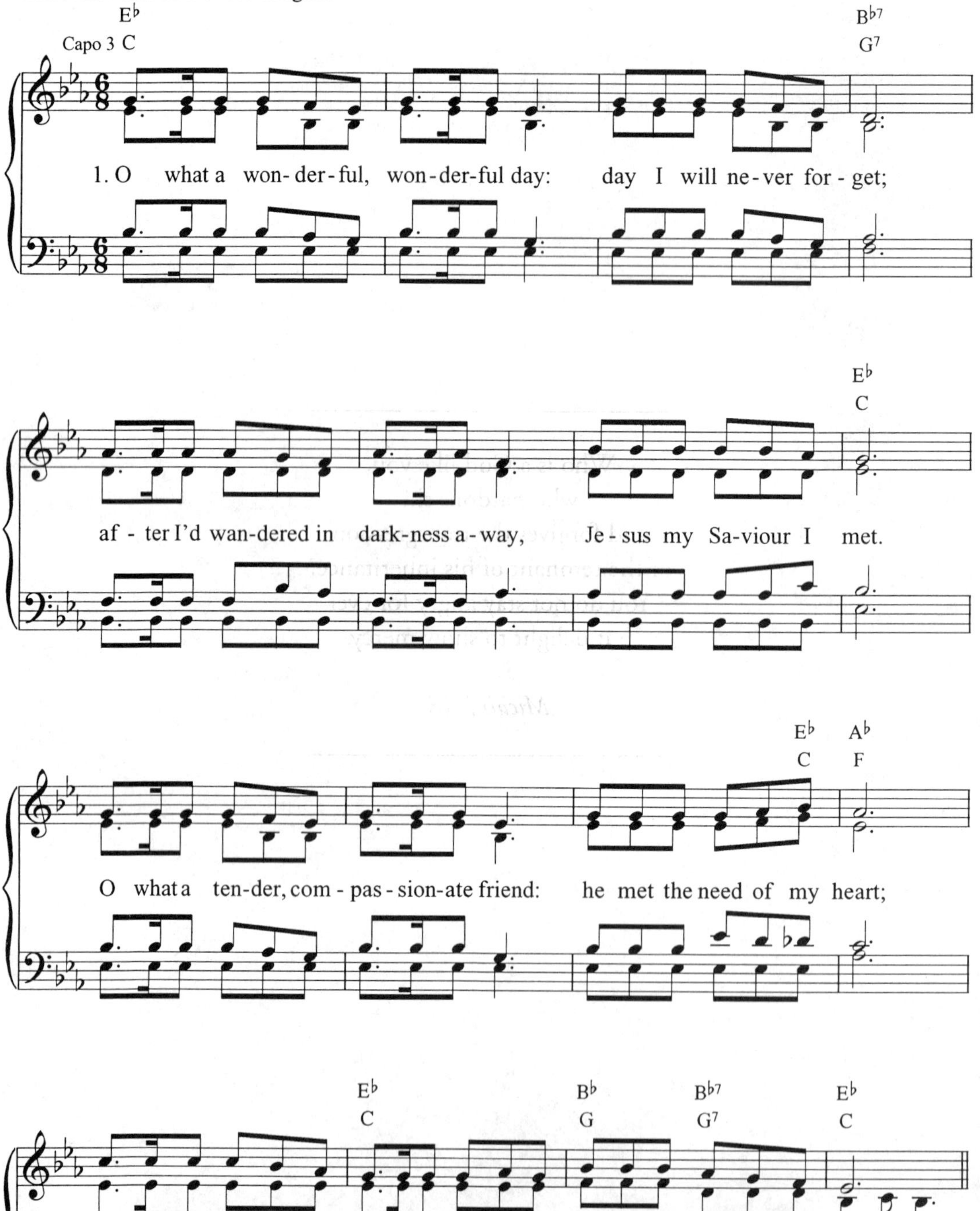

2. Born of the Spirit with life from above
into God's fam'ly divine,
justified fully thro' Calvary's love,
O what a standing is mine!
And the transaction so quickly was made
when as a sinner I came,
took of the offer
of grace he did proffer:
he saved me, O praise his dear name!

3. Now I've a hope that will surely endure
after the passing of time;
I have a future in heaven for sure,
there in those mansions sublime.
And it's because of that wonderful day
when at the cross I believed;
riches eternal
and blessings supernal
from his precious hand I received.

My soul glorifies the Lord
and my spirit rejoices in God my Saviour.

Luke 1:46b-47

1479 Pass me not, O gentle Saviour

Words and Music: Frances Jane van Alstyne (Fanny J. Crosby) Music: William H. Doane

PASS ME NOT 85 85 and Refrain

G C G D7 G D G
1. Pass me not, O gen - tle Sa - viour, hear my hum - ble cry;
C G D7 G D7 G
while on o - thers thou art call - ing, do not pass me by.
Chorus
C6 C G D
Sa - viour, Sa - viour, hear my hum - ble cry;
G C G D7 G D7 G
while on o - thers thou art call - ing, do not pass me by.

2. Let me at thy throne of mercy
find a sweet relief;
kneeling there in deep contrition,
help my unbelief.

3. Trusting only in thy merit,
would I seek thy face;
heal my wounded, broken spirit,
save me by thy grace.

4. Thou the spring of all my comfort,
more than life to me,
whom have I on earth beside thee?
Whom in heav'n but thee?

1480 Pierced for our transgressions

Words and Music: Phil Hart and Joanne Hogg

Gmaj7 Dmaj7/F# Em9 G6/A A7
love it knows no mea-sure and your mer - cy knows no bounds.
D F#m/C# Bm9
Je - sus, suff - 'ring ser-vant, Je - sus, Prince of
F#m/A Em G
Peace; Lamb of God, Mes - si - ah, how
Em G6/A 1, 2. D 3. G
wor - thy is your name. 2. You name.
3. One

2. You made your life a ransom
and paid for all our sin.
Hung crucified on Calv'ry,
despised and scorned by men.
You died that we might know you,
you died that we might live,
but rose again triumphant,
the Son of righteousness.

3. One day we'll see our Saviour
in clouds of glory come
to gather us, his children;
Christ, God's conquering Son.
That at the name of Jesus,
ev'ry knee shall bow,
and ev'ry tongue confess him
the King of glory now.

1481 Praise be to you, Father God *More than conquerors*

Words and Music: Greg Shepherd

D A/C♯ Bm A
God's for us, show-ing love to us, who can
Bm Esus4 E
be a - gainst us now? For your
D A/C♯ Bm A
Son who died is now glo - ri-fied, in - ter -
Bm Esus4 E
cedes for us now.
A Chorus D E
We are more than con - que - rors

D A D
through your migh - ty love. We are more than con - que - rors.
E F#m7 F#m7/E
Now I am con-vinced that
Last time to Coda
D A/C# Bm Bm/E
nei - ther death nor life can take me from the love of
1.
A Bm A/C#
Christ.
2.
D.S.
A
Christ. And if
3.
D.S.S. al Coda
A
Christ. We are more

CODA
F#m7
F#m7/E
D
Christ. Now I am con-vinced that nei - ther death nor life
A/C#
Bm
Bm/E
A
can take me from the love of Christ.

1482 Praise the Father

Words and Music: Charlie Hall, Kendall Coombes, Brian Bergman, Will Hunt and Tom Cromwell

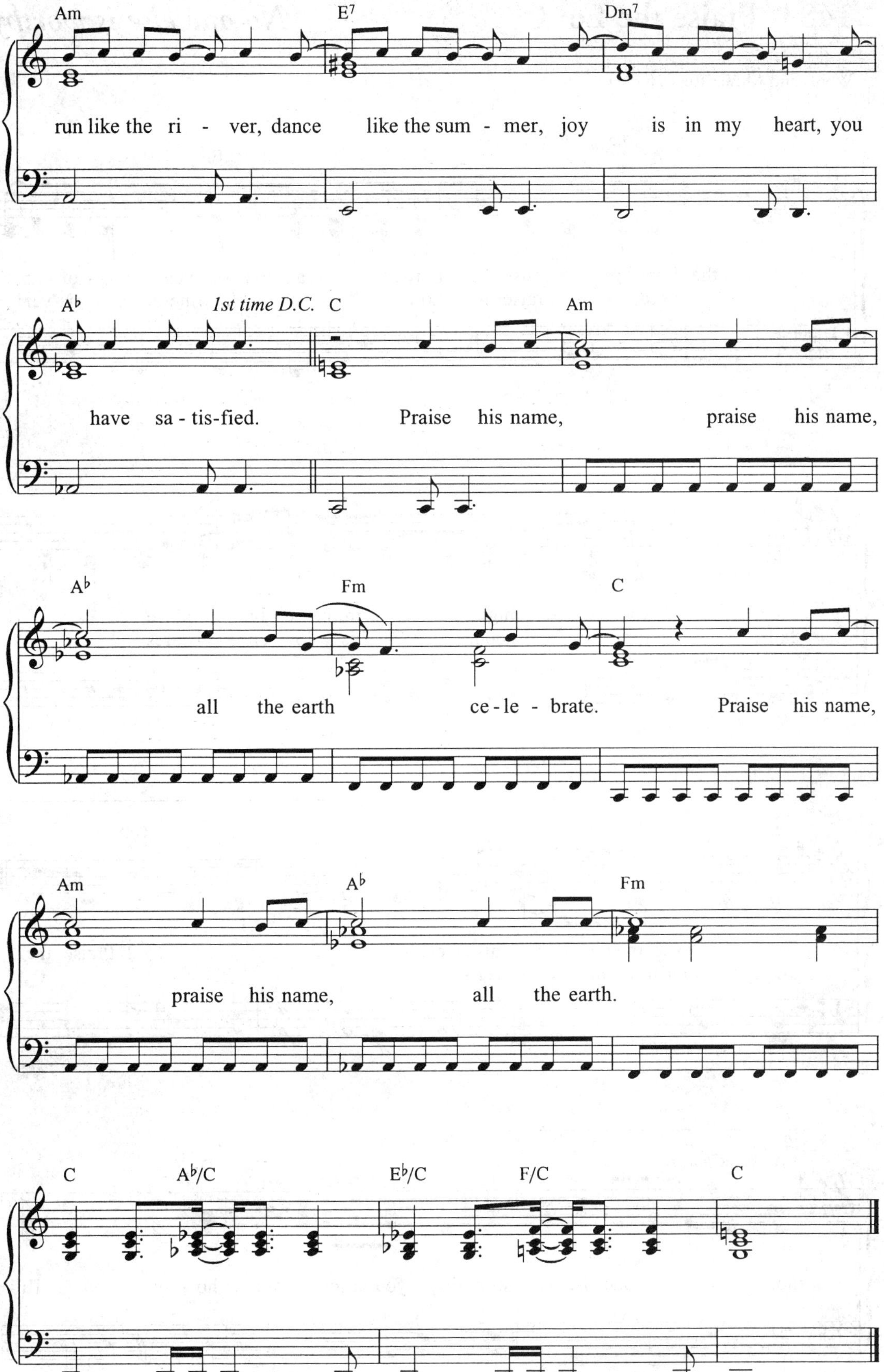
Am E7 Dm7
run like the ri - ver, dance like the sum - mer, joy is in my heart, you
A♭ 1st time D.C. C Am
have sa - tis-fied. Praise his name, praise his name,
A♭ Fm C
all the earth ce - le - brate. Praise his name,
Am A♭ Fm
praise his name, all the earth.
C A♭/C E♭/C F/C C

1483 Praise the Lord

No one else is worthy

Words and Music: Russ Hughes

1. Praise the Lord, praise the Lord, all you ser-vants of our
God, who stand by night in the ho-ly place, to come and seek his face.

Lord, praise the Lord, for his kind-ness ne-ver
fails, for he is good, his love en-dures, both now and e-ver-more.

For no one else is wor-thy, you a-lone are ho-ly. I'll

2. Praise the

E A E
bring you all hon - our and praise. Lord, you are strong and
A D E
migh - ty, the earth dis - plays your glo - ry, so I give you all my
F#m F#m/E F#m/D A/C# D E A
praise, Lord, I give you all my praise.

1484 Praise the Lord from the heavens

Let all creation praise the Lord

Words and Music: Lincoln Brewster

G C G
1. Praise the Lord from the hea - vens,
Lord from the moun - tain tops,
Lord, ev - 'ry na - tion,
D G
praise him in the skies. Praise the Lord from the hea -
praise him in the streets. Praise the Lord from the val -
praise him day and night. Praise the Lord, all cre - a -
C G D G
- vens, all you stars of light.
- leys and tell ev - 'ry - one you see.
- tion, lift his name on high.
C G Em D
Praise him all his an - gels, praise him all his
Tell them of his great - ness, and tell them of his
For he a - lone is wor - thy, the e - ver - last - ing

C2 C/B Am G D
hosts; let all cre - a - tion praise the
love; let all cre - a - tion praise the
King; let all cre - a - tion praise the
1. G Gsus4 G
2. G Chorus
Lord. 2. Praise the Lord. Praise the
D C7/E Am G D
Lord, praise the Lord; let all cre - a - tion sing. Praise the
C7/E Am G D
Lord, praise the Lord; let all cre - a - tion praise the
1. G Gsus4 G D.C.
Last time G Gsus4 G
Lord. 3. Praise the Lord.

2.
G Gsus4 G Em7/G D/G Em7/G
Lord. Praise him sun and moon,
D/G Em7/G D/G
praise him hea - ven of hea - vens. Praise him sons and
Em7/G D/G Em7/G
daugh-ters, praise him mo - thers and fa - thers;
Am G D Am G D
let all cre - a - tion praise, let all cre - a - tion praise,
Am G D G
Chorus
D.S.
let all cre - a - tion praise the Lord. Praise the

If I speak in the tongues of men and of angels,
but have not love,
I am only a resounding gong or a clanging cymbal.
If I have the gift of prophecy
and can fathom all mysteries and all knowledge,
and if I have a faith that can move mountains,
but have not love,
I am nothing.
If I give all I possess to the poor
and surrender my body to the flames,
but have not love,
I gain nothing.
Love is patient, love is kind.
It does not envy, it does not boast, it is not proud.
It is not rude, it is not self-seeking,
it is not easily angered, it keeps no record of wrongs.
Love does not delight in evil
but rejoices with the truth.
It always protects, always trusts,
always hopes, always perseveres.

1 Corinthians 13:1-7

1485 Praise the Lord from the heavens *Psalm 148*

Words and Music: Graham Kendrick

Steady 3

1. Praise the Lord, from the hea - vens, praise him from the skies. Praise the Lord, hosts of an - gels, sing ce - les - tial choirs. Praise him, sun and moon, praise him, shin - ing stars, clouds that ride on the wind: let ev - 'ry-thing with

Lord, earth and o - ceans, crea - tures of the deep. Fire and hail, ice and hur -ri-cane, let the thun - der speak. Beasts of for - est, field an des - ert, ev - 'ry bird in the sky: from least of all to

all praise the one name wor - thy of all praise. On - ly God, our cre - a - tor from e - ter - nal days. All his ex - cel - lence far out - shin - ing, all the worlds he has made: yet comes to us, de -

B♭ G Csus4 Asus4 Last time to Coda E♭/F C/D
life and breath prai - ses sing.
great - est king, sing for joy.
li - vers us, give him praise.
F D E♭/F C/D 1, 2. F D B♭ G 3. F D
2. Praise the
3. Let them
E♭/F C/D F D E♭/F C/D
To the Lord of all cre - a - tion, glo - ry and ma - jes - ty for -
To the Lord of all cre - a - tion, glo - ry and ma - jes - ty for -
Praise the Lord of all cre - a - tion, glo - ry and ma - jes - ty for -
1, 2. F D 3. F D D.S.
e - ver. e - ver. All his
e - ver.
CODA
F D
praise.

1486 Praise to Christ, the Lord incarnate

Words: Martin E. Leckebusch

Music: Graham Kendrick

1. Praise to Christ, the Lord in-car-nate, gift of God by hu-man birth: he it is who came a-mong us, shared our life and showed our worth; ours the tur-moil he en-coun-tered, ours the fight he made his own; now with-in our hearts his Spi-rit makes his way of free-dom known.

2. Praise to Christ, the Man of Sorrows,
tasting death for our release:
his the cup of bitter anguish,
ours the pardon, ours the peace;
his the blood that seals forgiveness,
ours the weight of guilt he bore –
so by death and resurrection
Christ has opened heaven's door.

3. Praise to Christ, the Priest eternal:
still for us he intercedes;
still he sees our pains and problems –
how he understands our needs!
Yesterday, today, forever,
always he remains the same:
pledged to bring us to the Father,
strong in grace, and free from blame.

1487 Press into the heart of the Father *With all faith*

Words and Music: Don Harris

2.
F C F B♭ F/A
D A D G D/F♯
Be-lieve on this, the word of life, our Lord, the
Gm F Csus4 C F/A C F
Em D Asus4 A D/F♯ A D
Christ has come to save us. Re-ceive by faith his blood sup-
B♭ F/A Gm F Dm7
G D/F♯ Em D Bm7
plied that the pow-er of sin be cursed and the
1.
B♭ C F B♭2 Dm7 Csus4
G A D G2 Bm7 Asus4
Fa-ther be glo-ri-fied.
2.
F B♭2 Dm7 Csus4 F B♭2 F
D G2 Bm7 Asus4 D G2 D
D.C.

1488 Princes and paupers

We all bow down

Words and Music: Lenny LeBlanc

A♭ E♭/G B♭sus4
F C/E Gsus4
Chorus
one day will see his face.
e - ver his love will reign.
And we
E♭ Cm B♭7sus4 B♭7 E♭ Cm7
C Am G7sus4 G7 C Am7
all bow down; kings will sur - ren - der their crowns
Gm A♭ E♭/G B♭/D Cm
Em F C/E G/B Am
and wor - ship Je - sus, for
Last time to Coda
A♭ B♭ A♭/C E♭/B♭ A♭ B♭7
F G F/A C/G F G7
he is the love, un-fail-ing love, he is the love of God.
1.
E♭ Cm A♭ E♭/G A♭ B♭7sus4 B♭7 E♭
C Am F C/E F G7sus4 G7 C

2.
Eb Gm/D Cm Ab Bbsus4 Bb
C Bridge Em/B Am F Gsus4 G
He's the light of the world, the
Cm Ab Bb/D Ab/C Eb/Bb Bb7
Am F G/B F/A C/G G7
Chorus D.S.
Lord of the cross. and we
CODA
Eb Cm Ab Eb/G Ab Bb7sus4 Bb7 Eb
C Am F C/E F G7sus4 G7 C

1489 Put peace into each other's hands

Words: Fred Kaan

Music: Traditional Irish melody

ST COLUMBA 87 87

D G/B A D A Bm
1. Put peace in - to each o - ther's hands and
D/A G D/F♯ G D Dsus4 D Bm Em/C♯ D Em
3
like a trea - sure hold it, pro - tect it like a
D/F♯ A Bm A6 D/F♯ G D/A A7 D G/D D
can - dle - flame, with ten - der - ness en - fold it.

2. Put peace into each other's hands
with loving expectation;
be gentle in your words and ways,
in touch with God's creation.

3. Put peace into each other's hands
like bread we break for sharing;
look people warmly in the eye:
our life is meant for caring.

4. As at Communion, shape your hands
into a waiting cradle;
the gift of Christ receive, revere,
united round the table.

5. Put Christ into each other's hands,
he is love's deepest measure;
in love make peace, give peace a chance,
and share it like a treasure.

1490 Rejoice and be glad!

Words: Horatius Bonar

Music: Traditional English melody

2. Rejoice and be glad! it is sunshine at last!
The clouds have departed, the shadows are past.

3. Rejoice and be glad! for the blood has been shed;
redemption is finished, the price has been paid.

4. Rejoice and be glad! now the pardon is free!
The Just for the unjust has died on the tree.

5. Rejoice and be glad! for the Lamb that was slain
o'er death is triumphant, and liveth again.

6. Rejoice and be glad! for our King is on high;
he pleadeth for us on his throne in the sky.

7. Rejoice and be glad! for he cometh again;
he cometh in glory, the Lamb that was slain.

Sound his praises, tell the story of him who was slain!
Sound his praises, tell with gladness he cometh again!

1491 Salvation and glory

We lift up your name

Words and Music: Jeff Hamlin

Cmaj7 D/C E B/E E B/E E
B♭maj7 C/B♭ D A/D D A/D D
glo - ry to the Lamb;
all cre - a - tion sings;
Cmaj7 D/C Cmaj7 C/D B7sus4
B♭maj7 C/B♭ B♭maj7 B♭/C A7sus4
hal - le - lu - jah to the great 'I Am'.
hal - le - lu - jah to the King of kings.
Chorus
E E/G♯ C♯m/B A2
D D/F♯ Bm/A G2
We lift up your name, O Lord,
E2/G♯ E2/F♯ F♯m7
D2/F♯ D2/E Em7
wor - thy the Lamb who was slain,

E/F♯ F♯m7 E/A Am(♯7)/C A/B E
D/E Em7 D/G Gm(♯7)/B♭ G/A D
taking all our pain; we lift up your name,
E/G♯ C♯m/B A2 E2/G♯ E2/F♯
D/F♯ Bm/A G2 D2/F♯ D2/E
O Lord, giving you hon-
F♯m7 E/F♯ F♯m7 E/A Am(♯7)/C B7sus4
Em7 D/E Em7 D/G Gm(♯7)/B♭ A7sus4
-our and praise with our hands upraised
A/B B E
G/A A D
to you, Lord.

1492 Salvation, spring up

Words and Music: Charlie Hall

With excitement
E
Sal - va - tion, spring up from the ground, Lord, rend the
hea-vens and come down. Seek the lost and heal the lame;
Je - sus, bring glo - ry to your name. Let all the
pro-di-gals run home, all of cre - a-tion waits and groans. Lord, we've heard
of your great fame; Fa - ther, cause all to shout your name.
Fine

N.C.
B C♯m A
Stir up our hearts, O God;
B C♯m A
o - pen our spi - rits to awe who you are.
B C♯m A²/C♯
Put a cry in us so deep

E/B A E/G# Bsus4/F# E
in - side that we can - not find the words
A2 E/G# E Cmaj7
we need, we just weep and cry out to you.
E/G# A2 E/B Cmaj7/E Em9/F# Em/G E/G# A2
E/B
1. C2 D.C.
2. C2 D.C. al Fine

‘Come now, let us reason together,’
says the Lord.
‘Though your sins are like scarlet,
they shall be as white as snow;
though they are red as crimson,
they shall be like wool.’

Isaiah 1:18

1493 Saviour, I will sing to you *Saviour of the world*

Words and Music: Tim Lomax

1. Sa-viour, I will sing to you a heart-felt song of love for
2. Je-sus, now you reach the lost in the sha-dow of the

you, and ev-'ry day I'll give my life
cross. It's there they taste your grace so sweet,

in wor-ship as a sac-ri-fice. You gave your all to set me
and there that love and jus-tice meet. You took the sting of death a-

free by dy-ing on the cross for me.
way and now we live in vic-to-ry.

Chorus
A G D/F♯ Bm A G
Je-sus, Sa-viour of the world, you're the King of love now reign-ing.
D/F♯ G Bm A
Sa - viour, you're the source of end - less mer - cy.
G D/F♯ Bm A G D/F♯ G
Sa-viour of the world, you're the ris - en Lord e - ter - nal. Sa - viour, you're the
1.
Bm A D Dsus4
D.C.
King who died for me.
2.
Bm A
D.S.
King who died. Je - sus,
3.
Bm A D
King who died for me.

Dsus4 Bm7 A
Je - sus,
G D/F# Bm A G D/F#
Sa-viour of the world, Je - sus, Sa-viour of the world,
Bm A G D/F# Bm A
Je - sus, Sa-viour of the world, you're the King who died
D G D
for me, you're the King who died for me,
G D G2 D
you're the King who died for me.

No, in all these things
we are more than conquerors
through him who loved us.
For I am convinced that neither death nor life,
neither angels nor demons,
neither the present nor the future,
nor any powers,
neither height nor depth,
nor anything else in all creation,
will be able to separate us
from the love of God
that is in Christ Jesus our Lord.

Romans 8:37-39

1494 See, what a morning *Resurrection hymn*

Words and Music: Keith Getty and Stuart Townend

2. See Mary weeping, 'Where is he laid?'
As in sorrow she turns from the empty tomb;
hears a voice speaking, calling her name;
it's the Master, the Lord raised to life again!
The voice that spans the years,
speaking life, stirring hope, bringing peace to us,
will sound till he appears,
for he lives, Christ is risen from the dead!

3. One with the Father, Ancient of Days,
through the Spirit who clothes faith with certainty,
honour and blessing, glory and praise
to the King crowned with power and authority!
And we are raised with him,
death is dead, love has won, Christ has conquered;
and we shall reign with him,
for he lives, Christ is risen from the dead!

1495 Send down the fire

Words and Music: Marty Haugen

Chorus

Capo 1

Send down the fire of your jus-tice, send down the rains of your love; come, send down the Spi - rit, breathe life in your peo - ple, and we shall be peo - ple of God.

Last time

1. Call us to be your com - pas - sion,

E♭ B♭/D A♭/C D♭ A♭/C B♭
D A/C♯ G/B C G/B A
teach us the song of your love; give us
Fm7 E♭ B♭/D E♭ B♭/D Cm
Em7 D A/C♯ D A/C♯ Bm
hearts that sing, give us deeds that ring, make us
Fm7 E♭/G A♭ F7/A B♭ Fm7 B♭
Em7 D/F♯ G E7/G♯ A Em7 A
D.C.
ring with the song of your love.

2. Call us to learn of your mercy,
teach us the way of your peace;
give us hearts that feel, give us hands that heal,
make us walk in the way of your peace.

3. Call us to answer oppression,
teach us the fire of your truth;
give us righteous souls, till your justice rolls,
make us burn with the fire of your truth.

4. Call us to witness your kingdom,
give us the presence of Christ;
may your holy light keep us shining bright,
ever shine with the presence of Christ.

1496 Send out your light

Words: from Psalm 43:3, John L. Bell

Music: John L. Bell

Quietly but firmly

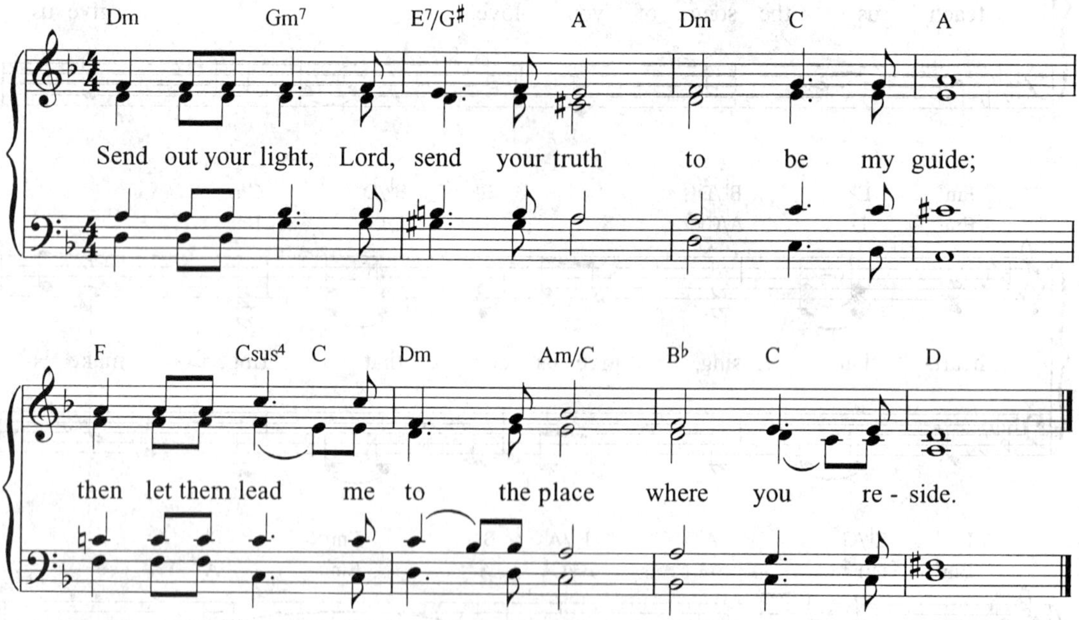

1497 Shall we gather at the river

Words and Music: Robert Lowry

D Em D A7 D A
1. Shall we ga-ther at the ri - ver, where bright an - gel-feet have trod,
D Em D G G6 Em7 A7 D
with its cry-stal tide for e - ver flow-ing by the throne of God?
Chorus
G D A7 D
Yes, we'll ga-ther at the ri - ver, the beau-ti-ful, the beau-ti-ful ri - ver;
G D G6 Em7 A7 D
ga-ther with the saints at the ri - ver that flows by the throne of God.

2. On the margin of the river,
washing up its silver spray,
we will walk and worship ever,
all the happy, golden day.

3. Ere we reach the shining river,
lay we ev'ry burden down;
grace our spirits will deliver,
and provide a robe and crown.

4. At the shining of the river,
mirror of the Saviour's face,
saints, whom death will never sever,
raise their songs of saving grace.

5. Soon we'll reach the silver river;
soon our pilgrimage will cease;
soon our happy hearts will quiver
with the melody of peace.

1498 Shalom, shalom *Shalom, Jerusalem*

Words and Music: Paul Wilbur

Sha-lom, sha-lom, Je-ru-sa-lem, peace be to

you; when Mes-si-ah comes to take us home, may his

praise be found in you. 1. Pray for peace, Je-

ru-sa-lem, ci-ty of our God;

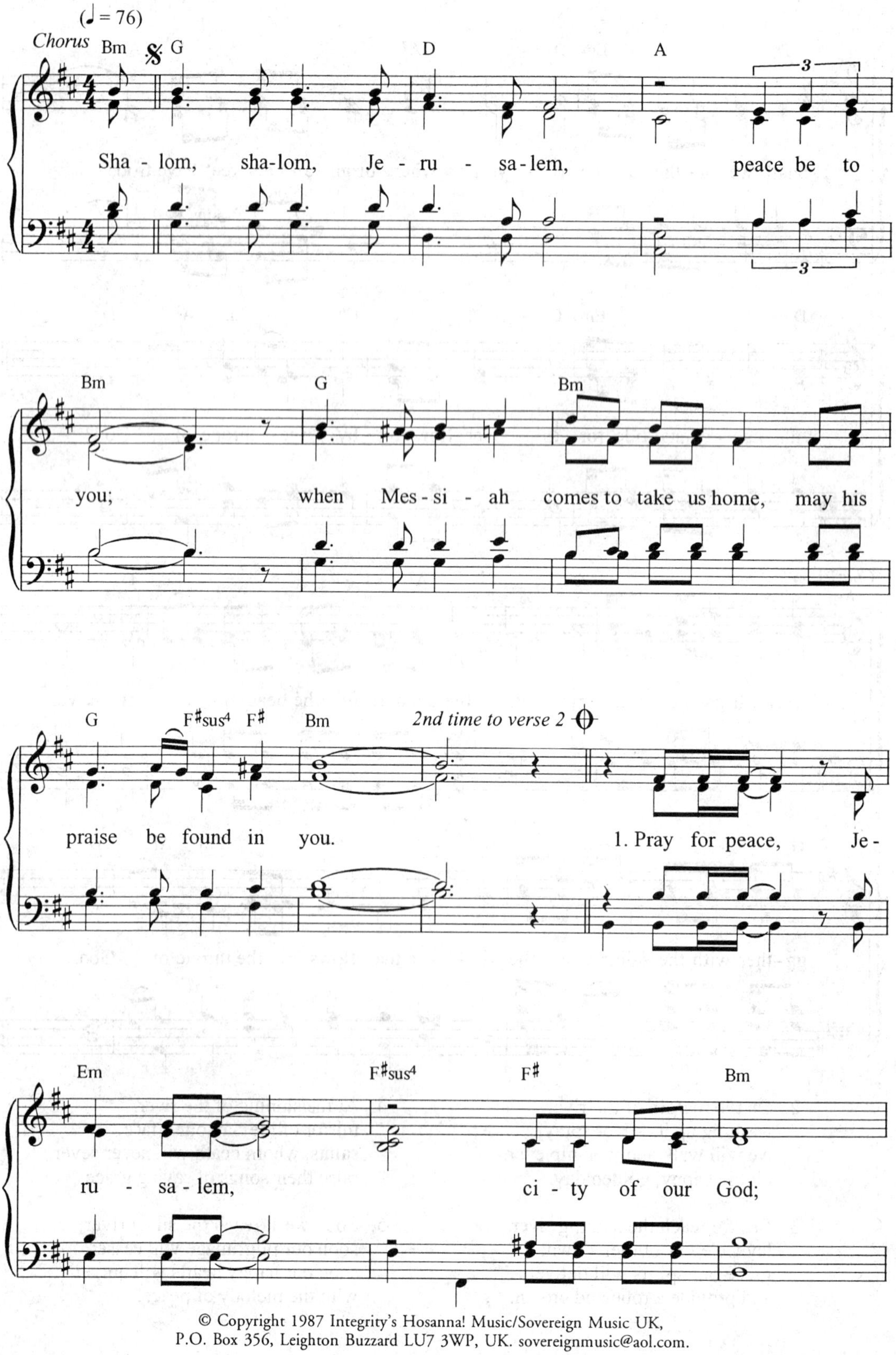

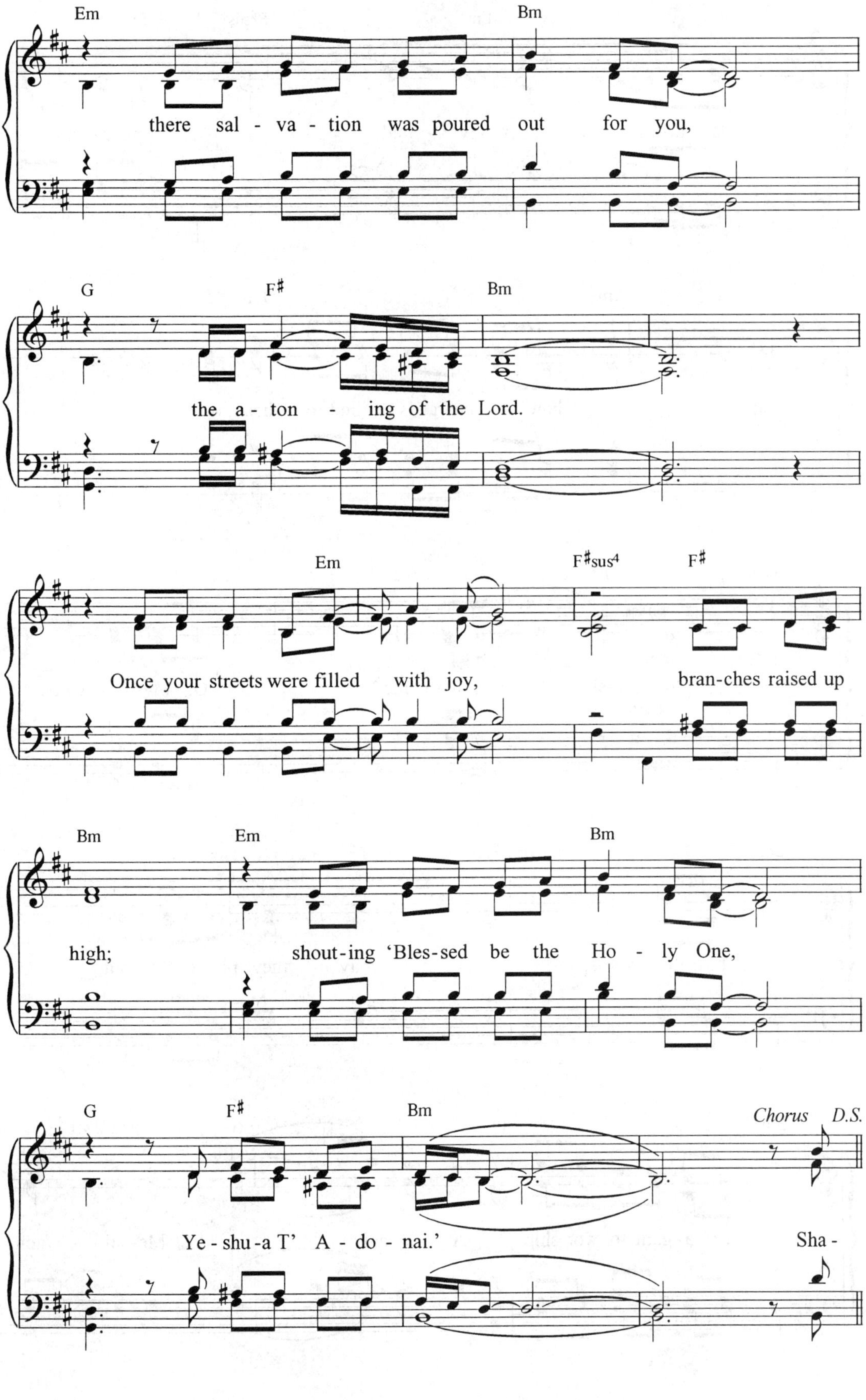
Em Bm
there sal - va - tion was poured out for you,
G F♯ Bm
the a - ton - ing of the Lord.
Em F♯sus4 F♯
Once your streets were filled with joy, bran-ches raised up
Bm Em Bm
high; shout-ing 'Bles-sed be the Ho - ly One,
G F♯ Bm
Chorus D.S.
Ye - shu - a T' A - do - nai.' Sha -

Em F#sus4 F#
2. Is - ra - el, be - lov - ed, Eph - ra - im, my
Bm Em Bm
son; how my heart is thrilled to hear you say,
G F# Bm
'Our Mes - si - ah has come.' O, my bro - thers,
Em F#sus4 F# Bm
hear these words, may they pierce your soul;
Em Bm G F#sus4 F#
turn a - gain to wor - ship A - do - nai, Me - shi - ach

Bm
Chorus
G
D
you will know.
Sha - lom, sha-lom, Je - ru - sa-lem,
A
Bm
G
peace be to you;
when Mes - si - ah
Bm
G
F#sus4
F#
Bm
comes to take us home, may his praise be found in you.

1499 Shepherd of my thankful heart

Words and Music: Paul Oakley

3. Sacrifice no words could tell,
Majesty on earth to dwell,
Living Word, Emmanuel,
I'll love you all my days.

4. Maker of the stars above,
praise of angels ever sung,
King of glory, King of love,
let all creation praise.

1500 Shine your light

Who you are

Words and Music: Dave Lubben

Shine your light in - to the dark;

speak your truth in - to my heart;

want to know who you are.

Chorus

O-pen my eyes

G2
D
so I can see you; o-pen my ears
G2
D
so I can hear you; I give my heart
To repeat
G2
Em
Bm/E
Chorus
to you, please, o-pen my eyes
To continue
Em
Bm/E
Lord; I want to
G/C
G/B
Dsus4
D
know who you are; I want to

G/C
G/B
Dsus4
D
A/D
Last time to Coda
know who you are.
G2
A/G
D
Please show me;
A/D
G2
A/G
D.S.
o-pen my eyes, Lord;
CODA
Dsus4
D
A/D
D2

1501 Shine your light on us *Shine*

Words and Music: Marc James and Tré Sheppard

Shine your light on us that all may see your good- -ness. Shine your face on us that all may see your glo - ry.

Verse

1. Ans-wer me when I call, you are my on- -ly prayer.
2. & 3. I wan-na be close to you, that my life would tell your sto - ry.

When dark-ness is all a-round
I wan-na be one with you,

G Gm Bm
I know you will be there.
changed by the light of your glo - ry.
Ma-ny are ask -
G D5 E
- ing who can show us some-thing real.
Bm G D5
Long-ing for hope be - yond the pain of what they feel.
E Gm G
So I will go down on my knees and say:
D5 Dm7 G
shine your light on us that all may see your good -
Gm D5 Dm7
- ness. Shine your face on us that all

1, 2.
G Gm D5
may see your glo - ry.
D G Gm
3.
D5 Dm7 G
Shine your light on us that all may see your good -
Gm D5 Dm7
- ness. Shine your face on us that all
G Gm rit. al fine D
may see your glo - ry.

1502 Shout out loud

Words and Music: Wayne Huirua and Chris de Jong

Funky, with swung 16s

Am7
G G#
Am7
praise the King. Bless the Lord in the house, so sing:
1, 2.
Last time
2nd time to Coda
N.C.
E7b9
G Am7
Fine
Je-sus, you are wel-come in this place. place. So sing!
Am7
G/A
Am7
When I'm walk-ing through the val-ley and I can-not find my way,
G/A
when I'm head-ing in-to trou-ble and I don't know what to say,
Am7
D7
Gm7
Eaug
got-ta lift my hands to hea-ven, stomp and sing and shout,

Am7 D7 Gm7
got - ta lift my heart to you, Je - sus, I'll shout a - loud.
D.S.al Coda
Eaug G G♯
Shout out
CODA
B♭/C C7 Fmaj7 Dm/B E7sus4 E7
Je - sus, you're all I need to take a - way my fear.
Am7 B♭/C C7 Fmaj7
You are my friend in - deed,
D.S. al Fine
Dm/B E7sus4 E7 G G♯
Je - sus, you're wel - come here. Shout out

1503 Show me how to stand for justice

Words: Martin E. Leckebusch

Music: Robert Lowry

DIM OND IESU 87 87 D

G D G C G
1. Show me how to stand for jus-tice: how to work for what is
D G D G C G D7
right, how to chal - lenge false as - sump-tions, how to walk with-in the
G D D7
light. May I learn to share more free - ly in a world so full of
G C G/D D7 G
greed, show-ing your im-mense com - pas-sion by the life I choose to lead.

2. Teach my heart to treasure mercy,
whether given or received –
for my need has not diminished
since the day I first believed:
let me seek no satisfaction
boasting of what I have done,
but rejoice that I am pardoned
and accepted in your Son.

3. Gladly I embrace a lifestyle
modelled on your living word,
in humility submitting
to the truth which I have heard.
Make me conscious of your presence
every day in all I do:
by your Spirit's gracious prompting
may I learn to walk with you.

1504 Sing glory to God the Father

Words: Michael Saward

Music: Marc-Antoine Charpentier

TE DEUM 8 12 8 8 13 13

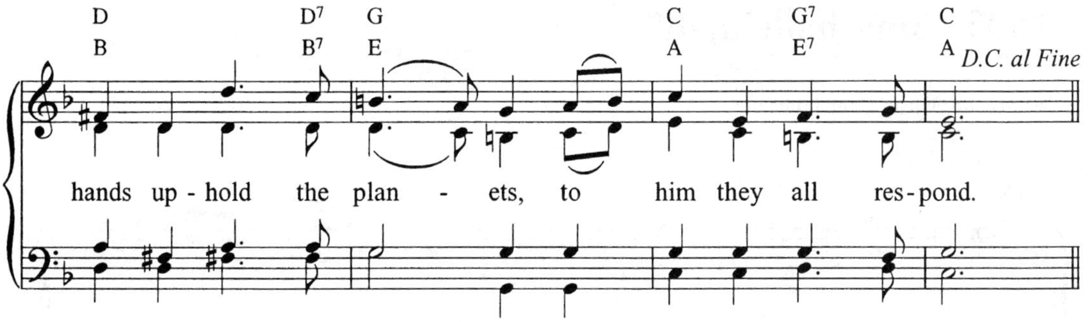

2. Sing glory to God the Saviour,
   the Lord of the galaxies, bearer of our shame.
   Sing praise to the world's redeemer
   and magnify his holy name.

   He suffered grief and torment, for sin he paid the price,
   he rose in glorious triumph, both priest and sacrifice.

3. Sing glory to God the Spirit,
   the power of the elements, setting hearts aflame.
   Sing praise to the world's life-giver
   and magnify his holy name.

   His gifts to all are given, his fruit transforms our hearts,
   his fellowship enriches, a grace which he imparts.

4. Sing glory, the whole creation!
   Give thanks to the Trinity, heaven's love proclaim.
   Sing praise to our God, almighty,
   and magnify his holy name.

1505 Sing hallelujah!

Words and Music: Tim Lomax

(♩ = 110)
Chorus D
Em7
F#m7
G2
Sing hal - le - lu - jah! Oh what a vict-'ry, death is de-feat-ed, life
Em7
A
D
Em7
has come. Sing hal - le - lu - jah! We are for - gi - ven, saved
Last time to Coda
F#m7
G2
Em7
A
D
D/F#
by the blood of Christ, our Lord. Sing hal - le - lu -
G2
Asus4
A
D
Dsus4
D
- jah! 1. Our on - ly
D
Em7
G
D/F#
boast is in the cross of Christ, the place of death

G2 Asus4 A Bm7
gave way to glo - rious life. There on the cross our sin was

Em7sus4 D/F♯ G Asus4 A *D.C.*

nailed, O gra-cious King, you saved the world!

CODA

D D/F♯ G2 Asus4 A D D/F♯

Sing hal - le - lu - jah! (Sing hal - le - lu -

G2 Asus4 A D D/F♯ G2 Asus4 A D

- jah!) Sing hal - le - lu - jah!

2. We are redeemed by your precious blood,
the cross of shame revealed the pow'r of God.
And by your wounds we shall be healed,
O suffering King, you saved the world!

1506 Sing out

Words and Music: Paul Baloche and Ed Kerr

D E C#/E# F#m Bm7 D
praises abound, his glory surrounds us, filling his temple here,
E7sus4 E/F# F#m Bm7 D/E A
Fine
sing out, the Lord is near.
D E D
1. The Lord inhabits the song of his
A D E D D/E A D
saints and lives in their praises; the Lord in-
Chorus
E D A D E D D/E D.S.
habits the song of his saints and lives in their praises. Sing out,

2. We come to worship together as one,
with music and singing;
rejoice in all that the Father has done,
let's lift up an offering.

1507 Sing them over again to me *Wonderful words of life*

Words and Music: Philip P. Bliss

WORDS OF LIFE Irregular and Refrain

F C7 C6 C7 F
Capo 3 D A7 A6 A7 D
1. Sing them o - ver a - gain to me, won-der-ful words of life;
C7 C6 C7 F
A7 A6 A7 D
let me more of their beau - ty see, won-der - ful words of life;
Bb F Bb F
G D G D
words of life and beau - ty, teach me faith and du - ty:
Chorus
C7 F C7 F
A7 D A7 D
Beau-ti - ful words, won-der - ful words, won-der - ful words of life;

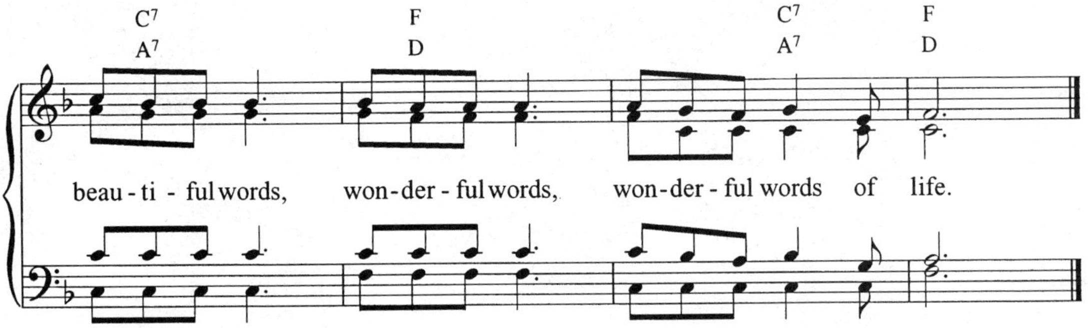
C7 A7
F D
C7 A7
F D
beau - ti - ful words, won - der - ful words, won - der - ful words of life.

2. Christ, the blessed One, gives to all
   wonderful words of life;
   sinner, list to the loving call,
   wonderful words of life;
   all so freely given,
   wooing us to heaven:

3. Sweetly echo the gospel call,
   wonderful words of life;
   offer pardon and peace to all,
   wonderful words of life;
   Jesus, only Saviour,
   sanctify forever.

Be very careful, then, how you live –
not as unwise but as wise,
making the most of every opportunity,
because the days are evil.
Therefore do not be foolish,
but understand what the Lord's will is.
Do not get drunk on wine.
Instead, be filled with the Spirit.

Ephesians 5:15-18

1508 Sing unto the Lord

Words and Music: Becky Fender

1509 Softly and tenderly Jesus is calling

For you and for me

Words and Music: Will L. Thompson

2. Why should we tarry when Jesus is pleading,
   pleading for you and for me?
   Why should we linger and heed not his mercies,
   mercies for you and for me.

3. Time is now fleeting, the moments are passing,
   passing from you and from me;
   shadows are gathering, deathbeds are coming,
   coming for you and for me!

4. Oh for the wonderful love he has promised,
   promised for you and for me!
   Though we have sinned, he has mercy and pardon,
   pardon for you and for me!

1510 So I sing of the cross

Words and Music: Anthony Taylor

C2 G
My life is hid-den now in you, Je-sus, lov-er of my
C2 C D
soul and I re-joice now you're my right-eous-ness.
G Chorus D/F#
So I sing of the cross, I sing of my Sa-viour,
C2
G D/F# Am7 D
and I sing of the mer-cy that I ne-ver de-served.
G Bm7 Am7
You poured out your grace, you showed me your fa-vour,

G D/F# C2
Je - sus, you bought the free - dom that I could nev-er earn.
To continue
G D/F# C2
G D/F# C2
Last time
G
G D/F# Em7 C2 G
2. So I sing of the King, who is clothed in ma - jes - ty.
D D/F# G D/F# Em7
How he chose to call me friend,

C2 G D
though I was still an e - ne - my.
C2 G
And now the ran - som has been paid, the sin of the world on him was
C2 G D
laid, I can't de-ny the love of God dis - played.
C2 G
No long - er now a slave to sin, Je-sus is my ev - 'ry -
C2 C D
D.S.
thing, and I re-joice that I be - long to him.

1511 Son of God *The greatest gift*

Words and Music: Vicky Beeching

B♭ B♭/D E♭2 F2
G G/B C2 D2
I've e-ver re-ceived is the cross, the cross. For there you gave
B♭ B♭/D E♭2 F2
G G/B C2 D2
your-self up for me on the cross, the cross. And with the blood
Gm7 B♭/D E♭2 F
Em7 G/B C2 D
you poured out for me you have saved my soul.
Cm7 B♭/D E♭2 F B♭
Am7 G/B C2 D G
You have giv-en me the great-est gift of all.

1512 Source of life *You are beautiful*

Words and Music: Gary Sadler

1. Source of life to wood and stream, sov-'reign Lord and gen-
2. Son of God up-on a cross, tast-ing death for all

-tle King, more than we could e- ver dream:
of us, reach-ing out when we were lost:

you are beau-ti-ful. Fa-ther to the fa-ther-less,
you are beau-ti-ful. Ri-sen Lamb up-on the throne,

heal-er of our bro-ken-ness, how you fill our emp-
roar-ing li-on com-ing soon, ev-'ry eye will see

- ti-ness: you are beau-ti-ful.
it's true: you are beau-ti-ful.

Chorus
E F#m A E
Je - sus, you are beau - ti - ful,
C#m B A E
there is none to com-pare with you.
F#m A E
Je - sus, you are beau - ti - ful, and you
C#m A7
show your love to me, and it gives me grace to see you are
F#m E/G# Bsus4
ev - 'ry-thing my heart de - sires. You are beau - ti - ful.
E/G# A2 E/G# A2 E

1513 Sovereign Lord

Words and Music: Martyn Layzell

Em7 D/F♯ C2 D Em7 A7
lu - jah, hal - le - lu - jah.
C2
Chorus
G Em7
Ma - jes - ty, reign in me, your right
D C2 G Em7
hand en-fold - ing me. Earth ap - plaud, hea - vens sing at the
1.
D C2
sight of Christ the King.
2.
C2
Chorus
D.S.
King. Ma - jes-
3.
C2 C/E D/F♯ G
King.

1514 Spirit, Holy Spirit

Words and Music: Geoff Roberts and Judith Roberts

2. Spirit, Holy Spirit,
fashion me, fashion me.
Spirit, Holy Spirit,
in your love fashion me.
You are the Potter, Lord, I am the clay;
change my heart that I might be like Jesus.
Spirit, Holy Spirit,
in your love fashion me.

3. Spirit, Holy Spirit,
flow through me, flow through me.
Spirit, Holy Spirit,
in mercy flow through me.
All I ask is to know more of you
and let all I do reflect my Saviour.
Spirit, Holy Spirit,
in mercy flow through me.

1515 Spirit of the Lord *Healing love*

Words and Music: Ian White

2. Give us just a glimpse of God, of Jesus' heart,
open ears to hear the voice say, 'Come':
look up, look up, look up and see
the light of healing love.

1516 Stand up and clap your hands *Lord most high*

Words and Music: Dave Lubben

G D/F♯ G A
throne; sing prai - ses to the Lord most
name; all praise to you, O Lord most
D D/F♯ G Bm Asus4
Chorus
high. Come, let us
high. Lord, we
C2 G/B Em7
praise him, praise him; he a - lone is
praise you, praise you; you a - lone are
D C2 Em7
good; come, let us praise our Lord most
good; Lord, we praise you, Lord most

D
C2
high;
come, let us praise him,
high;
we praise you,
G/B
Em7
D
praise him; he a - lone is good; come, let us
praise you; you a - lone are good; O we
Last time
C2
Em7
D
praise our Lord most high.
praise you, Lord most
To continue
D/F♯
G
Bm7
G
D.S.
high.
2. We

But when the kindness and love
of God our Saviour appeared,
he saved us,
not because of righteous things we had done,
but because of his mercy.
He saved us through the washing of rebirth and renewal
by the Holy Spirit,
whom he poured out on us generously
through Jesus Christ our Saviour,
so that, having been justified by his grace,
we might become heirs
having the hope of eternal life.

Titus 3:4-7

1517 Stand up, stand up for Jesus

Words: George Duffield, Jr.

Music: George J. Webb

WEBB 7 6 7 6 D

2. Stand up, stand up for Jesus,
the trumpet call obey.
Forth to the mighty conflict,
in this his glorious day:
ye followers now serve him,
against unnumbered foes;
let courage rise with danger,
and strength to strength oppose.

3. Stand up, stand up for Jesus,
stand in his strength alone;
the arm of flesh will fail you,
ye dare not trust your own:
put on the gospel armour,
each piece put on with prayer,
where duty calls, or danger,
be never wanting there.

4. Stand up, stand up for Jesus,
the strife will not be long;
this day the noise of battle,
the next the victor's song:
to him that overcometh
a crown of life shall be;
he with the King of Glory
shall reign eternally.

1518 Take not your Spirit from me *Take me higher*

Words and Music: Lincoln Brewster

D2 C2 D2
Won't you wrap me up in your arms?
C2 Chorus G2 Em7
And take me high-er, and draw
Dsus4 C2 G2
me clo-ser; and pull me deep-
Last time
Em7 Dsus4 C2 G2
er than I've e - ver been.
To continue
G2 Em7 Dsus4 C2 D.C.

1519 Take us to the river

Words and Music: Robin Mark

1. Take us to the ri - ver,
throne room,
- tain,

take us there in
give us ears to
lift us in the

u - ni - ty to sing
hear the cry of heav'n;
sha - dow of your hands;

a song of your sal -
for that cry is
is this your migh - ty

va - tion,
mer - cy,
an - gel,

to win this ge - ne - ra -
mer - cy to the fal -
who stands a - stride the o -

- tion for our King.
- len sons of man:
- cean and the land?

A song of your for - give -
for mer - cy it has tri -
For in his hand your mer -

G
- ness, for it is with
- umphed, tri-umphed o - ver
- cy sho - wers on a
D F#m7 G
grace that ri - ver flows; take us to the ri -
judge - ment by your blood; take us to the throne
dry and bar - ren place; take us to the moun -
D A D
- ver in the ci - ty of our God.
room in the ci - ty of our God.
- tain in the ci - ty of our God.
1. D.S.
2, 3. Chorus
G
2. Take us to your
For the Spi - rit of the
A Bm
Sov - 'reign Lord is up - on us:

G
D/F#
this is the year of the
Asus4
A
1.
Asus2
A
Lord.
The
2.
Asus2
A
D.S.
3. Take us to the moun-
Last time
Asus2
A
D

Then I saw a new heaven and a new earth,
for the first heaven and the first earth had passed away,
and there was no longer any sea.
I saw the Holy City, the new Jerusalem,
coming down out of heaven from God,
prepared as a bride beautifully dressed for her husband.
And I heard a loud voice from the throne saying,
'Now the dwelling of God is with men,
and he will live with them.
They will be his people,
and God himself will be with them and be their God.
He will wipe every tear from their eyes.
There will be no more death or mourning
or crying or pain,
for the old order of things has passed away.

I did not see a temple in the city,
because the Lord God Almighty and the Lamb are its temple.
The city does not need the sun or the moon to shine on it,
for the glory of God gives it light,
and the Lamb is its lamp.
The nations will walk by its light,
and the kings of the earth will bring their splendour into it.
On no day will its gates ever be shut,
for there will be no night there.
The glory and honour of the nations will be brought into it.
Nothing impure will ever enter it,
nor will anyone who does what is shameful or deceitful,
but only those whose names are written
in the Lamb's book of life.

Revelation 21:1-4, 22-27

1520 Teach us, O Lord, to number our days

To honour you

Words and Music: Bob Fitts

A2
Em7/G
D2
you, Lord.
A2
Em7/G
D2
And we will praise
you, Lord.
1.
2.
Em
And we will praise
Lord, as we set our hands to build
G
Asus4
A
this house in your praise,
may the
Em
G
Asus4
A
D.C.
beau-ty of our God be on our face.

I will extol the Lord at all times;
his praise will always be on my lips.
My soul will boast in the Lord;
let the afflicted hear and rejoice.
Glorify the Lord with me:
let us exalt his name together.
I sought the Lord, and he answered me;
he delivered me from all my fears.
Those who look to him are radiant;
their faces are never covered with shame.
This poor man called, and the Lord heard him;
he saved him out of all his troubles.
The angel of the Lord encamps
around those who fear him,
and he delivers them.
Taste and see that the Lord is good;
blessed is the man who takes refuge in him.

Psalm 34:1-8

1521 Tell me the stories of Jesus

Words: William H. Parker   Music: Frederic A. Challinor

STORIES OF JESUS Irregular

C F/C C G7/D G C
1. Tell me the sto-ries of Je - sus I love to hear;
F/C C A/C# G/D D7 G
things I would ask him to tell me if he were here:
G7 C6 C C9 Am/C C7 A/C# Dm
scenes by the way - side, tales of the sea,
G13 G7 Am Adim7 C/G G7 C
sto - ries of Je - sus, tell them to me.

2. First let me hear how the children
stood round his knee,
and I shall fancy his blessing
resting on me;
words full of kindness,
deeds full of grace,
all in the lovelight
of Jesus' face.

3. Into the city I'd follow,
there take my stand,
waving a branch of the palm tree
high in my hand;
one of his heralds,
yes, I would sing
loudest hosannas,
'Jesus is King!'

1522 Tender Saviour

Words and Music: Nick Haigh and Anita Haigh

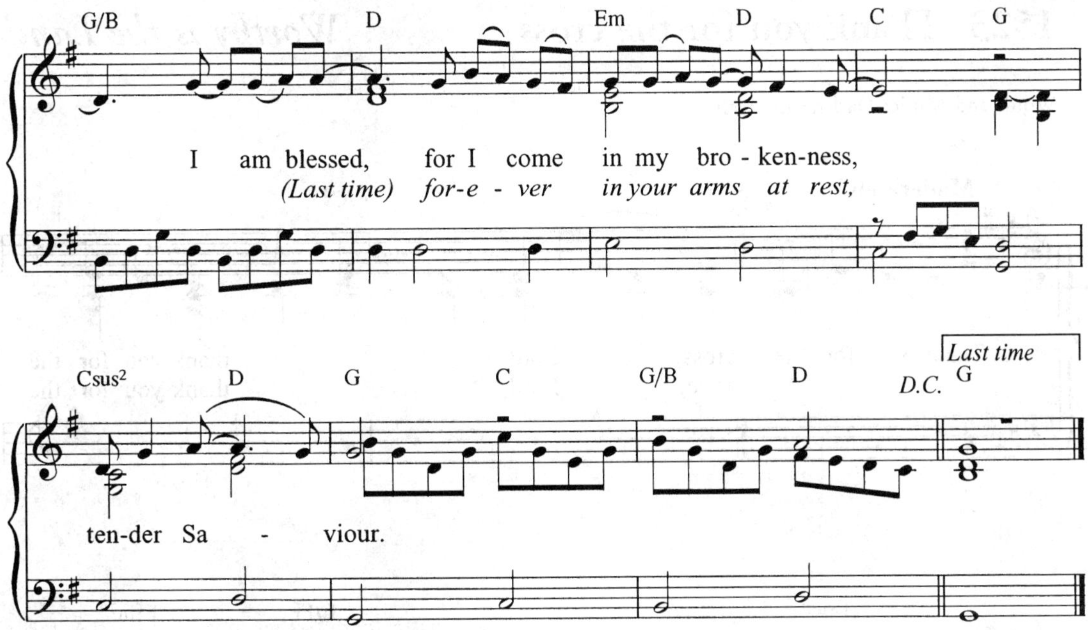
G/B D Em D C G
I am blessed, for I come in my bro - ken-ness,
(Last time) for-e - ver in your arms at rest,
Last time
Csus2 D G C G/B D D.C. G
ten-der Sa - viour.

2. Tender Saviour, speak to me,
   whisper words of hope and peace,
   and let the tumult in me cease,
   tender Saviour.

3. Tender Saviour, hear my cry,
   look with pity on this child;
   and show your mercy by and by,
   tender Saviour.

4. Tender Saviour, make it so,
   let your blessings overflow.
   Until you do, I won't let go;
   tender Saviour.

1523 Thank you for the cross *Worthy is the Lamb*

Words and Music: Darlene Zschech

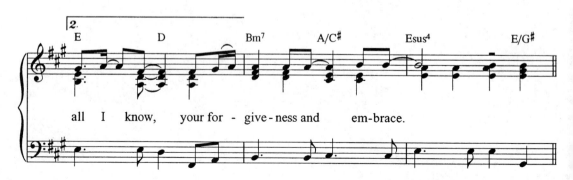

Moderately
D
A/C♯
1. Thank you for the cross, Lord, thank you for the
love, Lord, thank you for the
D Esus4 E A E/F♯ F♯m7
price you paid. Bear - ing all my sin and shame in
nail - pierced hands. Washed me in your cleans-ing flow, now
1.
E D Bm7 A/C♯ Esus4 E A A/C♯
love you came and gave a-maz - ing grace. 2. Thank you for this
2.
E D Bm7 A/C♯ Esus4 E/G♯
all I know, your for - give - ness and em-brace.

Chorus
A E/G♯ Bm7 A/C♯
Wor-thy is the Lamb, seat - ed on the throne.
D2 E E/D A/C♯ D
Crown you now with ma - ny crowns, you
Bm7 Bm7/A E E/G♯ A
reign vic-to - ri-ous. High and lift - ed up,
E/G♯ Bm7 A/C♯ D2
Je - sus, Son of God. The
E E/D A/C♯ D
dar-ling of hea - ven, cru - ci - fied.

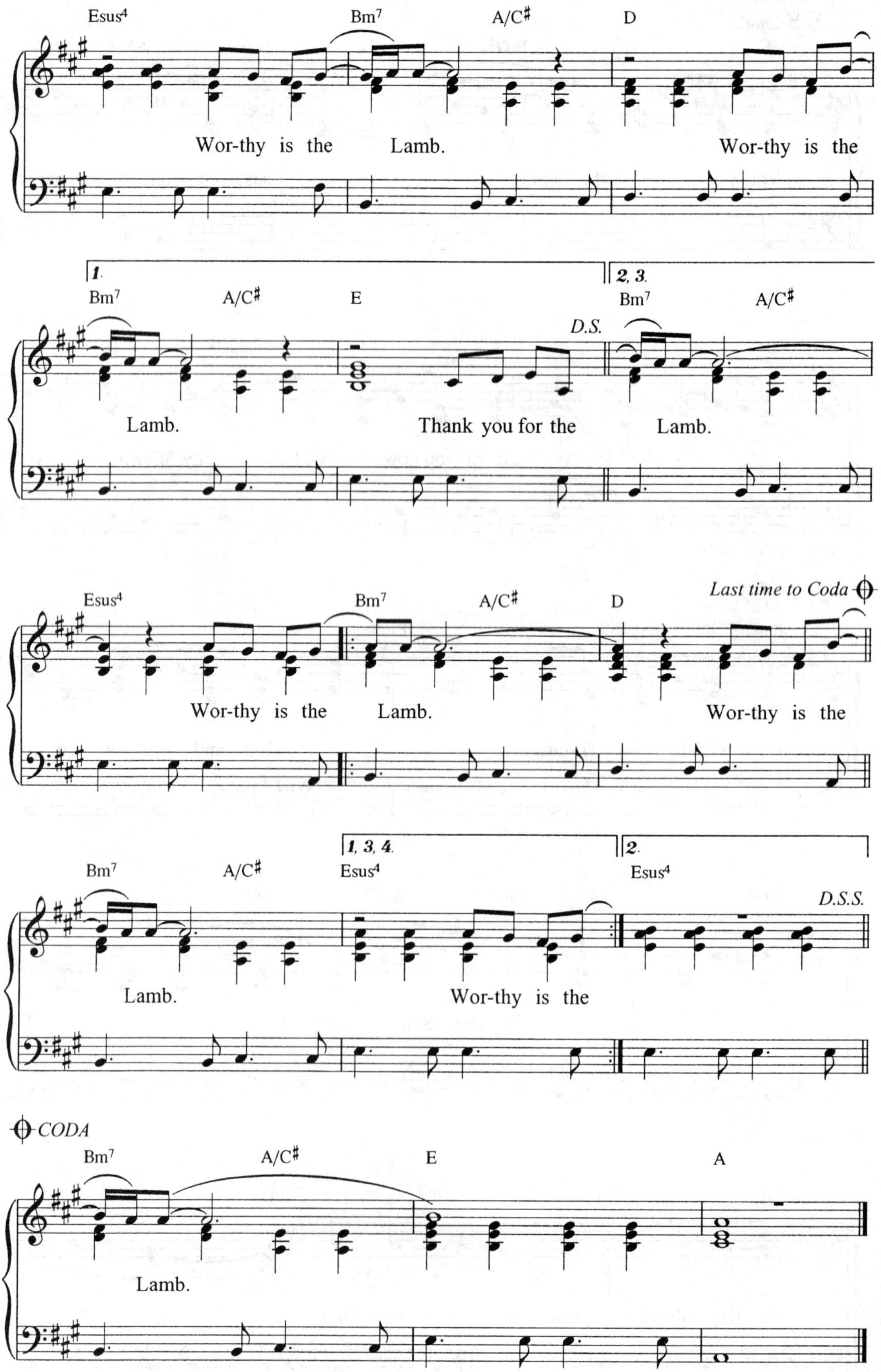
Esus4
Bm7
A/C#
D
Wor-thy is the
Lamb.
Wor-thy is the
1.
2, 3.
Bm7
A/C#
E
D.S.
Bm7
A/C#
Lamb.
Thank you for the
Lamb.
Esus4
Bm7
A/C#
D
Last time to Coda
Wor-thy is the
Lamb.
Wor-thy is the
1, 3, 4.
2.
Bm7
A/C#
Esus4
Esus4
D.S.S.
Lamb.
Wor-thy is the
CODA
Bm7
A/C#
E
A
Lamb.

May I never boast
except in the cross of our Lord Jesus Christ.

Galatians 6:14a

1524 Thank you, thank you for the blood

Words and Music: Matt Redman

Dm7 Bm7 Gm Em C7 A7 F D
e - ver as we sing these free - dom songs.
1. 2.
Eb2 C2 D.C. Eb2 C2 Bb G
We sing of all you've done,
Eb C2 C/E A/C# F D
we sing of all you've done, we
D/F# B/D# Gm Em Gm/F Em/D Eb C
sing of all you've done for us, won for us, paid for us. We
Eb C Bb G
for us.

1525 The cross before me

Not to us

Words and Music: Jesse Reeves and Chris Tomlin

Dsus4 C2 G
it's not for us, it's all for you.
it's not for us, it's all for you.
Gsus4 G
Chorus
Not to us, but to your name
F/C C F/C C G
be the glo - ry. Not to us,
F/C C
1.
F/C C
but to your name be the glo - ry.
G G2 Cmaj7 C F/C C

2.
F/C C G
- ry. The earth is shak - ing, the moun-tains shout - ing:
C6 C C6 C Em7
it's all for you. The waves are crash - ing, the
Dsus4 C
sun is rag - ing: it's all for you. The
G C6 C
u - ni - verse spin-ning and sing-ing: it's all for you.
C6 C Em7 Dsus4
Your child-ren danc - ing, danc - ing, danc - ing:

C
Gsus4 G
it's all for you, it's all for you,
Gsus4 G
C6 Cmaj7
C6 Cmaj7
my all for you.
Em7sus4 Em7
Dsus4
C6 C
1.
2.
C6 C
C6 C
G
My all for you,
My all for you.

1526 The giver of grace

Words and Music: Tim Lomax

(♩ = 96)
A
1. The gi - ver of grace
poured out his
flow - ing with

D
E/G♯
D
life for us, dy - ing up - on the cross,
truth and peace, a foun - tain of won - drous love

A
E
D/F♯
spill - ing his pre - cious blood.
has sprung from the heart of God.

E/G♯
A
What grace is this?
Beau - ti - ful grace,
Love that we
gi - ven so

D E/G♯ D
don't de - serve, for - give - ness for all our sin,
free - ly now, God's ri - ches are poured for all,
A E
free - dom and life.
there at the cross.
All
Chorus
A D E
praise to your glo - rious grace, all praise for your sav - ing blood,
A E/G♯ F♯m7 D
O Lord, you are our Sa - viour, our Re - deem -
D/E E A
- er. We live for the praise of your glo -

D E A E/G# F#m7
- ry, we live for the praise of your name, O Lord,
D E
you are our Sa - viour, our Re - deem - er.
1.
A Asus4 E
2. 3.
D.S. Asus4 Chorus Asus4 A
2. A ri - ver has come All

While they were eating,
Jesus took bread, gave thanks and broke it,
and gave it to his disciples,
saying, 'Take it; this is my body.'
Then he took the cup,
gave thanks and offered it to them,
and they all drank from it.
'This is my blood of the covenant,
which is poured out for many,'
he said to them.
'I tell you the truth,
I will not drink again of the fruit of the vine
until that day when I drink it anew
in the kingdom of God.'

Mark 14:22-25

1527 The glory of the cross

Words and Music: Andrew Rayner and Wendy Rayner

2. Deep mercy of the cross,
the wonder of my Lord
that he should suffer and die.
Amazing grace, the sweetest kind
that dries my tears and heals the blind;
guilty I stand, but Christ my plea,
the love of God streaming out for me.

3. The power of the cross,
the wonder of my Lord
that he should proclaim me free.
Amazing grace, the sweetest kind
that breaks my chains, restores my mind;
guilty no more, by royal decree
the love of God streaming out for me.

As I looked,
thrones were set in place,
and the Ancient of Days took his seat.
His clothing was as white as snow;
the hair of his head was white like wool.
His throne was flaming with fire,
and its wheels were all ablaze.
A river of fire was flowing,
coming out from before him.
Thousands upon thousands attended him;
ten thousand times ten thousand stood before him.

Daniel 7:9-10a

1528 The head that once was crowned with thorns

Words: Thomas Kelly

Music: Lucy Bunce

2. The highest place that heav'n affords
is his, is his by right.
The King of kings and Lord of lords,
and heav'n's eternal light.

3. The joy of all who dwell above,
the joy of all below,
to whom he manifests his love,
and grants his name to know.

4. To them the cross, with all its shame,
with all its grace is giv'n;
their name an everlasting name,
their joy the joy of heav'n.

5. They suffer with their Lord below,
they reign with him above,
their profit and their joy to know
the myst'ry of his love.

6. The cross he bore is life and health,
though shame and death to him;
his people's hope, his people's wealth,
their everlasting theme.

1529 The holiest place *Angels*

Words and Music: Marty Sampson

A2 E/G# F#m
him a-lone.
Bsus4 Chorus E F#m7 Amaj9 A2
Sing with the an - gels, sing with the
E F#m Amaj9 B C#m7
an - gels, sing-ing the name of the Lord,
A2 F#m7 E/G# E/B B
sing-ing the name of the Lord.
2nd time
E E/G# E A E/G# F#m D.S. Amaj7
him

E/G♯ F♯m7 Bsus4 A2(add6)
a-lone, in him
E/G♯ F♯m7 Bsus4
a-lone; sing with the
E F♯m7 Amaj9 A2 E F♯m
an - gels, sing with the an - gels,
Amaj9 B C♯m7 A2
sing-ing the name of the Lord, sing-ing the
F♯m7 E/G♯ Bsus4 B E/B B C♯m7
1. 2.
name of the Lord. Sing with the Lord.

F#2sus4 A2 E2 C#m7
F#2sus4 A2 E2
A2 E/G# F#m7
Je - sus, Je - sus,
Bsus4 B A2 E/G#
Je - sus,
C#m7 B E F#m E/G# E
Je - sus.
A E/G# F#m E F#m E/G# E A E/G# F#m E

1530 The image of the invisible God

What a wonderful Saviour

Words and Music: Tim Lomax

E
B/E
A/E
1. The i - mage of the in - vi - si - ble God, the
2. ways, O Lord, are just and true, for
3. Je - sus, you have saved the world, your
E
A
E/G♯
B
first - born o - ver cre - a - tion, the
you a - lone are ho - ly. Who
blood has cleansed the na - tions. There
E
B/E
A/E
first, the last, the liv - ing one, the
will not bring their prai - ses to you? For
on the cross our sin was nailed, your
E
A
E/G♯
B
rul - er o - ver the na - tions.
you a - lone are wor - thy.
death re-deemed cre - a - tion. In

© Copyright 2005 Kevin Mayhew Ltd.

E/G♯ A B
Je - sus, what a won - der you are! My
Na - tions, they will of - fer their praise, and
you we see the glo - ry of God, the
E/G♯ A C♯m
Sa - viour, my God, the Lord of my heart.
all of the earth will fol - low your ways.
glo - ry dis - played through suf - fer - ing love.
B Chorus E E/G♯ A E/G♯ B
What a won-drous Lord, what a migh-ty King, what a
E/G♯ A B E E/G♯ A
won - der-ful Sa - viour you are! What a won-drous Lord, what a

E/G♯ B E/G♯ A A/B E
migh-ty King, what a won-der-ful Sa-viour you are!
To verses
Last time
B/E A/E B/E A/E E
2. Your

Love the Lord your God with all your heart
and with all your soul
and with all your strength.

Deuteronomy 6:5

1531 The Lord bless you and keep you *The blessing*

Words and Music: Tim Lomax and A.P. Douglas

D
A/B
E
Fine
peace, and give you peace.
D
A
E
And give you peace, and
D
F♯m
B
D.S. al Fine
give you peace. The

1532 The Lord thy God

Words and Music: Blane Morris

Bm
F#m/A
I saw him high and lift - ed up with
Gmaj7 D/G Em/G Gmaj7 D/C C
pow - er and grace and au - tho - ri - ty: and
D2 Bm
he shall reign in the midst of thee for
Gmaj7 G6 Gmaj7/A Em7/A D
e - ver and e - ver, a - men.

1533 The love of God comes close

Words and Music: John L. Bell and Graham Maule

2. The peace of God comes close
to those caught in the storm,
foregoing lives of ease
to ease the lives forlorn.
The peace of God . . .

3. The joy of God comes close
where faith encounters fears,
where heights and depths of life
are found through smiles and tears.
The joy of God . . .

4. The grace of God comes close
to those whose grace is spent,
when hearts are tired or sore
and hope is bruised and bent.
The grace of God . . .

3. The Son of God comes close
where people praise his name,
where bread and wine are blest
and shared as when he came.
The Son of God . . .

1534 The power of your love

Words and Music: Gary Sadler

A2 E/G# A2
what else can I do; my heart is o - pen wide;
C#m7 F#m7 Bsus4 E/G#
my hands reach up to you; I'm
A2 E/G# A2
cal - ling out for more; I'm ask - ing in your name,
E/G# A2 C#m7
that by your Spi - rit, Lord, I will ne-
F#m7 Bsus4 B
- ver be the same. The
D.S.
CODA
I'm

A2
E/G#
sing-ing out my praise; I'm pour-ing out my thanks, for the
F#m7
Bsus4
E
pow-er of your love is chang - ing me; I'm
A2
E/G#
lift-ing up my voice; I'm danc-ing in the joy, for the
1.
2.
F#m7
Bsus4
E
Bsus4
E
pow-er of your love is chang - ing me. I'm - ing me.

1535 There are shadows cast across the sun

To the one God

Words and Music: Paul Field

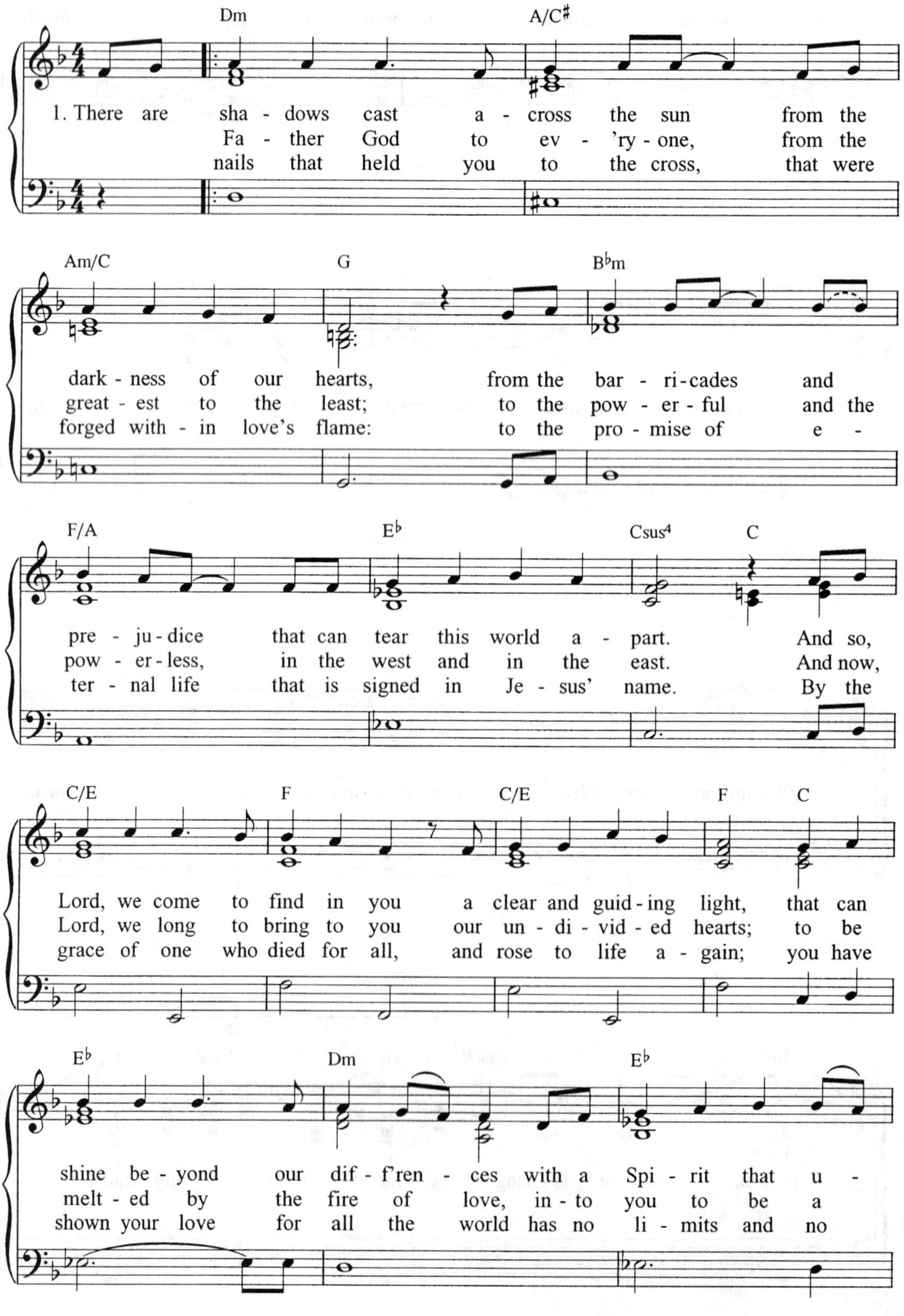

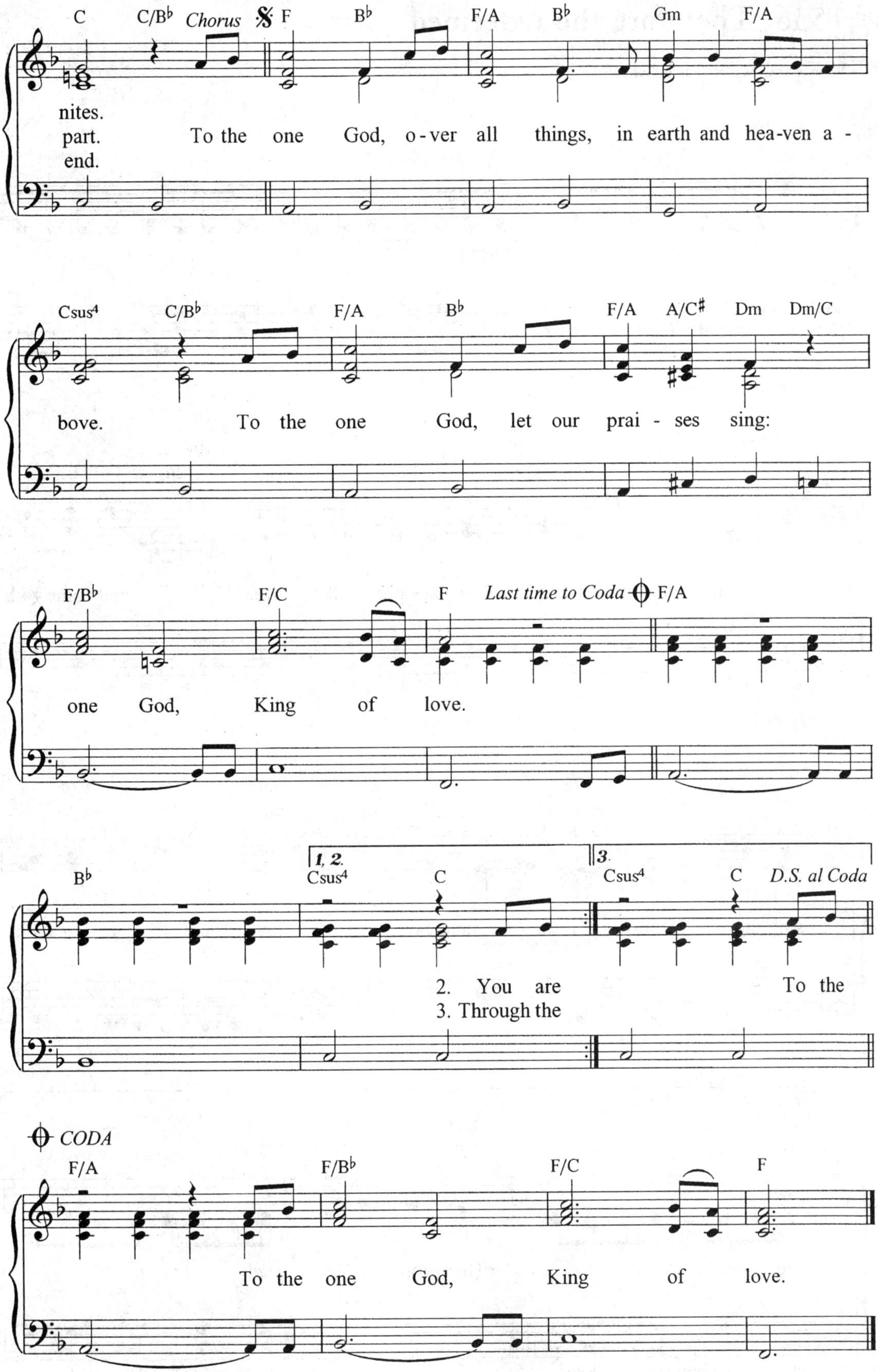

C C/B♭ Chorus F B♭ F/A B♭ Gm F/A
nites.
part. To the one God, o-ver all things, in earth and hea-ven a-
end.
Csus4 C/B♭ F/A B♭ F/A A/C♯ Dm Dm/C
bove. To the one God, let our prai - ses sing:
F/B♭ F/C F Last time to Coda F/A
one God, King of love.
B♭ 1, 2. Csus4 C 3. Csus4 C D.S. al Coda
2. You are To the
3. Through the
CODA
F/A F/B♭ F/C F
To the one God, King of love.

1536 Therefore the redeemed

Words and Music: Ruth Lake

B♭7 E♭maj7 Cm7 F7 B♭maj7
G7 Cmaj7 Am7 D7 Gmaj7
They shall ob - tain gladness and joy,
Gm7 B♭/C C9 F7
Em7 G/A A9 D7
and sor-row and mourn-ing shall flee a-way.
B♭ B♭7/D
G G7/B
There-fore the re-deemed of the Lord shall re - turn and come with
E♭ C7/E B♭/F Gm7
C A7/C♯ G/D Em7
sing-ing un - to Zi - on, and e - ver - last - ing joy shall
Cm7 E♭/F E♭ B♭ E♭/F B♭7(6)
Am7 C/D C G C/D G7(6)
D.C.
be up - on their heads.

1537 There is a day

Words and Music: Nathan Fellingham

Am F
will be like him, for we will see him as he is,
C G C
oh yeah! Then all hurt
G
and pain will cease, and we'll be with him for e -
Am F C
- ver, and in his glo - ry we will live. Oh yeah,
G Fmaj7
oh yeah!
1st time D.C. for v.3
Fine

2. The trumpet sounds and the dead will then be raised
   by his power, never to perish again.
   Once only flesh, now clothed with immortality;
   death has now been swallowed up in victory.

3. So lift your eyes to the things as yet unseen,
   that will remain now for all eternity.
   Though trouble's hard, it's only momentary,
   and it's achieving our future glory.

1538 There is a higher throne

Words and Music: Keith Getty and Kristyn Lennox

Majestically
E
A/E
B/E
1. There is a high - er throne than all this
2. And there we'll find our home, our life be -
E
B/D♯
C♯m
A
world has known, where faith - ful ones from ev - 'ry tongue
fore the throne; we'll hon - our him in per - fect song
F♯m7
Bsus4
B
E
A/E
will one day come. Be - fore the Son we'll stand,
where we be - long. He'll wipe each tear - stained eye,
B/E
E
B/D♯
C♯m
made fault - less through the Lamb; be - liev - ing hearts find
and thirst and hun - ger die; the Lamb be - comes our
A
F♯m7
Bsus4
B
E/G♯
Chorus
pro - mised grace: sal - va - tion comes.
Shep - herd King: we'll reign with him.
Hear hea - ven's

A B A/E E
voi - ces sing, their thun - d'rous an - them rings through
C#m C#m/B A A/G# F#m7
em - 'rald courts and sap - phire skies, their prai - ses
B E/G# E/A A
rise. All glo - ry, wis - dom, pow'r,
B A/E E C#m7 C#m/B
strength, thanks and hon - our are to God, our King who
A A/G# F#m7 Bsus4 B E
reigns on high, for e - ver - more.
A/E E A/E D.C. E

1539 There is a hope so sure

Words and Music: Graham Kendrick

Slowly (♩ = 70)
G D/F♯ G D/F♯
1. There is a hope so sure, a pro-mise so se-cure: the my-ste-
life so true, a life of love so pure, for all our
G A D
ry of God at last made known. Trea-sures so
sin a per-fect sa - cri - fice. And when that
Em7 D/F♯ G Bm
vast ap-pear, all wis-dom, know-ledge here: it's Christ in
life was nailed, on cru-el cross im-paled, our sin-ful
G Em7 A D
Chorus
us, the hope of glo - ry!
flesh with him was cru - ci - fied.
And the life that

G/D D G/D A/D Bm G
I now live, no long-er is my own, Je-sus lives in me the hope of
A D/F# G D G Em7 D/F#
glo - ry. And each day I live, no long-er is my own, Je-sus
G Em7 A D
lives in me the hope of glo - ry.
2. There is a
D.S.
ry. And the life that
D Bm E/G#
ry. 3. There is a
A E/G# A E/G#
life so strong, that a whole world of wrong, and all the

A B E F#m7 E/G#
pow'rs of hell could not de - feat. For Je-sus rose a-gain, and if we
A C#m A F#m7 B
died with him, with him we'll rise to share his end - less
E Chorus A/E E
life. And the life that I now live, no long - er
A/E B/E C#m A B E/G#
is my own, Je - sus lives in me the hope of glo - ry. And each
A E A F#m7 E/G#
day I live, no long - er is my own, Je - sus
A F#m7 B 1. E 2. E
lives in me the hope of glo - ry. And the life that ry.

1540 There is a place of quiet rest

Words: Anon.

Music: C.B. McAfee

QUIET REST 86 86 and Refrain

D Aaug D Adim A7 Adim A7 A A7 D
1. There is a place of qui - et rest, near to the heart of God; a
Aaug D Adim A7 Adim A7 A D A D
place where sin can - not mo-lest, near to the heart of God.
Chorus
G D F#m A7 A D
O Je - sus, blest Re - deem - er, sent from the heart of God; hold
G D A7 F#m A7 D
us, who wait be - fore thee, near to the heart of God.

2. There is a place of comforts sweet,
near to the heart of God;
a place where we our Saviour meet,
near to the heart of God.

3. There is a place of full release,
near to the heart of God;
a place where all is joy and peace,
near to the heart of God.

1541 There is one name

Words and Music: Robert Critchley

Worshipfully, with strength
E♭/F B♭ Dm⁷
Capo 3 C/D G Bm⁷
There is one name un - der hea - ven
E♭ B♭/F
C G/D
by which men can be saved, Je - sus a-lone.
F E♭/F B♭ Dm⁷
D C/D G Bm⁷
On - ly one name un - der hea - ven,
E♭ Fsus⁴ F E♭/G F/A
C Dsus⁴ D C/E D/F♯
Je - sus, and Je - sus a - lone.

B♭ F/A A♭ E♭/G
G D/F♯ F C/E
One sac - ri-fice, one ho - ly Lamb
Cm7 B♭/D E♭ F
Am7 G/B C D
shed his own blood, paid for my sin; and
B♭ F/A A♭ E♭/G
G D/F♯ F C/E
this right-eous One, God's on - ly Son,
Cm7 B♭/D Fsus4 F
Am7 G/B Dsus4 D
I sing my prai - ses to him,
Cm7 Fsus4 F B♭
Am7 Dsus4 D G
I sing my prai - ses to him.

1542 There must be more *Consuming fire*

Words and Music: Tim Hughes

Em7 D/F# G C
1. There must be more than this: O Breath of God,
Em7 D/F# C Em7 D/F#
come breathe with-in. There must be more than this:
G C Em7 D/F# C
Spi-rit of God, we wait for you.
Am7 G/B D Am7 G/B
Fill us a-new, we pray; fill us a-new, we pray.
D G D/F#
Chorus
Con-sum-ing fire, fan in-to flame a
3

Em7
C
G
pas - sion for your name. Spi - rit of God, fall in this
D/F#
Em7
D/F#
place. Lord, have your way, Lord, have your way with us.
C
D.C.
G

2. Come like a rushing wind,
clothe us in power from on high.
Now set the captives free;
leave us abandoned to your praise.
Lord, let your glory fall;
Lord, let your glory fall.

1543 There's a call — *Come and worship*

Words and Music: Don Moen

D
C/D
1. There's a call, it's com-ing from the moun-tain
G/D
D
to one and all;
there's a call, a call to ev - 'ry
C/D
G/B
G
tribe and na - tion, wor - ship him,
D/F♯
Em7
D/F♯
G
G/A
Chorus
the Lamb who sits up - on the throne. Come and

D C/D D Cmaj7/D D
wor - ship, roy - al priest - hood, come and
C/D D Cmaj7/D D
praise him, ho - ly na - tion;
Bm7 D/C♯ D D♯dim Em D/F♯ Em7 Em7/F♯ Em/G Em/G♯
show forth his praise,
G/A F♯7/A♯ Bm A/C♯ D D♯dim Em D/F♯ Em7
show forth his pow - er, this is the day,
Em7/F♯ Em/G Em/G♯ G/A F♯7/A♯ Bm Bm/A
this is the hour. For

G
D/F♯
Last time to Coda
Em7
G/A
this is the day that the Lord has made, let us re-joice and be glad.
D A/D D A/D D
2nd time to Bridge
D
2. A - rise
C/D
and come in - to his ho - ly moun - tain,
G/D
D
wor - ship him and bow be - fore his throne;
a - rise and wor-ship him be -

C/D
G/B
G
fore the na - tions, lift your voice
D/F♯
Em7
D/F♯
G
G/A
Chorus
D.S.
and make his glo - ry known. Come and
D
A/D
D
A/D
C/D
Bridge
Cmaj9
D2/F♯
Come in - to his gates
Em7
Em7/A
Dmaj7
with thanks - giv - ing in your heart,
F/G
Cmaj9
D/G
en - ter his courts with praise;

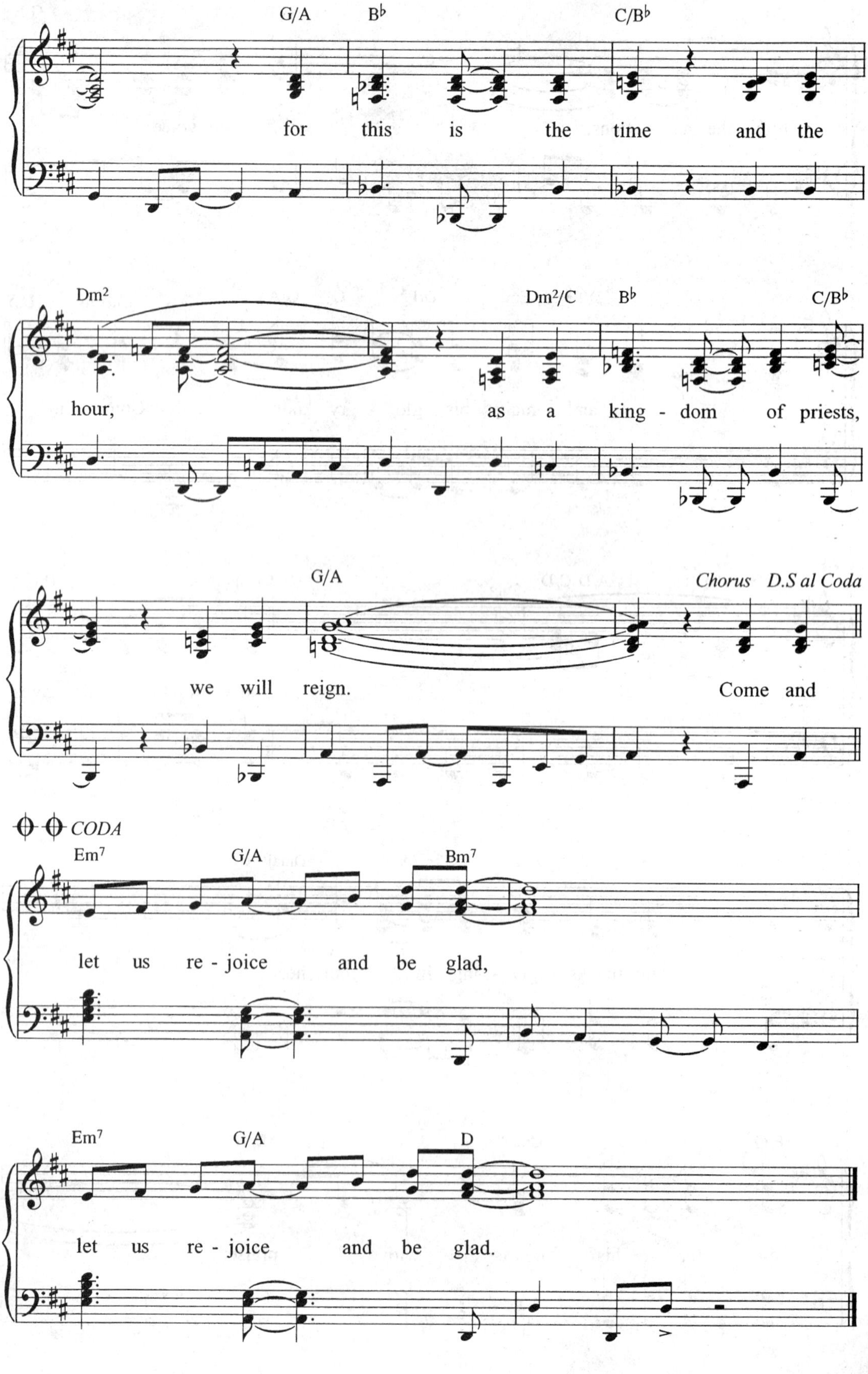
G/A B♭ C/B♭
for this is the time and the
Dm² Dm²/C B♭ C/B♭
hour, as a king - dom of priests,
G/A
Chorus D.S al Coda
we will reign. Come and
CODA
Em⁷ G/A Bm⁷
let us re - joice and be glad,
Em⁷ G/A D
let us re - joice and be glad.

1544 There's a call *We will go*

Words and Music: Stuart Townend

With life
D
G/D
1. There's a call to the peo - ple of Zi - on,
We have stayed long e - nough on this moun-tain,
2. We have drunk of the wine of his pre-sence,
He will give us the ground that we walk on,
D
G/D
to a - rise and pos - sess the land;
now we're called to new realms of faith;
we have feast - ed up - on his word;
for the bat - tle be - longs to God;
Em7
Bm7
A
ev - 'ry town has its heirs to the pro - mise,
we are more than a tem - ple of wor - ship,
now we're hun - gry for works of pow - er,
do not fear, for his grace is suf - fi - cient,
1.
Em7
Bm7
A
G/A
ev - 'ry na - tion its sons of light.
now we're thirs - ty to share his love.

2.
Em7 A7sus4 Chorus D
we're an ar - my of praise! We will go to ev-'ry place,
when we're weak, he is strong!
G/D D G/D G A
shar-ing mer - cy and preach-ing grace, for the
Bm F#m7 Em7 Bm7 Em7 A7sus4
fields are white for har - vest, and la - bou-rers are few.
D G/D
No place too dark, no soul too lost for the pow -
D G/D G A Bm F#m7 Em7
- er of the cross; for his light will shine in dark-

Bm7 Em7 A7sus4
ness, and ma - ny will be - lieve, so we will go.
D G/D Bm7
1. Em7 G/A
Chorus
We will go
2. Em7 G/A
D.C.
Last time
Em7 G/A D

1545 There's a cry

Words and Music: Robin Mark

(♩ = 72)
Am
G/B
C
Dm7
1. There's a cry that is ris - ing from the
tree by a ri - ver giv - ing
watch - man is wait - ing for the
C/E
F
C
Dm7
depths of cre - a - tion; there's a call on the lips of ev - 'ry
fruit in due sea - son, and the leaves of the tree are for the
sun in its dawn - ing, and his heart is re - joic - ing at the
C/E
F
G
peo - ple, ev - 'ry na - tion. It's the cry of the child - ren for the Fa -
heal - ing of the na - tions. You have plant - ed a king - dom that shall ne -
light of the morn - ing, so my soul waits for you and your un - fail -
C
G/B
Am
Em/G
F
G
- ther's heart, it's the call of the lost sheep for the Shep -
- ver fall, to the ends of the earth is your sal - va -
- ing love, for the Lord our Re - deem - er has be - come

C G/B Am Em
- herd's voice. Hear their
- tion call. Hear our
their hope. Hear our
Am G Em
cry from the depths, O Lord, hear their
cry from the depths, O Lord, hear our
cry from the depths, O Lord, hear our
1. 2, 3.
Am F G G Chorus
cry from the depths, O Lord. 2. Like a Lord. Those who
cry from the depths, O
cry from the depths, O
Am F
weep re-turn with songs of joy; you have
G Am
turned their mourn-ing in - to danc - ing. Those who

F
seek shall find the Lord of lords; Je - sus
1.
G Am G D.S.
Christ, de-sire of all the na - tions. 3. As the
2. 3.
Am G D.S.S. Am G
- tions. Those who - tions.
Am F G Em
Your king-dom, your name and your throne will last for e - ver.
(optional harmony)
Last time
(done) Your king - dom come, your will be done.
Am F G Em Am
Your king-dom, your name and your throne will last for e - ver.

God is spirit,
and his worshippers must worship in spirit
and in truth.

John 4:24

1546 There's a land that is fairer than day

Sweet by and by

Words: S.F. Bennett

Music: J.P. Webster

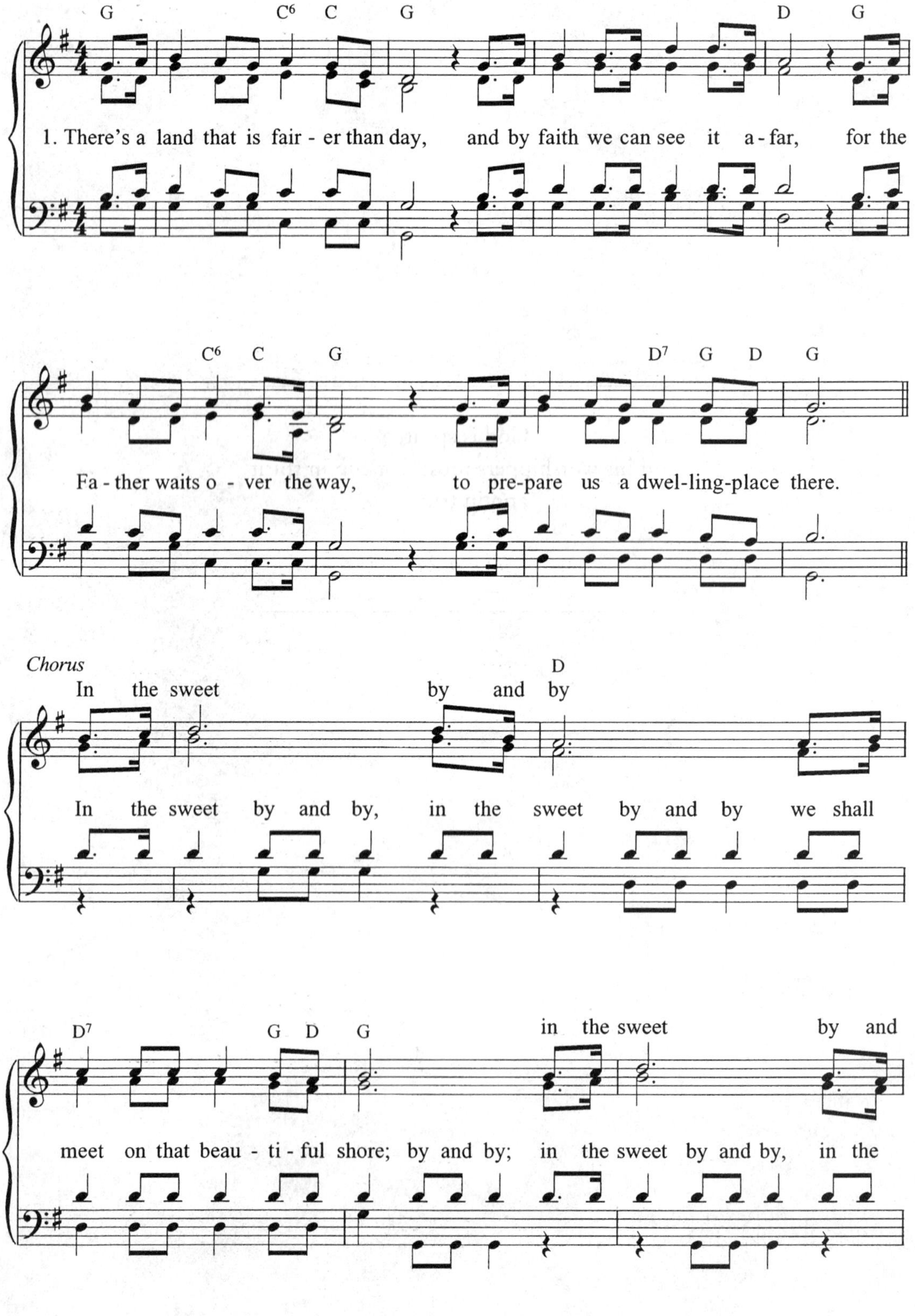
G C6 C G D G
1. There's a land that is fair - er than day, and by faith we can see it a - far, for the
C6 C G D7 G D G
Fa - ther waits o - ver the way, to pre-pare us a dwel-ling-place there.
Chorus
In the sweet by and by
D
In the sweet by and by, in the sweet by and by we shall
D7 G D G
in the sweet by and
meet on that beau - ti - ful shore; by and by; in the sweet by and by, in the

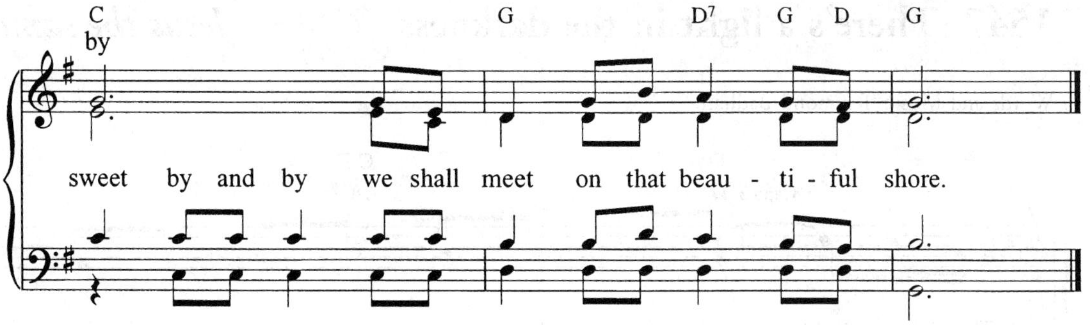
C G D7 G D G
by
sweet by and by we shall meet on that beau - ti - ful shore.

2. We shall sing on that beautiful shore
the melodious songs of the blest,
and our spirits shall sorrow no more,
not a sigh for the blessing of rest.

3. To our bountiful Father above
we will offer the tribute of praise,
for the glorious gift of his love,
and the blessings that hallow our days.

1547 There's a light in the darkness *Jesus the same*

Words and Music: Raymond Badham

Capo 3
F D
C/E A/C♯
1. There's a light in the darkness that shines,
Dm7 Bm7
C A
B♭2 G2
Gm7 Em7
giv-ing hope to all the world, hope to all the world.
Csus4 Asus4
C A
F D
C/E A/C♯
There's a door that's been o - pened to all,
Dm7 Bm7
C A
B♭2 G2
Gm7 Em7
in-to a new and liv - ing way, a new and liv - ing way.
Csus4 Asus4
C A
Chorus
B♭2 G2
F/A D/F♯
Praise the name of Je - sus.

Gm7 F/A Bb2 F/C C F C/E
Em7 D/F# G2 D/A A D A/C#
Per - fect Re - deem - er, Star of the Morn - ing. Yes - ter-day, to - day
Bb/D Csus4 C Bb2 Gm7 Csus4 C
G/B Asus4 A G2 Em7 Asus4 A
and for e - ver, Je - sus the same,
Bb2 F/A Gm7 C Dm Bb
G2 D/F# Em7 A Bm G
Je - sus the same.
Gm9 Dm Bb Gm9
Em9 Bm G Em9
2. There's a fire
F C/E Dm C
D A/C# Bm A
that burns in our hearts, to see the lost re - turn

B♭2 Gm7 Csus4 C Dm7 C/E
G2 Em7 Asus4 A Bm7 A/C♯
to the Fa - ther. It's a pas - sion that's not of our own,
F F/A B♭2 Gm7
D D/F♯ G2 Em7
we have seen it in the Son, in the face of the Son.
C B♭2 F/A
A Chorus G2 D/F♯
Praise the name of Je - sus.
Gm7 F/A B♭2 F/C C F C/E
Em7 D/F♯ G2 D/A A D A/C♯
Per - fect Re - deem - er, Star of the Morn - ing. Yes - ter-day, to - day
B♭/D Csus4 C B♭2 Gm7 Csus4 C
G/B Asus4 A G2 Em7 Asus4 A
and for e - ver, Je - sus the same.

B♭2 F/A Csus4 C Last time to Coda Gm7
G2 D/F♯ Asus4 A Em7
Je - sus the same. Won - der - ful
F F/B♭ C Gm7
D D/G A Em7
Coun - sel - lor, Migh - ty God, E - ter - nal Fa -
F F/B♭ C
D D/G A
D.S. al Coda
- ther, Prince of Peace.
CODA
B♭2 Gm7 Csus4 C
G2 Em7 Asus4 A
Je - sus the same,
B♭2 F/A Gm7 F
G2 D/F♯ Em7 D
Je - sus the same.

1548 There's a lot of pain *Outrageous grace*

Words and Music: Godfrey Birtill

Slowly
C
F
1. There's a lot of pain, but a lot more heal - ing,
lot of fear, but a lot more free - dom;
C
Dm7
G7sus4
G7
there's a lot of trou - ble, but a lot more
there's a lot of dark - ness, but a lot more
C
G7sus4
G7
C
peace. There's a lot of hate, but a lot more
light. There's a lot of cloud, but a lot more
(v.2)
F
C
Dm7
lov - ing, there's a lot of sin,
vis - ion; there's a lot of pe - rish - ing,

G7sus4 G7 Csus4 C
Chorus
but a lot more grace. Oh, out -
but a lot more life. Oh, out -
G7sus4 C G7sus4
ra - geous grace! Oh, out - ra - geous grace!
ra - geous grace! Oh, out - ra - geous grace!
Last time to Coda
1.
C F C/E Dm7 C/E G7sus4
Love un - furled by hea - ven's hand.
Through my Je - sus I can
2.
G7 Chorus G7sus4 G7
1st time D.S. for v.2
Oh, out - stand. 2. There's a
There's an

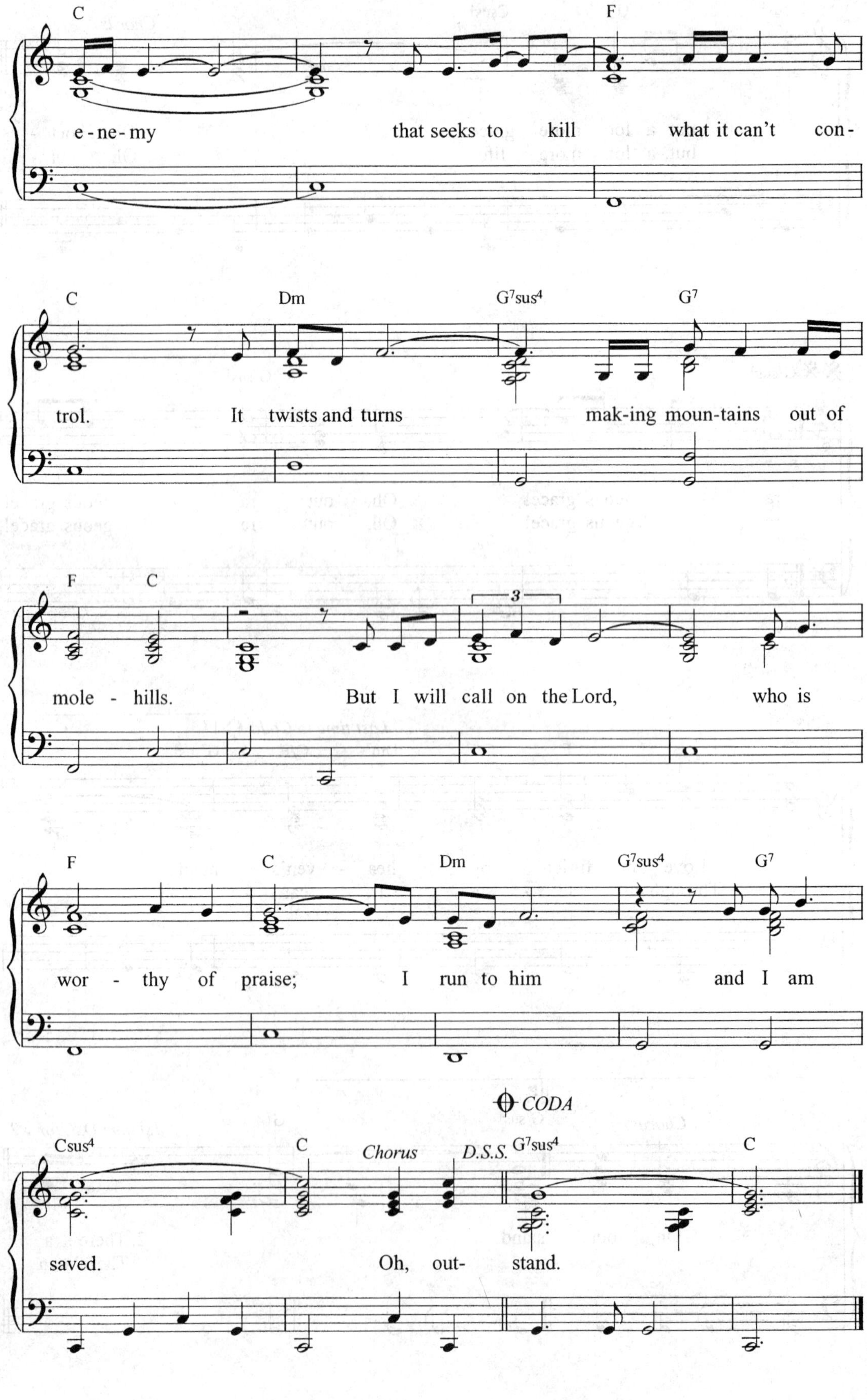
C F
e - ne - my that seeks to kill what it can't con-
C Dm G7sus4 G7
trol. It twists and turns mak-ing moun-tains out of
F C
mole - hills. But I will call on the Lord, who is
3
F C Dm G7sus4 G7
wor - thy of praise; I run to him and I am
CODA
Csus4 C Chorus D.S.S. G7sus4 C
saved. Oh, out- stand.

I will sacrifice a thank-offering to you
and call on the name of the Lord.
I will fulfil my vows to the Lord
in the presence of all his people,
in the courts of the house of the Lord –
in your midst, O Jerusalem.
Praise the Lord.

Psalm 116:17-19

1549 There's a new generation *New generation*

Words and Music: Billy Funk

G
1. There's a new ge - ne - ra - tion (there's a new ge - ne - ra - tion), that is
new ge - ne - ra - tion (there's a new ge - ne - ra - tion), that is
C2
seek - ing your face (that is seek - ing your face); there's a
run - ning by faith (that is run - ning by faith); there's a
G
new ge - ne - ra - tion (there's a new ge - ne - ra - tion), that is
new ge - ne - ra - tion (there's a new ge - ne - ra - tion), that is
C2
tak - ing their place (that is tak - ing their place); Lord,
wil - ling to pray (that is wil - ling to pray); wind

Am7
D7sus4
D7
we sur - ren - der to your will,
of re - vi - val, come and sweep
G
G/B
C2
let it be done; come this day,
a - cross this land; what a change,
Am7
D7sus4
have your way, let your King - dom
with one move of your migh - ty
G
1.
2.
Chorus
come. There's a We will rise
hand.
C2
D
G/D
C2
(we will rise), we will run (we will run);

D G/D C2 Dsus4 D
we will ex-alt the name of Je - sus, by your blood
Em C2
we o - ver-come. We will sing (we will sing),
D G/D C2 D G/D
we will dance (we will dance); come on and ce -
Am7 C Dsus D G
- le-brate the King - dom of our God.
1.
D.S.
2.
2. There's a

I consider everything a loss
compared to the surpassing greatness
of knowing Christ Jesus my Lord,
for whose sake I have lost all things.
I consider them rubbish,
that I may gain Christ and be found in him,
not having a righteousness of my own
that comes from the law,
but that which is through faith in Christ –
the righteousness that comes from God
and is by faith.

Philippians 3:8-9

1550 There's a people *Oh, that we might see your glory*

Words and Music: Stuart Townend and Terry Virgo

2. We're that people
you have rescued from our blindness,
you have come to live within us,
to share your peace, to share your joy.
Come and fill us,
flood our spirits with your fullness,
let us taste the wine of heaven,
only you can satisfy.

1551 There shall be showers of blessing

Words: Daniel W. Whittle

Music: James McGranahan

A E7 D/E E7 A E E7 D/E E7 A
1. There shall be show-ers of bles - sing: this is the pro-mise of love!
D A F#m C# F#m E7
There shall be sea-sons re - fresh - ing sent from the Sa-viour a - bove.
Chorus A E7 A E
Show - ers of bles - sing,
Show - ers, show-ers of bles - sing, show-ers of bles-sing we need;
A7 D A E7 D/E E7 A
mer-cy-drops round us are fall - ing but for the show-ers we plead.

2. There shall be showers of blessing:
   precious reviving again;
   over the hills and the valleys,
   sound of abundance of rain.

3. There shall be showers of blessing:
   send them upon us, O Lord!
   Grant to us now a refreshing:
   come and now honour thy word.

4. There shall be showers of blessing:
   O that today they might fall,
   now as to God we're confessing,
   now as on Jesus we call!

1552 There's nowhere else *My God reigns*

Words and Music: Darrell Evans

A
E
re - joice, for my God reigns. So, re -
joice, be glad, your Fa - ther and your friend is the Lord, your God, whose
A
rule will ne - ver end; I re - joice, for my God
E
Chorus
B
reigns. My God reigns and I
A
E
B
dance the dance of praise, my God reigns

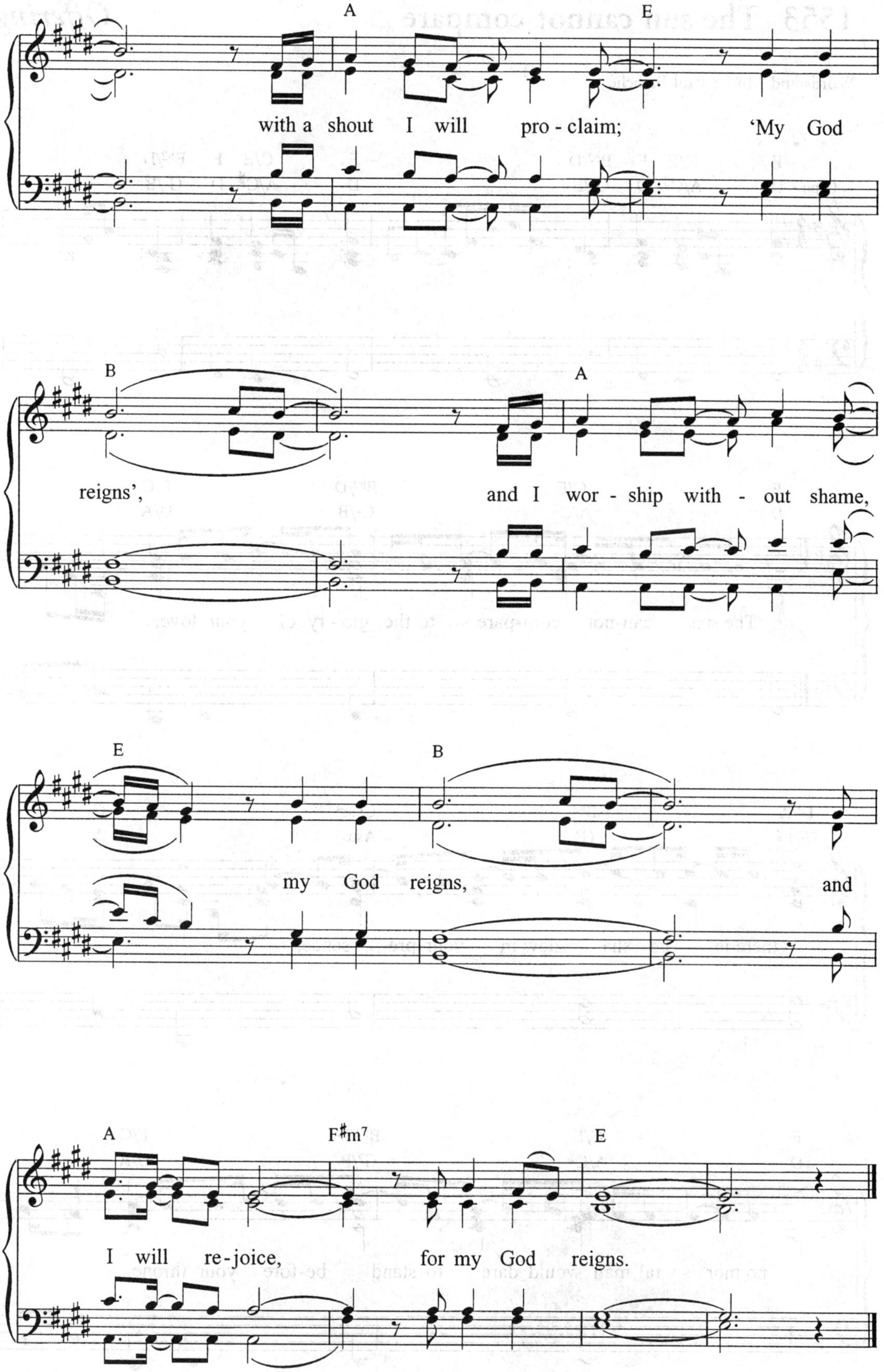
A E
with a shout I will pro - claim; 'My God
B A
reigns', and I wor - ship with - out shame,
E B
my God reigns, and
A F#m7 E
I will re - joice, for my God reigns.

1553 The sun cannot compare

Offering

Words and Music: Paul Baloche

F2/A D2/F# Bb2 G2 Csus4 Asus4 C A
be-fore the Ho - ly One of hea - ven; it's
Bb2/D G2/B C/E A/C# F D A7sus4 F#7sus4 A7/C# F#7/A# Dsus4 Bsus4 Dm7 Bm7
on - ly by your blood, and it's on - ly through your mer - cy,
C A Bb2 G2 F D F2/A D2/F# Bb2 G2 Csus4 Asus4
Lord, I come. I bring an of - fer-ing of wor - ship to my King;
F D F2/A D2/F# Bb2 G2 Csus4 Asus4
no one on earth de-serves the prai - ses that I sing;
F D F2/A D2/F# Bb2 G2 Csus4 Asus4
Je - sus, may you re-ceive the hon - our that you're due;

F F2/A Bb2 Csus4
D D2/F# G2 Asus4
O Lord, I bring an of - fer-ing to you.
1.
F C/E F Bb2/D Bb2
D A/C# D G2/B G2
I bring an of - fer-ing to you.
F C/E F Bb2
D A/C# D G2
2.
F F2/A Bb2 Csus4
D D2/F# G2 Asus4
I bring an of - fer-ing of wor - ship to my King;
F F2/A Bb2 Csus4
D D2/F# G2 Asus4
no one on earth de-serves the prai - ses that I sing;

F F2/A Bb2 Csus4
D D2/F# G2 Asus4
Je - sus, may you re-ceive the hon - our that you're due;
G(add 4) Bb2 Csus4
G(add 4) G2 Asus4
O Lord, I bring an of - fer-ing to you;
G(add 4) Bb2 Csus4
G(add 4) G2 Asus4
O Lord, I bring an of - fer-ing to you;
Eb2 Bb2 Csus4
C2 G2 Asus4
O Lord, I bring an of - fer-ing to you;
F C/E F Bb/D
D A/C# D G/B
I bring an of - fer-ing to you.

F D
C/E A/C♯
F D
B♭/D G/B
F D
C/E A/C♯
F D
B♭/D G/B
F D
C/E A/C♯
F D
B♭/D G/B
repeat ad lib.
F D

Those who are wise
will shine like the brightness of the heavens,
and those who lead many to righteousness,
like the stars for ever and ever.

Daniel 12:3

1554 The way the sun breaks through

Words and Music: Paul Baloche

C5
Dm7
waves of blue come crash-ing in;
shows my heart your faith-ful - ness;
C/E
the way a mo-ther holds her child,
the way the morn-ing star re-turns,
Dm7
B♭2
the way you make me smile.
the way a fire burns.
F2
Chorus
C
Am7
I see you, I feel you like the
F2
C
wind a-gainst my face; I hear you, I'm near

Am7
F2
you in ev - 'ry step I take; I want
Am7
Am7/G
F2
to fol - low you more and more each day,
Am7
Dm7
Fmaj7
Last time to Coda
'cause you are the way, you are the
1.
C5
way.
2. The way
2.
Fmaj7
A2
Am
Am/G
way.
Instrumental

D
A2
Am
Am/G
D
F
F2
D.S. al Coda
I see
CODA
Fmaj7
C2
way,
you are the way.

1555 The wonder of your cross

Words and Music: Robin Mark

(♩ = 85)
A F♯m7 Bm7 E
1. The won - der of your cross shall be our me - di - ta -
2. To steal a - way at night when they took down your bo -
3. Were hea - ven's prai - ses si - lent in those hours of dark -
A D/A A D/A A F♯m7
- tion, to ga - ther in that sha -
- dy, with love and tears to leave
- ness? Your Ho - ly Spi - rit brood -
Bm7 E A D/A A D/A
- dow as the sun went down.
you in a bor - rowed grave.
- ing 'round that emp - ty throne?
E Bm7 E
To weep with those who thought that you were leav -
To go with Ma - ry to that place they laid
Un - til the de - cla - ra - tion 'He is ris -

F#m
D
- ing, you were leav - ing, Je - sus;
you, where they laid you, Je - sus;
- en!' You are ris - en, Je - sus;
A
F#m7
Bm7
E
the hum - ble King who ne - ver wore an earth - ly
and in the morn - ing find the stone was rolled a -
he is not dead: be - hold, he lives for e - ver -
1.
A D Bm7 A E A D Bm7 A E
crown.
2, 3.
A D Bm7 A
Chorus
D
way.
more.
The cross, O the
A/C#
E/G#
D/F#
E
won - der-ful cross. What

D A/C♯ E/G♯ D/F♯
glo - ry, what vic - t'ry I've found.
E D A/C♯
I'll come to the won - der-ful cross
E/G♯ D/F♯ E D F♯m
and my whole life
Bm7 E A D Bm7 A E
I lay down.
Last time
A D Bm7 A E D.C. A

Praise the Lord.
Praise the Lord, O my soul.
I will praise the Lord all my life;
I will sing praise to my God as long as I live.

Do not put your trust in princes,
in mortal men, who cannot save.
When their spirit departs, they return to the ground;
on that very day their plans come to nothing.

Blessed is he whose help is the God of Jacob,
whose hope is in the Lord his God,
the Maker of heaven and earth,
the sea, and everything in them –
the Lord, who remains faithful for ever.
He upholds the cause of the oppressed
and gives food to the hungry.
The Lord sets prisoners free,
the Lord gives sight to the blind,
the Lord lifts up those who are bowed down,
the Lord loves the righteous.
The Lord watches over the alien
and sustains the fatherless and the widow,
but he frustrates the ways of the wicked.

The Lord reigns for ever,
your God, O Zion, for all generations.

Praise the Lord.

Psalm 146

1556 Think about his love

Words and Music: Walt Harrah

Gmaj7 Asus4 D
1. How could I for - get his love?
2. E - ven when I've strayed a - way
Bm7 Am7 C/D Gmaj7 Asus4 A A7sus4
How could I for - get his
his love has sought me out and
D A/C# Bm
mer - cy?
found me.
He sa - tis-fies, he
F#m G Em7
sa - tis-fies, he sa - tis-fies my de-sires.
Em7/A A Gmaj7 Em7 G/A

Your ways, O God, are holy.
What god is so great as our God?
You are the God who performs miracles;
you display your power among the peoples.

Psalm 77:13-14

1557 This is a time

Seeing you

Words and Music: Matt Redman

G7sus4
C
a great - er glimpse;
the glo - ry of you,
F/A
Fm/A♭
C/G
the glo - ry of you.
D7/F♯
F
Dm7
God, o - pen our eyes
to-wards
a great - er glimpse.
C
Chorus
F/C
Wor - ship starts with
see - ing you,
C
wor - ship starts with
see - ing you.

F/C
C
Our hearts res-pond to your re - ve - la - tion.
1, 3.
2.
D.S.
Wor - ship starts with
No one can sing
Last time
B♭2
Wor - ship starts with see - ing you,
F/A
Fm/A♭
C/G
wor - ship starts with see - ing you.
F
Dm7
C
Our hearts res-pond to your re - ve - la - tion.

1558 This is my song of praise *with* Certain as the rivers

Faithful Father with *Your faithfulness*

Words and Music: Brian Doerksen

C D G
this kind of grace. I know
and say my name. I know
D/F♯ Em C
I still break your heart and yet you run to wel - come
when my life is through my heart will find its home in
D
3rd time
me. This is my song from be -
you.
Em C D C²
fore the world be - gan you have been faith - ful,
G/B D C² G/B D
you will be faith - ful, for - e - ver faith -

C2 G/B D G
- ful, Fa - ther. Cer - tain as the
Am Em G
ri - vers reach the sea, cer - tain as the sun - rise in the east,
D C C/D D
I can rest in your faith - ful - ness.
G Am Em
Sur - er than a mo - ther's ten - der love, sur - er than the
G D C
stars still shine a - bove I can rest

C/D D G C
in your faith - ful - ness, we can rest
C/D D G
in your faith - ful - ness;
Em D C2
you have been faith - ful,
G/B D C2 G/B D
you will be faith - ful, for - e - ver faith-
C2 Am7 G/B C2 G
- ful, Fa - ther.

1559 This is the anthem of the free *Anthem of the free*

Words and Music: Matt Redman

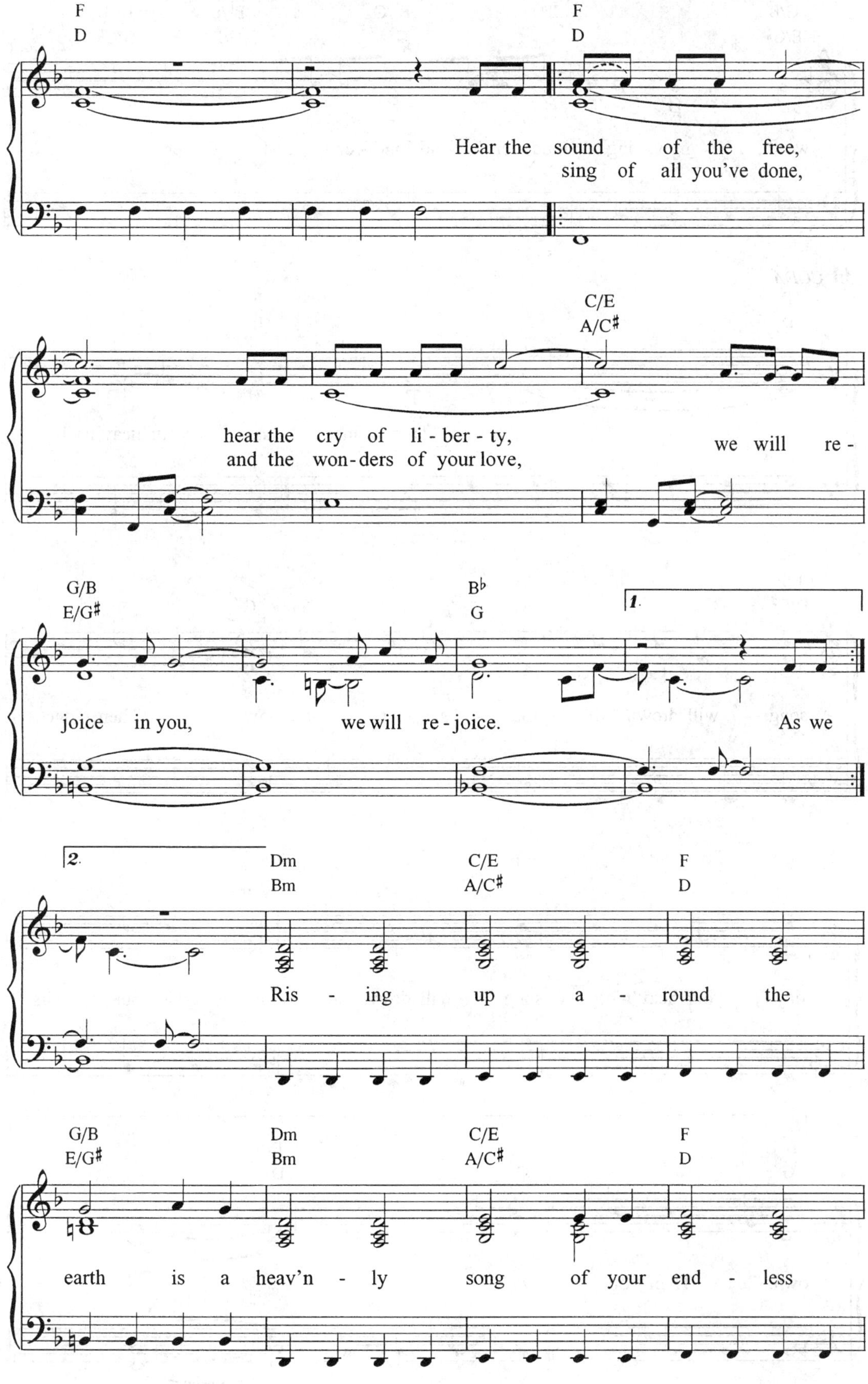
F D F D
Hear the sound of the free,
sing of all you've done,
C/E A/C♯
hear the cry of li - ber - ty, we will re -
and the won - ders of your love,
G/B E/G♯ B♭ G
1.
joice in you, we will re - joice. As we
2.
Dm Bm C/E A/C♯ F D
Ris - ing up a - round the
G/B E/G♯ Dm Bm C/E A/C♯ F D
earth is a heav'n - ly song of your end - less

G/B E/G♯ B♭ G B♭/C G/A B♭/D G/B B♭/E G/C♯
D.C. al Coda
worth, grow - ing loud - er and loud - er and loud - er.
CODA
F D F D
Then one day your heav'n - ly
F/E D/C♯ G/B E/G♯ B♭ G
song will drown all mu - sic but its own. Then one
F D F/E D/C♯ G/B E/G♯
day your heav'n - ly song will drown all mu - sic but its
1. B♭ G
own. Then one
2. B♭ G F D
own.

No one lights a lamp
and hides it in a jar
or puts it under a bed.
Instead, he puts it on a stand,
so that those who come in
can see the light.

Luke 8:16

1560 Though I've seen troubles

Words and Music: Godfrey Birtill

1. Though I've seen trou - bles, you will re - store
 - ments you breathe en -

my life a - gain. Though I've been wound - ed, and tast - ed bit-
cou - rage-ment and hope. My lack of wis - dom you've of - ten o -

- ter - ness from the depths of the earth, you al - ways bring
- ver - looked. Blown a - way by your grace and by the pow -

me up a - gain, in-crease my hon - our, and com-
- er in the blood I grow in free-

Chorus
2.
Chorus
F C G G F C G
- fort me. Thank - dom, root-ed in love. Thank
C F C G C
you for your faith - ful-ness, O my God. I love you,
G F C
and my lips will shout for joy, and my
F C G F G C
song de-clare your glo - ry all day long,
1.
2.
D.S.
F G C C
all day long. 2. Through dis - ap-point- long.

I am the true vine, and my Father is the gardener.
He cuts off every branch in me that bears no fruit,
while every branch that does bear fruit he prunes
so that it will be even more fruitful.
You are already clean
because of the word I have spoken to you.
Remain in me, and I will remain in you.
No branch can bear fruit by itself;
it must remain in the vine.
Neither can you bear fruit
unless you remain in me.

I am the vine; you are the branches.
If a man remains in me and I in him,
he will bear much fruit;
apart from me you can do nothing.

John 15:1-5

1561 Through all the changing scenes of life

Words: Psalm 34 in *New Version*
(Tate and Brady, 1696)

Music: George Thomas Smart

WILTSHIRE CM

2. O magnify the Lord with me,
with me exalt his name;
when in distress to him I called,
he to my rescue came.

3. The hosts of God encamp around
the dwellings of the just;
deliv'rance he affords to all
who on his succour trust.

4. O make but trial of his love:
experience will decide
how blest are they, and only they,
who in his truth confide.

5. Fear him, ye saints, and you will then
have nothing else to fear;
make you his service your delight,
your wants shall be his care.

6. To Father, Son and Holy Ghost,
the God whom we adore,
be glory as it was, is now,
and shall be evermore.

1562 Through our God *Victory song*

Words and Music: Dale Garratt

E♭ C
Fm Dm
G7 E7 Fm Dm F7 D7 G7 E7
Ah,
D.S. al Coda
e - ne-my, the earth shall stand and see that through our
CODA
G7 E7
Cm Am
G7 E7
Christ is King! Christ is
Cm Am
G7 E7
Cm Am
King! Christ is King!

1563 Thy word is a lamp unto my feet *Thy word*

Words: Amy Grant
Music: Michael W. Smith

1564 Times of refreshing

Words and Music: Don Harris and Martin J. Nystrom

(♩ = 92)
G7sus4 C2 C2/E Fmaj7
Times of re - fresh - ing, here in your pre - sence;
G7sus4 C2 Am7 Fmaj7 G7sus4
no great - er bles - sing than be - ing with you.
G/F Em7 Am7 Am/G D2/F♯
My soul is re - stored, my mind is re - newed;
Dm6/F Em7 Am7 Dm7 Fmaj7/G C
there's no great - er joy, Lord, than be-ing with you.

Let us not become weary in doing good,
for at the proper time we will reap a harvest
if we do not give up.

Galatians 6:9

1565 ’Tis so sweet to trust in Jesus

Words: Louisa M.R. Stead | Music: William James Kirkpatrick

TRUST IN JESUS 87 87 and Refrain

G C G D A7 D
1. ’Tis so sweet to trust in Je - sus, just to take him at his word;
G C G C C6 G D G
just to rest up - on his pro - mise, just to know, ‘Thus saith the Lord.’
Chorus
D7 Em G D G D A7 D
Je - sus, Je - sus, how I trust him! How I’ve proved him o’er and o’er!
G C G C C6 G D7 G
Je - sus, Je - sus, pre - cious Je - sus! O for grace to trust him more!

2. O how sweet to trust in Jesus,
just to trust his cleansing blood;
just in simple faith to plunge me
’neath the healing, cleansing flood!

3. Yes, ’tis sweet to trust in Jesus,
just from sin and self to cease;
just from Jesus simply taking
life and rest, and joy and peace.

4. I’m so glad I learned to trust him,
precious Jesus, Saviour, Friend;
and I know that he is with me,
will be with me to the end.

1566 Today I awake

Words and Music: John L. Bell and Graham Maule

SLITHERS OF GOLD 11 10 11 10

Capo 3
F C7 F B♭ Am Dm7 Am C7
D A7 D G F♯m Bm7 F♯m A7
1. To - day I a-wake and God is be - fore me. At
F C7 F B♭ Am D7 Am7
D A7 D G F♯m B7 F♯m7
night, as I dreamt, he sum-moned the day; for
B♭maj7 C7 Am Dm Gm Am7 B♭ C7
Gmaj7 A7 F♯m Bm Em F♯m7 G A7
God ne - ver sleeps but pat-terns the morn - ing with
Am Dm7 Gm7 C7 B♭ B♭6 F
F♯m Bm7 Em7 A7 G G6 D
sli - thers of gold or glo - ry in grey.

2. Today I arise and Christ is beside me.
He walked through the dark to scatter new light.
Yes, Christ is alive, and beckons his people
to hope and to heal, resist and invite.

3. Today I affirm the Spirit within me
at worship and work, in struggle and rest.
The Spirit inspires all life which is changing
from fearing to faith, from broken to blest.

4. Today I enjoy the Trinity round me,
above and beneath, before and behind;
the Maker, the Son, the Spirit together –
they called me to life and call me their friend.

1567 Today I choose

Words and Music: Brian Doerksen and Sandra Gage

A
D/F♯
To - day
I choose
Esus4
A
A
to fol - low you;
to-day
I choose
D/F♯
Esus4
A
to give my 'yes' to you;
to-day
A
D/F♯
Esus4
I choose
to hear your voice
A
D/F♯
Last time to Coda
and live;
to-day
I choose

Esus4 A E Chorus
to fol - low you. As for me
Bm D Asus4 A
and my house, we will serve you;
E Bm D
as for me and my house, we will
Esus4 E A
spend our lives on you to-day.
1.
D/F# Esus4 A
To-day

2.
Esus4 Bm A/C#
Won - der - ful, Coun - sel - lor,
D E Bm
E - ver - last - ing Fa - ther, E - ter - nal King,
A/C# D Esus4
Lord of Hosts, wil - ling - ly we fol -
CODA
E D.S. al Coda Esus4 A
low. To - day to fol - low you.
D/F# Esus4 A

My command is this:
Love each other as I have loved you.
Greater love has no one than this,
that he lay down his life for his friends.
You are my friends if you do what I command.
I no longer call you servants,
because a servant does not know his master's business.
Instead, I have called you friends,
for everything that I learned from my Father
I have made known to you.

John 15:12-15

1568 To the river *The river*

Words and Music: Brian Doerksen, Michael Hansen
and Brian Thiessen

Capo 3
F D
B♭ G
1. To the ri - ver I am go - ing, bring-ing
F D
C A
sins I can - not bear; come and
F D
B♭ G
cleanse me, come, for - give me; Lord, I
F D
C A
F D
need to meet you there.

B♭ G
In these wa - ters, heal - ing mer - cy flows with
F D C A F D
free - dom from des - pair; I am go - ing to that
B♭ G F D C A F D
ri - ver; Lord, I need to meet you there. Pre-cious
Chorus
B♭ G F D
Je - sus, I am rea - dy to sur - ren - der ev - 'ry care;
C A F D B♭ G
Last time to Coda
take my hand now, lead me clo - ser; Lord, I

F D C A F D
need to meet you there.
B♭ G
2. Come and join us in the ri - ver; come, find
F D C A
life be - yond com - pare; he is
F D B♭ G
call - ing, he is wait - ing; Je - sus
F D C A F D
longs to meet you there. He is

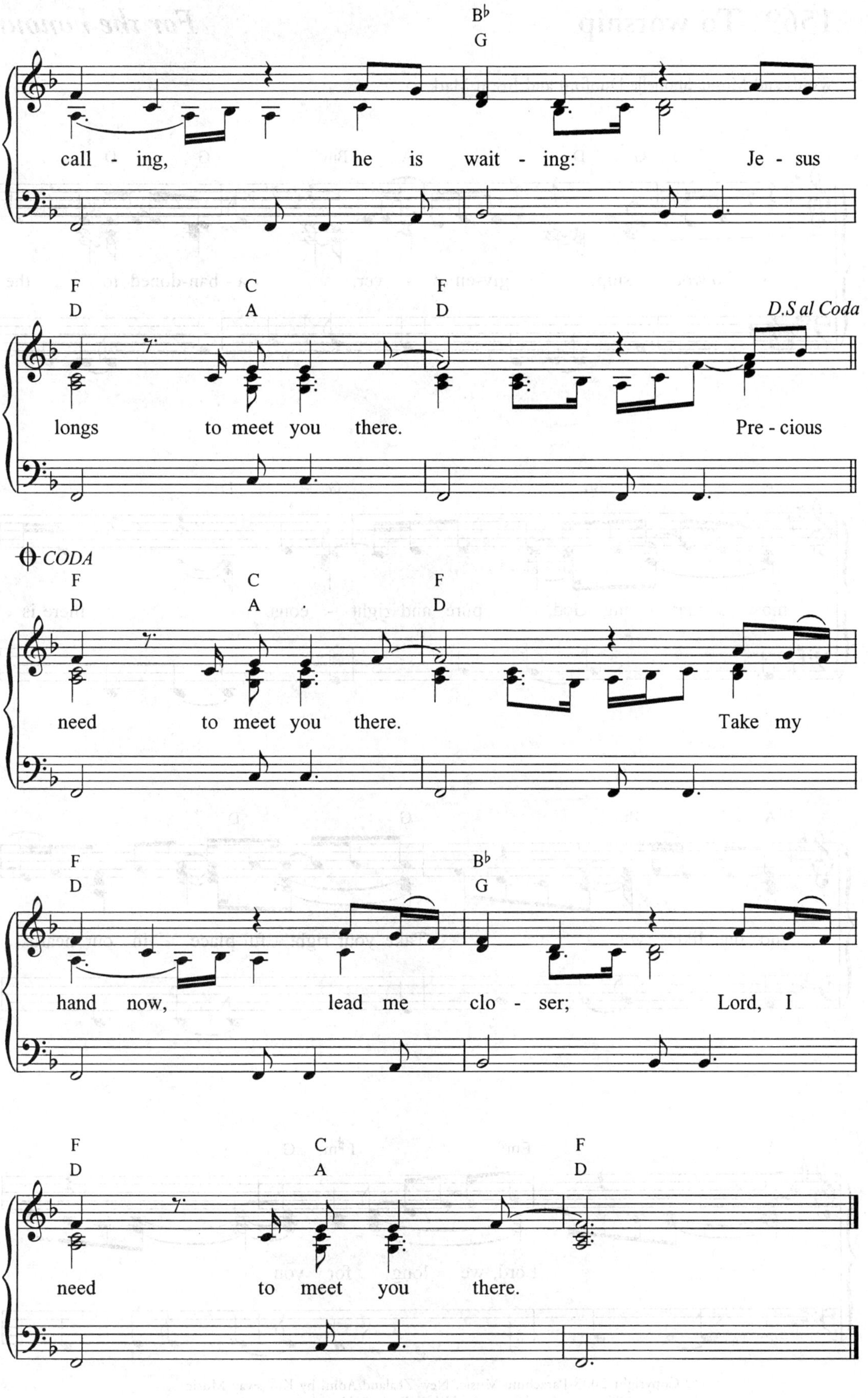
B♭
G
call - ing, he is wait - ing: Je - sus
F
D
C
A
F
D
D.S al Coda
longs to meet you there. Pre - cious
CODA
F
D
C
A
F
D
need to meet you there. Take my
F
D
B♭
G
hand now, lead me clo - ser; Lord, I
F
D
C
A
F
D
need to meet you there.

1569 To worship *For the honour*

Words and Music: Shonelle Dunford and Justin Mark

G D A Bm G D
To wor - ship, giv-en o - ver, a - ban-doned to the
A Bm G D
most a - maz - ing God, pure and right - eous, there is
A Bm G D
no one like you. Take your right - ful place in our hearts.
A Em7 F#m G
Lord, we long for you

Em7 D/F# G Asus4 A
Chorus
des - p'rate to see your pow - er fill this place. For the
D D/F# Asus4 A Bm D/F#
hon - our of the King, to de - clare your fame e -
G A D D/F#
ter - nal - ly. For the hon - our of the King,
Asus4 A Bm D/F#
ev - 'ry day I live my life
G A D
for the hon - our of the King.

1570 Trade your heavy heart *Celebrate the Lord of love*

Words and Music: Paul Baloche and Ed Kerr

(♩ = 116)
Chorus
E A² B E A² B
Trade your hea-vy heart for a heart of joy, ce-le-brate what God
has done;
E A² B E
join the song of praise as we ga-ther here,
A² B E A² B
ce-le-brate the Lord of love. Je-sus is our Lord,
E A² B
he is reign-ing here, we de-clare, 'His king - dom's come';

E A2 B E A2 B
dark-ness has to flee in his ho-ly light, ce-le-brate the Lord
E Fine A Verse B E
of love. All cre-a-tion sings,
A B E C#/E# F#m7
hear the o-ceans roar; let the earth pro-claim
B7sus4 D.C. al Fine
that Christ is Lord.

1571 Trust in the Lord

Words and Music: Paul Critchley

(♩ = 80)
D2 D D2 D
Trust in the Lord with all your heart and
G A G A
ne - ver re - ly on what you think you know. Trust in the Lord
D2 D D2 D
with all your heart and
G A G A
ne - ver re - ly on what you think you know, and in

F#m7
G
all your ways ac - know-ledge him, and in
F#m7
G
F#m7
all your ways ac-know-ledge him, and he
G
G/A
D2
D
Dsus4
D
will di - rect your path.

1572 Trust, trust in the Lord

Words and Music: Amy Sandstrom

D A/D G/D
Chorus
D A/D G/D D
Trust, trust in the Lord, lean not on your own un - der-
G/D A/D D A/D
stand - ing; in all, all of your ways ac - know-ledge
Bm A/G G D
him, he'll make your path straight. Trust, trust in the
A G/D D G/B A/C♯
Lord, lean not on your own un - der - stand - ing; in

D A/D F#/A# Bm
Last time to Coda
all, all of your ways ac - know-ledge him, he'll make your
A/G G D
2nd time to v.2
3rd time to Bridge
Verse 1
G2
path straight. (2. My) 1. You'll be my guide for
D/F# G D/F# D G A
life; I'll walk by your side with your hand in
Bm D/C Asus4 A7
Chorus D.S.
mine; I'll go where you lead me. O,
Verse 2
G2 D/F# G
(2.) eyes can on - ly see the ground be - neath my

D/F# D G A
feet; your dreams are great - er, your
Bm D/C C Em7 A/C# Chorus D.S.
ways are high - er; O Lord, please show me.
Bridge
G D/F# Em7 A7sus
Bless my thoughts, my dreams, my i - ma - gi - na - tions;
G2 D/F# Bm Em7
step by step, your de - light, your cre -
Chorus D.S. CODA
G/B Asus4 A/C# A A/G G D
a - tion. path straight.

1573 Turn your ear *O praise him*

Words and Music: David Crowder

G
D/F♯
1. Turn your ear to hea - ven and hear the noise
2. Turn your gaze to hea - ven and raise a joy-
C
G
in - side, the sound of an -
- ous noise. The sound of sal - va -
D/F♯
- gels' awe, the sound of an - gels' songs and all
- tion come, the sound of res - cued ones and all
C
Am7
this for a king, we could join and sing
this for a king, an - gels join to sing,
C
all to Christ the King.
all for Christ our King.

D/F# C D/F#
How con - stant, how di-vine this song of ours
C D/F# C
will rise. Oh, how con - stant, how di-vine
D/F# C
this love of ours will rise, will rise.
Chorus
G G/F#
Oh praise him, oh praise him;
1: D.C.
2: Repeat Chorus
3: Continue
Em7 C Am7
he is ho - ly, he is ho - ly, yeah.

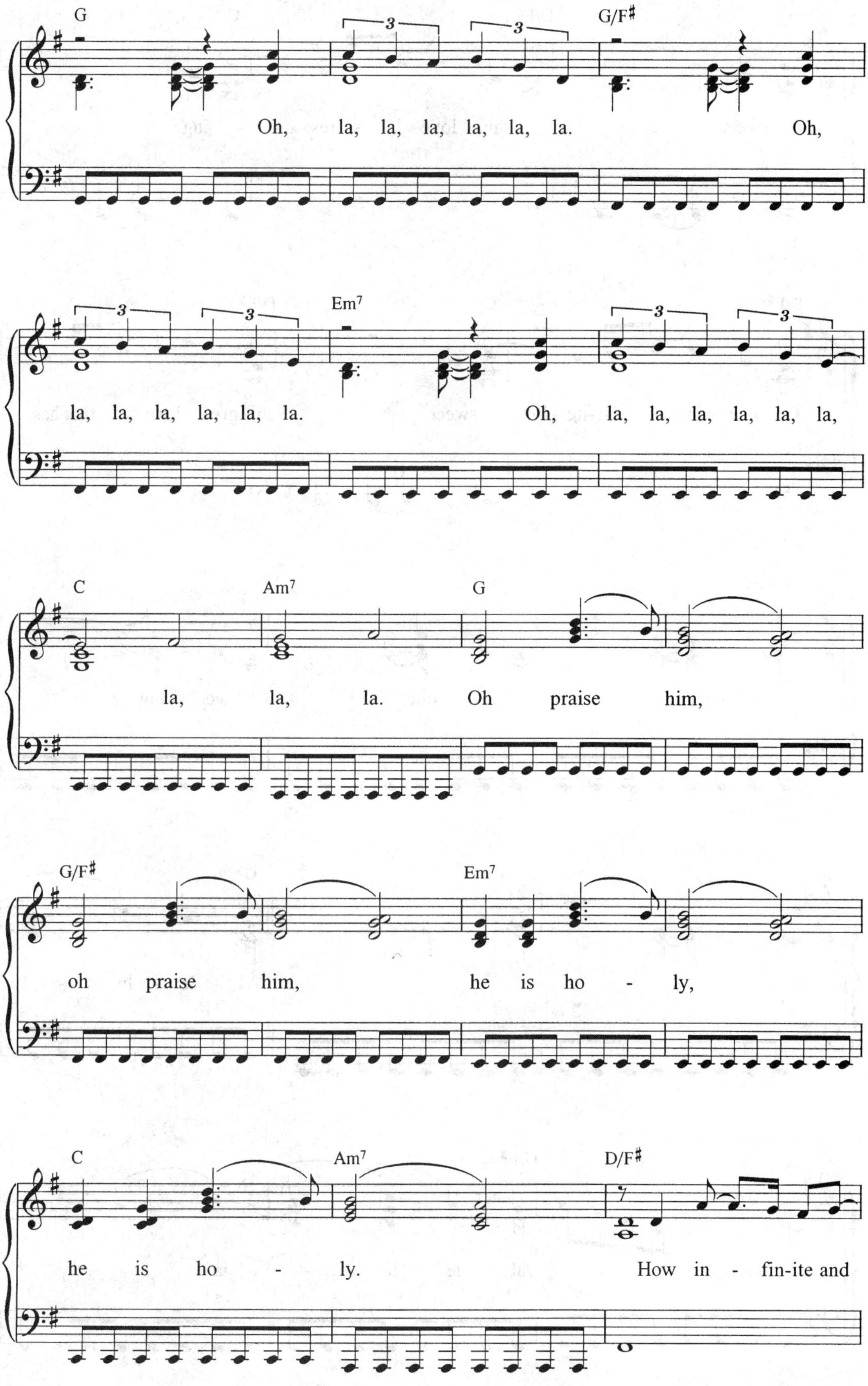
G
3
3
G/F♯
Oh, la, la, la, la, la, la. Oh,
3
3
Em7
3
3
la, la, la, la, la, la. Oh, la, la, la, la, la, la,
C
Am7
G
la, la, la. Oh praise him,
G/F♯
Em7
oh praise him, he is ho - ly,
C
Am7
D/F♯
he is ho - ly. How in - fin-ite and

C D/F# C
sweet this love so res - cu - ing.
D/F# C D/F#
Oh, how in - fin -ite - ly sweet this great love that has
C
re - deemed. As one we sing:
G
Al - le - lu -
G/F#
- ia, al - le - lu - ia.

Em7
C
He is ho - ly, he is ho -
Am7
G
- ly, yeah. Oh praise him,
G/F#
Em7
oh praise him, he is ho -
C
Am7
G
ly, he is ho - ly.

1574 We are a shining light *Do something beautiful*

Words and Music: Graham Kendrick

(♩ = 106)
G C Em C
1. We are a shin - ing light, ci - ty on a hill that can't be hid - den,
2. We are the salt of the earth, here to pu - ri - fy and fla - vour,
G C G F C G C
a shin-ing light. And this shin-ing light
salt of the earth. Sent through all the earth
Em C G C
is the life of Je - sus in us, oh what a light!
to love God and love our neigh-bour, salt of the earth.
G C
The fire of his Spi - rit burns with jus - tice,
As free - ly as we re-ceived so free - ly
G F
joy and peace and works through our hands and feet.
we must give, and we are his hands and feet.

Chorus
G C Em C
Go do some-thing beau - ti - ful,
G C Em F C
in the name of Je - sus do some-thing beau - ti - ful.
G C Em C
1.
Go do some-thing Je - sus would, do some-thing
G C Em D G C
beau-ti - ful, do some-thing beau-ti - ful.
Em D
2.
G C
do some-thing beau-ti - ful.

Em D Em D C Em
Let your light so shine be - fore the world,
Am7 D Em D
that all may see the good you do, and give their praise
C Em A Dsus4
D.S.
to God our Fa - ther.
3.
D.S. ad lib.
Last time
do some-thing
G C Em D rpt. x3 G
beau-ti - ful, do some-thing beau-ti - ful.

Therefore God exalted him to the highest place
and gave him the name that is above every name,
that at the name of Jesus every knee should bow,
in heaven and on earth and under the earth,
and every tongue confess that Jesus Christ is Lord,
to the glory of God the Father.

Philippians 2:9-11

1575 We are called to be prophets *Miracle in my heart*

Words and Music: Brian Houston

(♩ = 104)
A D2
1. We are called to be pro - phets to this na - tion,
A D2
to be the word of God in ev - 'ry si - tu - a - tion; change my
Bm7 E A Asus4 A
heart, change my heart to-day.
D Dsus4 A
Who'll be the salt if the salt
D2 A
should lose its fla - vour; who'll be the salt if the salt

D2
Bm7
should lose its fla - vour? Change my heart, change my
E
A
Asus4
A
D
Dsus4
heart to-day.
C#m7
D2
Lord, loose the chains of op - pres - sion;
C#m7
D2
Lord, set the cap - tives free;
C#m7
D2
Lord, fill my life with your com-pas - sion;

E
shine your light, shine your light,
Chorus
shine your light through me. Work a
D2
mi-ra-cle in my heart, work a
A
D2
mi-ra-cle in my heart; work a
F#m
E
D
E
E/F#
mi-ra-cle in my heart, O Lord,

E/G♯ A D2
to-day, to - day.
A Last time to Coda D2 A
2. Lord, take all my lies,
D2 A
take all of my greed; let me be a sac - ri - fice to those
D2 Bm7
who are in need; change my heart, change my
E A Asus4 A D Dsus4
heart to-day;

A
D2
Lord, with-out your pow'r it's all just good in - ten - tions;
A
D2
Lord, with-out your grace, who could find re-demp - tion? Change my
Bm7
E
heart, change my heart to - day.
A Asus4 A D Dsus4
D.S. al Coda
CODA
Chorus
Work a

D2
A
mi-ra-cle in my heart, work a mi-ra-cle in my heart;
D2
F♯m
E
work a mi-ra-cle in my heart,
D
E
O Lord, to-day,
A
D2
A
to-day.
1, 2.
3.
D2
Chorus
D2
A2
Work a

1576 We are your people *Hear from heaven*

Words and Music: Kevin Boese

(♩= 77)
G
C²
We are your peo - ple, called by your name; we
Dsus⁴ D G
hum-ble our - selves and pray. We are your peo - ple,
C²
called by your name; we hum-ble our-selves and pray.
Dsus⁴ D Em⁷ Am⁷
We turn from our sin and come to seek your face.

D G
Hear from hea - ven and for -
C2 Em7
give our wic - ked ways; hear from hea - ven
1. D C2
and heal our land to-day.
2. C2 G

1577 We believe in God

Because we believe

Words and Music: Nancy Gordon and Jamie Harvill

(♩ = 78)
D2
Men:
1.We be-lieve in God, the Fa - ther,
Women:
we be-lieve in God, the Fa - ther;
C2 D2 C2 D2
Men:
we be-lieve in Christ, the Son,
Women:
we be-lieve in Christ, the Son;
G2
Men:
we be-lieve in the Ho - ly Spi - rit,
Women:
we be-lieve in the Ho - ly Spi - rit;
Men:
we
D2 C2 D2 C2 D2
Men:
are the church and we stand as one,
Women:
we are the church and we stand as one.
G2 A/G G A D2
All:
Ho - ly, ho - ly, ho - ly is our God;

G2 A/G G A
wor-thy, wor - thy, wor-thy is our King.
D2 G D/F#
All glo-ry and hon-our are
G E/G# D/A C2
his to re - ceive; to Je - sus we sing,
G2 G/A D C/D G/D D
be-cause we be - lieve.

2. *Men:* We believe in the Holy Bible,
Women: we believe in the Holy Bible;
Men: we believe in the virgin birth,
Women: we believe in the virgin birth;
Men: we believe in the resurrection,
Women: we believe in the resurrection;
Men: Christ, one day, will return to earth,
Women: Christ, one day, will return to earth.

Holy, holy . . .

3. *Men:* We believe in the blood of Jesus,
Women: we believe in the blood of Jesus;
Men: we believe in eternal life,
Women: we believe in eternal life;
Men: we believe in his love that frees us,
Women: we believe in his love that frees us;
Men: to become the bride of Christ,
Women: to become the bride of Christ.

Holy, holy . . .

1578 We call upon your name *Arise, King of kings*

Words and Music: Mick Goss, Becky Heaslip and Eoghan Heaslip

Em7
3
God of all cre - a - tion, O Lord, we
C2
D
G
cry: a - rise,
D2/F#
King of kings, a fa - ther to the
Em7
D2/F#
C2
na - tions, the Rock of our sal - va-tion,
D
3
C2
G
O God, a - rise.
C2
1.
G
D.C.
2.
G

1579 We come to your mountain

Call to worship

Words and Music: Matt Redman

Am/F
Am/G
ev - 'ry step is praise. En-coun-ter - ing the
Am
Am/G
glo - ry of your name, your throne of ho - li-ness, the
F♯m7sus4(omit5)
1.
D.C.
2.
won - ders of your grace. Oh
Em
G
A7/C♯
come, come let us wor - ship, come let us re - cog - nise what a sac -
C
D/F♯
Em
G
- red thing we do. Come let us bow down, God, as we bring
A7/C♯
C
D/F♯
Em
our hearts, let them please the heart of you.

1580 We could watch you from afar

Rejoice with trembling

Words and Music: Matt Redman

Moderately

1. We could watch you from a - far, and for - e -
2. Who could ful - ly voice the praise of the God

- ver be a - mazed at how glo - ri - ous you are.
of end - less days, tell a frac - tion of your worth?

Yet you've drawn
For we on -

us close to you, where the won - der's great - er still,
- ly sing in part of the grace of who you are;

and you o - ver-whelm us, God.
just an e - cho, just a glimpse.

Chorus
B♭2 G2 F D C/E A/C♯
And we re-joice with trem - bling in our hearts,
Am7(♭5) F♯m7(♭5) B♭/D G/B B♭ G B♭/A G/F♯ Gm7 Em7 F/A D/F♯
bring you a song of re - ve-rence and love.
B♭2 G2 F D C/E A/C♯
Je - sus, how good, how great you are,
Am7(♭5) F♯m7(♭5) B♭ G Gm7 Em7 F/A D/F♯
and we re - joice with trem - bl-ing
B♭2 G2 F D
be - fore your throne.

He who dwells in the shelter of the Most High
will rest in the shadow of the Almighty.
I will say of the Lord,
'He is my refuge and my fortress,
my God, in whom I trust.'

Psalm 91:1-2

1581 We fall down

Words and Music: Chris Tomlin

Intensely
E B C#m A2
We fall down, we lay our crowns at the feet of Je-
F#m4 E B C#m
-sus. The great-ness of mer-cy and love, at the feet
A2 A/B B E2/G# A E/G# F#m7 E2/G#
of Je - sus. And we cry ho - ly, ho - ly, ho - ly. And we cry
A E/G# F#m7 E/B B A E/G#
ho - ly, ho - ly, ho - ly. And we cry ho - ly, ho - ly, ho-
F#m7 Bsus4 1. E Esus4 E Esus4/D 2. E
-ly is the Lamb.

1582 We give thanks

Words and Music: Mark Altrogge

Cmaj7 G/C Am/C G/C G Am7 Cmaj7
-dom have all come and you are Lord of
D Bm7 Em D/C Cmaj7
all; the ac-cus-er of the bro-thers has been
Em D/E Em D/C Cmaj7 G/D Am/D G/D C/D
hurled down for e-ver, o-ver-come by the blood,
G/D D G Am7 G/B C G/C C G/C Am/C G/D
o-ver-come by your blood, o-ver-come
Am/D G
D.C. al Fine
by the blood of the Lamb. So,

1583 We have cried out

Come, Lord Jesus

Words and Music: Barry Hart

C2 G/B D/A G
peo - ple say when the times are full of dan - gers, where's God
o - pen wide and can see this great sal - va - tion, the lost
C2 G/B Am7 Dsus4 D
and why won't he in - ter-vene? But we say
will re - turn from near and far; ev - 'ry voice
C2 G/B D/A Em
now by faith we will sing with all the an - gels that the
will re - joice at the heal - ing of the na - tions as they
C G/B Am7 Em/G
Fa - ther's on his throne in hea - ven where he's al - ways been.
wor - ship in the light that's stream - ing from the Morn - ing Star.
D/F# G6 C2
Chorus
Am/D G D
And his mer - cy flows and his Spi - rit blows

Em C G Am7
and a dark world knows the hope of glo - ry in God's
D/F# G6 C2 Am/D G D B7
Son; so let the thir - sty drink, let the Christ-life
Em C G D/F# Em Am7 Am/D
spring and the Spi-rit and the bride say, 'Come, Lord Je - sus, come!'
Em C G D/F# Em Am7 Am/D
And the Spi-rit and the bride say, 'Come, Lord Je - sus, come!'
To verses
Last time
G D/F# Em7 C2 D Em7 C2 D G

1584 We have nothing to give *Breathing the breath*

Words and Music: Matt Redman

A
Chorus
D/F♯
Lord, we're breath - ing the breath that you
sing - ing these songs with the
G
Bm7
D/F♯
Last time to Coda
gave us to breathe, to wor - ship you, to wor - ship you.
ve - ry same breath, to wor - ship you, to wor - ship you.
1, 3, 5.
2.
4.
G
G
D.C.
G
And we're
D/F♯
G
We are breath-ing the breath that you gave us to breathe, we are
Bm7
G
breath - ing the breath that you gave us to breathe, we are

D/F♯
G
breath - ing the breath that you gave us to breathe, we are
Bm7
G
breath - ing the breath that you gave us to breathe.
CODA
D.C.
G
D
To wor - ship you.

1585 We humbly pray *Lord, send the rain*

Words and Music: Russ Hughes

2. Move through our land,
give to each one the power of your Spirit.
Heal broken lives,
sweep sin aside, come rain down on ev'ry life.
That all may know that Jesus reigns,
that all may see you in your sov'reign pow'r,
send your Holy Spirit.

1586 We journey on *Lord of the harvest*

Words and Music: Matt Redman

C/E A/C♯ F D Gm Em F D
we will re-turn with songs of joy. And, Lord, in faith we'll per-se-vere
C/E A/C♯ F D D B
un-til we see the har-vest come.
B♭ G E♭ C
You're the Lord, Lord of the har-vest, we're
Gm7 Em7 Gm7/F Em7/D C/E A/C♯ D B
Chorus
sing-ing out and shout-ing out your fame. You're the
B♭ G E♭ C
Lord, Lord of the har-vest. You

Gm7 Em7 Gm7/F Em7/D C/E A/C# D B
Last time to Coda
send us in the pow - er of your name, Lord of the
Gm7 Em7
1. 2.
D.S. D.S.S. al Coda
har - vest. 2. So let your truth
CODA
Gm7 Em7 B♭maj7 Gmaj7 E♭maj9 Cmaj9
har - vest. This will be our wor - ship,
C/E A/C# D B Gm7 Em7
this will be our wor - ship.

It is written:
'As surely as I live,' says the Lord,
'Every knee will bow before me;
every tongue will confess to God.'

Romans 14:11

1587 Welcomed in to the courts of the King *Facedown*

Words and Music: Beth Redman and Matt Redman

1. Wel-comed in to the courts of the King, I've been ush-ered in to your pre - sence. Lord, I stand on your mer - ci - ful ground yet with ev - 'ry step tread with rev - 'rence. And I'll fall face - down as your

2. There is none in the hea - vens like you and up - on the earth who's your e - qual? You are far a - bove, you're the high - est of heights, I am bow-ing down to ex- alt you.

Chorus

Em D C G C
glo - ry shines a-round. Yes, I'll fall face - down as your
1. 2, 4.
Em D C D.C. C
glo - ry shines a-round. And I'll
Last time 3.
C G Fine C C
So let your glo-ry shine a-
D C
round, let your glo - ry shine a - round, King of glo - ry here be
D Repeat ad lib. C D.S. al Fine
found, King of glo - ry. And I'll

1588 We place you on the highest place

Words and Music: Ramon Pink

Majestically

We place you on the high-est place, for you are the great High Priest, we place you high a-bove all else; and we come to you and wor-ship at your feet.

1589 We pray for peace

Words: Alan Gaunt

Music: Paul Bateman

REAL PEACE 46 66 58

2. We pray for peace,
but not the cruel peace,
leaving God's poor bereft
and dying in distress,
we pray for real peace,
enriching all the human race.

3. We pray for peace,
and not the evil peace,
defending unjust laws
and nursing prejudice,
but for the real peace
of justice, mercy, truth and love.

4. We pray for peace:
holy communion
with Christ our risen Lord
and every living thing;
God's will fulfilled on earth
and all creation reconciled.

5. We pray for peace,
and for the sake of peace,
look to the risen Christ
who gives the grace we need,
to serve the cause of peace
and make our own self-sacrifice.

6. God, give us peace:
if you withdraw your love,
there is no peace for us
nor any hope of it.
With you to lead us on,
through death or tumult, peace will come.

1590 We're here because of grace

We've come to bless your name

Words and Music: Don Moen

(♩= 152)

E♭/F Dm/F E♭/F B♭maj7 Am7 Dm7
C/D Bm/D C/D Gmaj7 F♯m7 Bm7
that we just want to thank you for
that we just want to thank you for
Gm7 B♭/C F B♭ C F
Em7 G/A D G A D
all you've done for us.
all you've brought us through.
Chorus
Dm/C C Dm/C C B♭/F
Bm/A A Bm/A A G/D
We've come to bless your name, King of kings and Lord
F F2sus4 F Dm/C C
D D2sus4 D Bm/A A
of lords; we've come to give you praise,

Dm/C C B♭/F F B♭/F F C/E
Bm/A A G/D D G/D D A/C♯
you are the one that we a-dore. O Lord,
Dm C/D Dm C B♭2
Bm A/B Bm A G2
cleanse our hearts with fire and fill us with de-sire
F2 C2 B♭2
D2 A2 G2
for your courts and for your pre-sence in our lives.
F B♭/D C/E F Dm7 Fmaj7/A Gm7 C Dm B♭ C F
D G/B A/C♯ D Bm7 Dmaj7/F♯ Em7 A Bm G A D

He is not here;
he has risen, just as he said.

Matthew 28:6a

1591 We're here to bless your name *We give you glory*

Words and Music: Don Moen and Claire Cloninger

(♩ = 116)
Capo 3
F D
E♭ C
B♭ G
1. We're here to bless your name, ga - thered as your
here to seek your face, to ga - ther in your
Dm Bm
C A
F D
E♭ C
fa - mi-ly; to praise you and pro-claim your
pre - sence; to ce - le-brate your grace, to
B♭ G
Dm Bm
C A
Chorus
faith - ful-ness and mer - cy.
praise you for your bles - sings. We give you glo-
Am7 F♯m7
Dm7 Bm7
Gm7 Em7
C A
- ry, we give you hon - our, we give you ev -

F D Dm Bm Gm7 Em7
-'ry-thing we are, lift-ing our hearts and hands be-fore
B♭maj7/C Gmaj7/A C/B♭ A/G Am7 F♯m7 Dm7 Bm7 Gm7 Em7 C A
you; we give you glo - ry, we give you hon-
Am7 F♯m7 Dm7 Bm7 Gm7 Em7 C A F D
- our, we give you ev - 'ry-thing we are,
Dm Bm Gm7 Em7 B♭maj7/C Gmaj7/A C A
3rd time to Coda
lift-ing our hearts and hands be-fore you,
F D B♭/F G/D F D B♭/F G/D F D F/A D/F♯
1. 2.
Bridge
Lord. 2. We're There is

C Gm7 C
A Em7 A
no o - ther rea - son why we came than to
Gm7 C F B♭ F/A
Em7 A D G D/F♯
glo - ri - fy your name; for you are wor - thy
Gm7 F C Gm7 C
Em7 D A Em7 A
to be praised. Now we of - fer up our lives as a
Gm7 C F B♭ F/A Gm7 F
Em7 A D G D/F♯ Em7 D
liv - ing sac - ri - fice; ho - ly, ac - cept - a - ble to
CODA
C/E C C/B♭ D.S. al Coda F B♭/F F
A/C♯ A A/G D G/D D
you. We give you glo - Lord.

1592 Were you there when they crucified my Lord?

Words: Spiritual

Music: Spiritual, adapt.
John W. Work and Frederick J. Work

WERE YOU THERE Irregular

E♭ B♭ Cm Gm B♭7 E♭
Capo 1 D A Bm F♯m A7 D
1. Were you there when they cru - ci - fied my Lord? Were you
Gm E♭ B♭ Cm B♭ E♭ B♭ E♭ B♭7 E♭ A♭ Gm B♭7 E♭ E♭maj7
F♯m D A Bm A D A D A7 D G F♯m A7 D Dmaj7
there when they cru - ci - fied my Lord? Oh,
A♭ E♭ G G7 Cm A♭6 A♭ E♭ A♭ B♭
G D F♯ F♯7 Bm G6 G D G A
some-times it caus - es me to trem-ble, trem-ble, trem-ble.
A♭ E♭ Gm B♭7 Cm Gm B♭7 E♭
G D F♯m A7 Bm F♯m A7 D
Were you there when they cru - ci - fied my Lord?

2. Were you there when they nailed him to the tree? *etc.*

3. Were you there when they laid him in the tomb? *etc.*

4. Were you there when he rose up from the grave? *etc.*

1593 We see the Lord *Everything cries 'Holy'*

Words and Music: Robin Mark

Steadily
C
Verse
Em7
We see the Lord, and he is
One like a Lamb who was
F
C
high up - on the throne, and his
slain is on the throne, and I
F
1.
Am
G
glo - ry fills the hea - vens and the earth.
cast my crown be - fore
2.
Am
Gsus4
you, and bow down to

C
Chorus
F
C/E
praise. For ev - ’ry - thing cries ‘Ho - ly’, oh, ev-
Dm7
C/E
F
- ’ry - thing cries ‘Ho - ly’ oh, ev - ’ry - thing cries ‘Ho-
Am7
Gsus4
- ly’ to you, Lord.
1.
G
Oh, ev -
2.
G
D.C.
3.
C

1594 We stand and lift up our hands *Holy is the Lord*

Words and Music: Chris Tomlin and Louie Giglio

G C Dsus4 G/B C
We stand and lift up our hands for the joy of the Lord is our strength.
Dsus4 G C Dsus4
We bow down and wor - ship him now, how great,
G/B C Dsus4 A
how awe - some is he. And to - ge - ther we sing,
C2 A C2
Chorus
ev - 'ry - one sing: ho - ly is the Lord
G/B C Dsus4 D Em C
God Al - migh - ty, the earth is filled with your glo-

D G/B C Dsus4 D
-ry, ho-ly is the Lord God Al-migh-ty, the earth
Em C D Em C
is filled with your glo-ry, the earth is filled with your glo-
Dsus4
-ry.
1. D D.C.
Last time D G Fine
2. D G D/F# G/F
It's ris-ing up all a-round, it's the an-them of the Lord's
1. C 2. C D.S. al Fine
re-nown. It's ris- re-nown. And to-ge-ther we sing

1595 We stand in the gap *Stand in the gap*

Words and Music: Paul A. Jacobsen

(♩ = 120)
We stand in the gap, we're cry-ing for mer-cy, Lord, for those who can-not cry out for them-selves; we're cry-ing to you.
de-fy-ing the dark-ness, Lord, the ar-my of light, in pow-er and might, de-clar-ing your word.
1. We stand in the gap,
2. So come in your pow'r,

D G A G
set the peo - ple free; here in this hour
and your daugh - ters, Lord; come heal the land,
D G A G
we are on our knees. O - pen our eyes
ev - 'ry heart re - store. We'll give you the glo -
Last time to Coda
D G A Em7
- to e - ter - ni - ty; we are call - ing out to you.
- ry for e - ver - more; we are call - ing out to you.
1. 2.
A A D G
De - li - ver your sons We stand in the gap.
C G D G C G D.S. al Coda
We stand in the gap,

CODA
Em7
A
D
G
- ing out to you. We stand in the gap.
C
G
D
G
C
G
D

1596 We turn our eyes to you

Words and Music: Claire Cloninger, Bob Fitts and Paul Smith

B♭ C Am7 Dm B♭ Csus F
Capo 3 G A F♯m7 Bm G Asus D
Chorus
We
B♭ C F B♭ C
G A D G A
turn our eyes to you, we turn our eyes to
Dm7 B♭ C Am7 Dm7
Bm7 G A F♯m7 Bm7
you; in the beau-ty of your pre - sence, Lord, we
B♭ Csus4 F B♭ C
G Asus4 D G A
turn our eyes to you; we lift our hands to you,

F D Bb G C A Dm7 Bm7
we lift our hands to you; in the
Last time to Coda
Bb G C A Am7 F#m7 Dm7 Bm7 Bb G Csus4 Asus4
com-fort of your pre - sence, Lord, we lift our hands to you.
F D Verse Bb G Gm7 Em7
For here in your pre - sence, all our fear
F D C/E A/C# Dm Bm F/C D/A Bb G
just melts a-way; for here in your pre - sence,

Gm7 F C/E Dm F/C
Em7 D A/C♯ Bm D/A
our hearts just melt in praise; Lord, we're so thank -
B♭ Gm7 F C/E
G Em7 D A/C♯
- ful and grate - ful and al - ways want to stay
Dm F/C B♭ Gm7
Bm D/A G Em7
here where you heal us and keep us for - e -
CODA
F/C C F
D/A A D
D.S.
- ver. We

1597 We've come to praise your name

Words and Music: Wes Sutton

(♩ = 126)
G
C/G
G
We've come to praise your name in ev - 'ry way. We live to
F
G
wor-ship you all our days. We are the church re - deemed, this is the
C/G
G
day you've made. This is the time and place to
F
G
Chorus
ce - le - brate. This is a

G C2 G
house of praise, you are the God we wor - ship, this an awe-some place to
Am7 D G C2
which we've come. It is by sov-'reign grace we've been in - vit - ed to
Am7 1. D G
praise and wor - ship you, the liv - ing one.
Gsus4 G Gsus4 D.S.
We've come to
2. D Chorus 3. D G
you, this is a you, the liv - ing one.

1598 We've come to sing *Everybody sing*

Words and Music: Dave Bilbrough

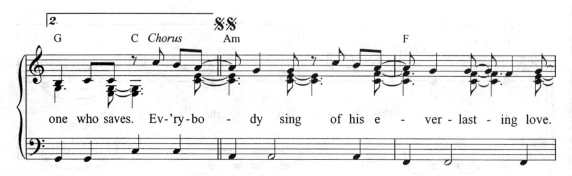

With a slight driving feel
C
Verse
F(add B♭)
We've come to sing our songs of wor - ship;
C
G7
C
we've come to give our - selves in praise, to of - fer thanks to our
F(add B♭)
C
1.
G
C
cre - a - tor, and ce - le-brate the one who saves.
2.
G
C
Chorus
Am
F
one who saves. Ev-'ry-bo - dy sing of his e - ver - last - ing love.

C
Am
Ev - 'ry - bo - dy sing of his e -
F
Gsus4
G
- ver - last - ing love. He's
Am
F
C
slow to an - ger, rich in mer - cy; let all the earth de - clare
G
C
F
G
his glo - ry. Ev - 'ry - bo - dy sing of his e - ver - last - ing love.
Last time to Coda
1.
C
F(add B♭)
C
F(add B♭)
D.C.

2.
C
Am
F
C
Am
F
Gsus4
D.S.
3.
C
D.S.S.
Ev-'ry-bo-
CODA
F(addB♭)
C
Repeat ad lib.
F(addB♭)
C
Al - le - lu - ia!
E-ver-last - ing love.

'Jesus, remember me
when you come into your kingdom.'
Jesus answered him,
'I tell you the truth,
today you will be with me in paradise.'

Luke 23:42-43

1599 We wait

Words and Music: Wes Tuttle

(♩ = 80)
D A/C♯ Bm D/A Em7 Gmaj9/A A
1. We wait,
D A/C♯ Bm D/A Em7
we're not in a hur - ry; oh, we need
A7sus4 A7 D A/C♯ Bm D/A
you, Lord. We wait, all our cares and wor-
Em7 A A♯dim Bm
- ries we lay a-side for you; oh, how we long

F#m Em7 A A#dim
to see your face;
Bm F#m Em7
oh, how we long for your em-brace.
A7sus4 A7 D A/C# Bm D/A
2. We wait, we're not a- fraid to tar -
Em7 A7sus4 A7 D A/C#
- ry; we yearn for you, Lord. We wait, for your
Bm D/A Em7 A A#dim
migh - ty wind to car - ry us in - to your pre - sence, Lord;

Bm F#m Em7
and as we fill this house with praise,
A A#dim Bm F#m
let your ho - ly fire fill this place,
Em7 A7sus4 A D A/C#
as we wait,
1.
Bm D/A Em7 Gmaj7/A A
we wait, we wait,
2.
A A#dim Bm F#m
and as we fill this house with praise,

Em7
A
A#dim
Bm
let your ho - ly fire
F#m
Em7
fill this place,
A7sus4
D
A/C#
Bm
D/A
as we wait,
we wait,
Em7
A7sus4
A7
D
we wait.

1600 We want to see your glory *Lord, we welcome you*

Words and Music: Gerrit Gustafson

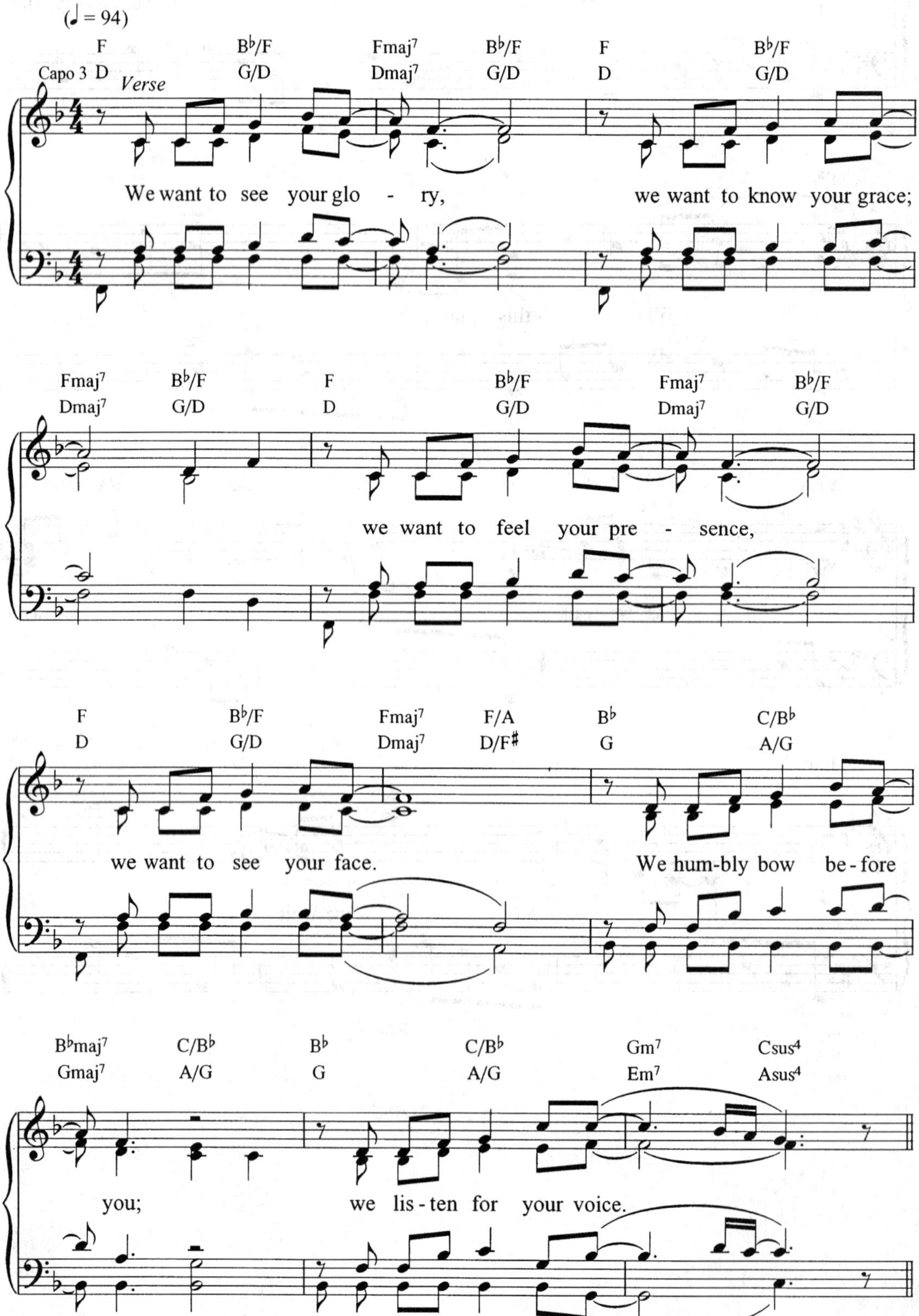
(♩ = 94)
F B♭/F Fmaj7 B♭/F F B♭/F
Capo 3 D G/D Dmaj7 G/D D G/D
Verse
We want to see your glo - ry, we want to know your grace;
Fmaj7 B♭/F F B♭/F Fmaj7 B♭/F
Dmaj7 G/D D G/D Dmaj7 G/D
we want to feel your pre - sence,
F B♭/F Fmaj7 F/A B♭ C/B♭
D G/D Dmaj7 D/F♯ G A/G
we want to see your face. We hum-bly bow be-fore
B♭maj7 C/B♭ B♭ C/B♭ Gm7 Csus4
Gmaj7 A/G G A/G Em7 Asus4
you; we lis-ten for your voice.

Chorus
F D
B♭/F G/D
Fmaj7 Dmaj7
B♭/C G/A
Women
F D
B♭/F G/D
Lord, we wel - come you
Men
Lord, we wel - come you in - to this place.
Fmaj7 Dmaj7
B♭/F G/D
F D
B♭/F G/D
Fmaj7 Dmaj7
B♭/C G/A
in - to this place.
Lord, we wel - come you in - to this place.
F D
B♭/F G/D
Fmaj7 Dmaj7
B♭/F G/D
Repeat ad lib.
Lord, we wel - come you in - to this place.

1601 We will proclaim

Words and Music: Geraldine Latty

Steadily
Chorus
Capo 3
F Dm7 Eb Cm7
D Bm7 C Am7
We will pro - claim your love in the morn - ing, we will pro -
claim your love in the morn - ing, we will pro - claim your love in the morn-
Last time to Coda
Eb Cm7 Bb Gm7 Ab Ab/Bb Bb/C
C Am7 G Em7 F F/G G/A
- ing, and your faith - ful - ness at night. We will pro-
Ab Ab/Bb Bb/C F F/A C C7/Bb F/A C7/G
F F/G G/A D D/F# A A7/G D/F# A7/E
1. It is good to praise you,

F Bb Dm7 C7 F Bb/F
D G Bm7 A7 D G/D
Lord, sing and make mu - sic to your name.
F F/A C C7/Bb F/A C7/G F7 Gm/Bb
D D/F# A A7/G D/F# A7/E D7 Em/G
For your deeds have made us glad, O
F/C C7 F Eb Bb/C
D/A A7 D C G/A
D.S.
Lord, our Lord. We will pro-
CODA
F Dm7 Eb Cm7 F
D Bm7 C Am7 D
at night. And your faith - ful - ness at night.

2. Lord, great miracles you do,
oh, the wisdom of your thoughts.
We will sing for joy to you, O Lord, our Lord.

3. Though we see much evil near,
we will take refuge in our God.
'You are good' we will declare, O Lord, our Lord.

1602 We will seek you first, Lord *O Lord, to you*

Words and Music: Gary Sadler

(♩ = 104)
Chorus E♭
Capo 1 D
A♭2
G2
We will seek you first, Lord, you will hear our
E♭2/G
D2/F♯
Fm11
Em11
voi - ces, ear - ly in the morn - ing and
B♭7sus4
A7sus4
E♭
D
E♭/G
D/F♯
A♭2
G2
late in the night; we will sing your prai - ses,
E♭2/G
D2/F♯
B♭/C
A/B
Cm7
Bm7
giv - ing you the glo - ry, of - fer - ing our

Last time
Fm11 Bb7sus4 Eb
Em11 A7sus4 D
lives to you, a ho - ly sac - ri-fice.
Eb Bb/Eb Ab/Eb Eb Eb/G Ab Ab/C
D A/D G/D D D/F# G G/B
Verse
May our praise a - rise as in -
Bb Cm Ab Eb Abmaj9 Eb/G
A Bm G D Gmaj9 D/F#
- cense, O Lord, to you;
Bb Bb/Ab Eb/G Ab Ab/C Bb
A A/G D/F# G G/B A
may our wor - ship be a fra -
Cm Ab Eb Abmaj9 Eb/G Bb
Bm G D Gmaj9 D/F# A
D.S.
grance, O Lord, to you. We will seek you

1603 We will see the glory of the Lord *Face to face*

Words and Music: Paul Baloche, Marc Byrd and Steve Hindalong

(♩= 119)
G2
We will see the glo - ry of the Lord;
we will see the glo - ry of the Lord.
G5
C2
Em7
Dsus4
G5
C2
1. The eyes of the blind will o - pen, the ears

Em7
Dsus4
of the deaf will hear;
G5
C2
the tongue of the mute will shout for joy, and the Lord
Em7
Dsus4
Em7
will cause the lame to leap like deer; we will see
Cmaj7
Dsus4
G5
G5/F#
the glo - ry of the Lord;
Em7
Cmaj7
Dsus4
we will see the glo - ry of the Lord.

G5 C2
2. Streng - then the arms of weak - ness, stea -
Em7 Dsus4 G5
- dy the fee - ble knees; say to those with anx -
C2 Em7 Dsus4
ious hearts: be strong in the Lord and do not fear:
Em7 Cmaj7 Dsus4
we will see the glo - ry of the Lord;
G5 G5/F# Em7 Cmaj7
we will see the

Dsus4
G5
Dsus4 Chorus
glo - ry of the Lord.
Hal - le - lu - jah,
Em7
C2
for the Lord Al - migh - ty reigns;
Dsus4
Em7
C2
hal - le - lu - jah,
we will wor - ship Je - sus
Dsus4
Em7
face to face;
hal - le - lu - jah,
for the
C2
Dsus4
Lord Al - migh - ty reigns;
hal - le - lu - jah,

Last time
Em7
C2
Gomit3
we will wor-ship Je - sus face to face.
Em7
Cmaj7
Dsus4
Instrumental
G5
Em7
Cmaj7
Dsus4
G5
D.C.

But God demonstrates his own love for us in this:
While we were still sinners, Christ died for us.

Romans 5:8

1604 What a wonderful change

Since Jesus came into my heart

Words: Rufus H. McDaniel

Music: Charles H. Gabriel

MCDANIEL 12 8 12 8 and Refrain

1. What a won - der - ful change in my life has been wrought since
Je - sus came in - to my heart! I have light in my soul for which
long I had sought, since Je - sus came in - to my heart!
Chorus
Since Je-sus came in - to my heart, since Je-sus came in - to my heart, floods of

C G D G C G D6 D7 G
joy o'er my soul like the sea bil-lows roll, since Je-sus came in-to my heart.

2. I have ceased from my wand'ring and going astray
   since Jesus came into my heart!
   And my sins, which were many, are all washed away,
   since Jesus came into my heart!

3. I shall go there to dwell in that city, I know,
   since Jesus came into my heart!
   And I'm happy, so happy, as onward I go,
   since Jesus came into my heart!

1605 What have we to show our Saviour

Words: Elizabeth Cosnett

Music: Cyril Vincent Taylor

ABBOT'S LEIGH 87 87 D

C D7 Em C6 Am D7 Gsus4 G
We have bro - ken his com - mand - ment,
A D6 Em G C#m7 Bm Em7 F#7 Bm
made his love a mock - er - y,
D A6 Bm D C D Bm7 Em B7
so we stand be - neath his judge - ment,
Em A7 D G D A7 D
once for all on Cal - va - ry.

2. See the soldiers pierce and leave him,
one dead body on a cross.
See his mother's arms receive him,
final fruit of Eden's loss.
To what end did she conceive him?
Why did angels hail his birth?
Must the friends he loved believe him
gone for ever, earth to earth.

3. When to Caesar he had tendered
everything that was his due,
to his God alone he rendered
what from God alone he drew.
He accepted our condition,
all that human sin could do:
we accept his full submission,
made in faith to One he knew.

4. In this last humiliation
God is strong to meet our need,
brings to birth a new creation,
fills with hope the life we lead.
Here the great retaliation
promised once to Adam's seed
through divine renunciation
ends in victory indeed.

1606 What love is this

I surrender

Words and Music: Dave Bilbrough

Slow and intense

1. What love is this, that took my place?

In-stead of wrath, you poured your

grace on me. What can I do but sim-ply come and

wor - ship you? I sur - ren - der,

2. What love is this
that comes to save?
Upon the cross
you bore my guilt and shame.
To you alone
I give my heart
and worship you.

3. A greater love
no man has seen;
it breaks sin's pow'r
and sets this pris'ner free.
With all I have
and all I am,
I worship you.

1607 What wisdom once devised the plan

The glory of the cross

Words and Music: Bob Kauflin

E B F#m7 Amaj7
that you would send your Son for us. I
B C#m E B/D#
glad - ly count my life as loss that I might come to
A F#m7 A
know the glo - ry of, the glo - ry of the cross.
To next verse
Last time
C#m A B A B
2. What

2. What righteousness was there revealed
that sets the guilty free,
that justifies ungodly men
and calls the filthy clean?
A righteousness that proved to all
your justice has been met,
and holy wrath is satisfied
through one atoning death.

3. What mercy now has been proclaimed
for those who would believe?
A love incomprehensible,
our minds could not conceive.
A mercy that forgives my sin
and makes me like your Son.
And now I'm loved for evermore,
because of what you've done.

1608 What wondrous love is this *Upon a cross of shame*

Words and Music: James Wright

2, 3.
C#m F#m7 Bsus4 B
grace poured out for us all.
same drawing all men to you.
Chorus
E E/G# A E
Up-on a cross of shame you bled and died, poured out your life
B A/C# B/D# E E/G# A2
with arms o-pen wide. And there you hung with a heart full of love
E/G# E
poured out for all of the world
1.
B A/C#
B/D# B E E/G# A2 A/C# B/D#
with a heart full of love.
D.C. to v.3

2.
B A/C♯ B/D♯ B
D.S.
3.
B A/C♯
B/D♯ B E E/G♯
with a heart full of love.
A2 A/C♯ B/D♯ E E/G♯ A2 A/C♯ B/D♯
Poured out for all of the world with a heart full of love,
E E/G♯ A2 A/C♯ B/D♯
poured out for all of the world
E E/G♯ A2 A/C♯ B/D♯ E
with a heart full of love.

Blessed are they whose ways are blameless,
who walk according to the law of the Lord.
Blessed are they who keep his statutes
and seek him with all their heart.

Psalm 119:1-2

1609 When all around is fading *Whole world in his hands*

Words and Music: Tim Hughes

Chorus
C F G
He's got the whole world in his hands,
C F G
he's got the whole world in his hands. I'll fear no e -
Am F E
- vil, for you are with me, strong to de - li - ver, migh-ty to save.
F Em G
He's got the whole world in his hands.
D.C.
Last time
Repeat and fade to end
C F G C
He's got the whole world in his hands.

1610 When I sing my praise *When I worship you*

Words and Music: Noel Richards and Tricia Richards

Verse 2
can see, love is pour - ing o - ver me.
B/E E A E/G♯ A
my face, a cool breeze in a de - sert place.
B Emaj7 Choruses
1. When I wor - ship you,
2. I will wor - ship you,
Amaj7 A/B
hea - ven comes to me, hea - ven comes to me.
hea - ven come to me, hea - ven come to me.
Emaj7
When I wor - ship you,
I will wor - ship you,

Amaj7
A/B
D.C.
hea - ven comes to me, hea - ven comes to me.
hea - ven come to me, hea - ven come to me.
Last time
C#m/E
B/E
A/E
B/E
C#m/E
B/E
A/E
B/E
E2

1611 When I think about the Lord

Words and Music: James Huey

Capo 3
F D
C/E A/C♯
C♯dim7 A♯dim7
Dm7 Bm7
When I think a-bout the Lord, how he saved me, how he
Cm7 Am7
E♭/F C/D
B♭maj7 Gmaj7
F/A D/F♯
raised me, how he filled me with the Ho - ly Ghost, how he
Gm7 Em7
B♭/C G/A
F D
healed me to the ut - ter-most; when I think a-bout the Lord,
C/E A/C♯
C♯dim7 A♯dim7
Dm7 Bm7
Cm7 Am7
E♭/F C/D
how he picked me up and turned me a-round, how he

B♭maj7 F/A Gm7
Gmaj7 D/F♯ Em7
Chorus
placed my feet on so - lid ground. It
B♭/C F C/E C♯dim7
G/A D A/C♯ A♯dim7
3
makes me wan - na shout hal - le - lu - jah, thank you, Je -
Dm7 Cm7 E♭/F B♭maj7
Bm7 Am7 C/D Gmaj7
- sus; Lord, you're wor - thy of all the glo - ry and all the hon -
F/A Gm7 B♭/C
D/F♯ Em7 G/A
- our and all the praise; it makes me wan - na shout

F C/E C♯dim7 Dm7
D A/C♯ A♯dim7 Bm7
hal - le - lu - jah, thank you, Je - sus; Lord, you're wor -
3
Cm7 E♭/F B♭maj7
Am7 C/D Gmaj7
- thy of all the glo - ry and all the hon -
F/A Gm7
D/F♯ Em7
- our and all the praise; it
1. 2.
B♭/C B♭/C F
G/A G/A D
makes me wan - na shout makes me wan - na shout.

1612 When I think about you

You're the strength of my life

Words and Music: Greg Shepherd

Driving (♩ = 128)
D G D
1. When I think a-bout you and your love for me,
2. For the joy be-fore you, you en-dured the cross,
3. When I think a-bout you, the Al-migh-ty Lord,
A G D
how your lov - ing kind - ness is
and how you suf - fered to
sus-tain - ing all things
Em7 Asus4 A D
poured out o - ver me, how you'll ne-ver leave
seek and save the lost. And as you died for
by your pow'r - ful word, I know you've re-deemed
G D A
me, faith-ful to the end,
us, as your e - ne - mies,
me, bought at such a price,

© Copyright 2005 Kevin Mayhew Ltd.

G
D
Em7
(v.3)
God of all com - pas - sion, you're the sin - ner's friend.
sure - ly to your child - ren you'll free - ly give all things.
ne - ver se - pa - ra - ted from the love of Christ.
Asus4
A
F#m
G
Now I see my bur - dens
D
A
Em7
in their right - ful place, and I know that all - suf - fi -
Asus4
A
Chorus
- cient is your grace. You're the

G
D
Em7
strength of my life though my heart and flesh may fail.
D/F#
G
D
You're the strength of my life, though my
Em7
Em7/A
1, 2.
D
G
heart and flesh may fail.
D
A
Em7/A
3.
D
D.S.
4.
D
You're the

How good and pleasant it is
when brothers live together in unity!
It is like precious oil poured on the head,
running down on the beard,
running down on Aaron's beard,
down upon the collar of his robes.
It is as if the dew of Hermon
were falling on Mount Zion.
For there the Lord bestows his blessing,
even life for evermore.

Psalm 133

1613 When it's all been said and done

Words and Music: Jim Cowan

2. When it's all been said and done,
all my treasures will mean nothing;
only what I've done for love's reward,
will stand the test of time.

3. Lord, your mercy is so great,
that you look beyond our weakness;
and find purest gold in miry clay,
making sinners into saints.

4. I will always sing your praise;
here on earth and ever after;
for you've shown me heaven's my true home,
when it's all been said and done,
you're my life when life is gone.

1614 When I turn my eyes *Lift my eyes*

Words and Music: Steve James

F2 Dm7 F2
who a - lone can be my help? O lift my
none can snatch me from his hand, O lift my
C Chorus F
eyes. Lift my eyes, lift my
eyes.
Am7 F
eyes, lift my eyes be-yond the
Am7 Dm7 F2
hills to the God who keeps me still, O lift my
1.
Last time
C C
Fine
eyes. 2. For all eyes.

2.
C
Bridge
B♭
eyes. His pre-sence with me as I
Dm7
F
Am7
start on the way, sus-tained by his grace in the heat of the day. No
C
Em7
G
D.S. al Fine
e-vil pre-vails in his pur-pose for me, till his face I see. Lift my

1615 When I was lost

Words and Music: Kate Simmonds and Miles Simmonds

B♭/C G/A
Chorus
F D F7/A D7/F♯ F/B♭ D/G B♭ G
There is a new song in my mouth, there is a
stand firm on this rock, my life is
C A C7/E A7/C♯ Gm/F Em/D F D A7/E F♯7/C♯ Dm Bm Dm7 Bm7
deep cry in my heart, a hymn of praise to Al-
hid - den now with Christ in God. The old has gone and the
Gm Em
1. C7sus4 A7sus4
migh - ty God, hal - le - lu - jah! And now I
new has come, hal - le - lu-
2. C7sus4 A7sus4
jah! Your love has lift - ed me.
1. F D F7/A D7/F♯ B♭ G
E♭/B♭ C/G F D F7/A D7/F♯ B♭ G E♭/B♭ C/G D.C.
Last time F D
me.

2.
B♭ G B♭/C G/A
me. Ma - ny are the won - ders you have done,
B♭ G B♭/C G/A
and ma - ny are the things that you have planned.
B♭ G Dm7 Bm7
How beau - ti - ful the grace that gives to us all that we don't
Gm Em F/A D/F♯
de - serve, all that we can - not earn, but is a gift
B♭/C G/A F D F7/A D7/F♯ B♭ G
of love. Your love has lift - ed me.
E♭/B♭ C/G F D F7/A D7/F♯ B♭ G E♭/B♭ C/G D.S.
There is a

1616 When the sunlight is shining *Rest in his promise*

Words and Music: David Ruis

(♩ = 66)
C F C Gsus4 G C F C Gsus4 G
1. When the sun - light is shin - ing and it's touch - ing my face, and your fa - vour is rest-ing and it seems all is grace,
sun - light has fad - ed and the dark - ness my friend, when the sor - rows are roll-ing and the suf- f'ring just won't end,
wars and their ru-mours are en - circ - ling the earth, and your judge - ments are fall-ing and there's no - where to turn,
hea - vens are o - pened and you ride like the wind, and your king - dom of jus-tice, it will come with-out end,
Chorus
I will
F G Am G F
lift up my eyes and give glo - ry to your name and I'll

To verses
C F C
rest in your pro-mise o - ver me.
2. When the
3. When the
4. When the
Last time
C Am Am/G Am/F
Gsus4 G Am G F
You are sov - 'reign Lord,
Am G F
you are ho - ly, Lord;
Am G F
you are faith - ful, Lord.
Csus4 F C

1617 When the trumpet of the Lord shall sound

When the roll is called up yonder

Words and Music: James M. Black

ROLL CALL Irregular and Refrain

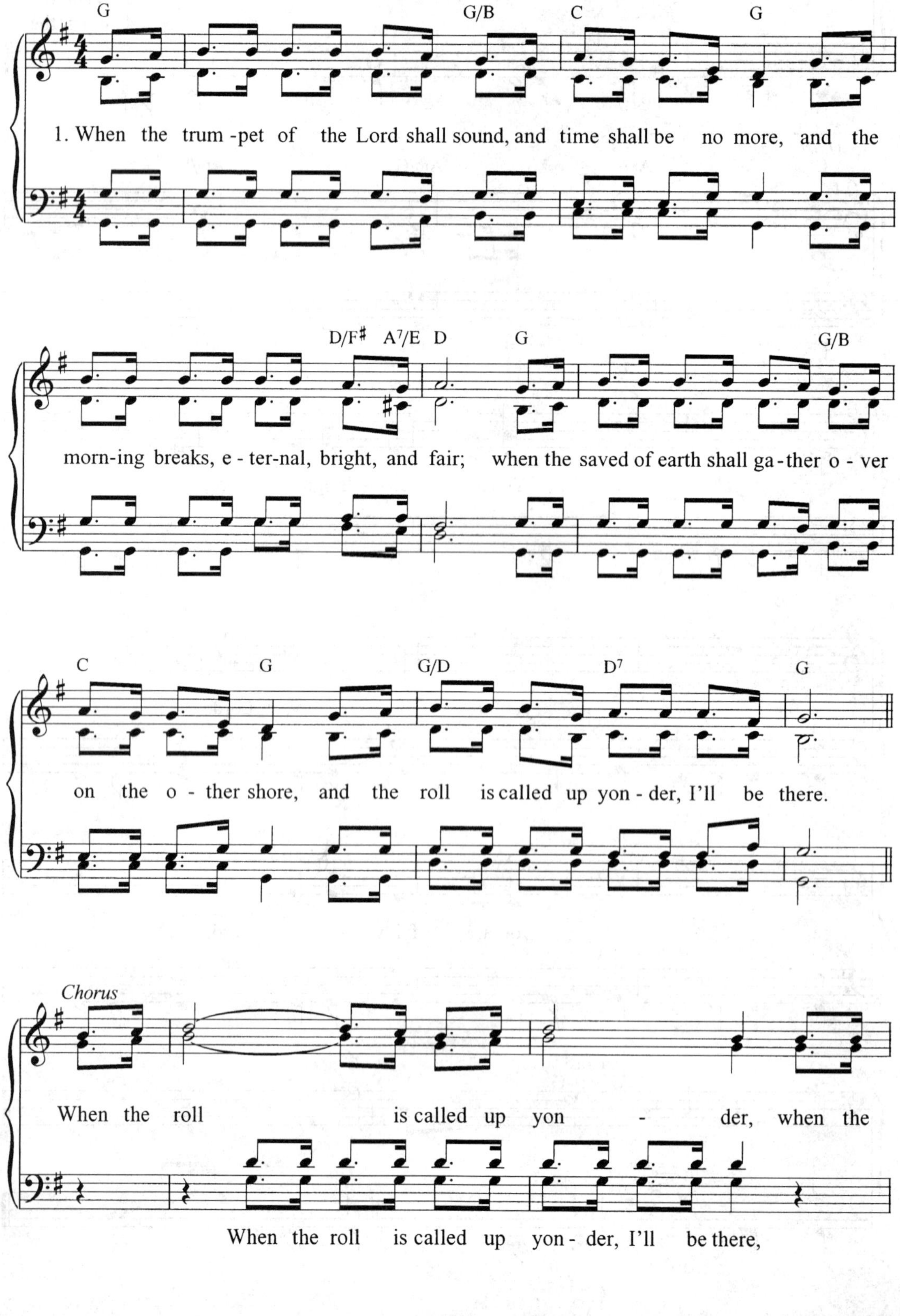
G G/B C G
1. When the trum-pet of the Lord shall sound, and time shall be no more, and the
D/F♯ A7/E D G G/B
morn-ing breaks, e-ter-nal, bright, and fair; when the saved of earth shall ga-ther o-ver
C G G/D D7 G
on the o-ther shore, and the roll is called up yon-der, I'll be there.
Chorus
When the roll is called up yon - der, when the
When the roll is called up yon-der, I'll be there,

D7
G
roll is called up yon - der, when the roll is called up
when the roll is called up yon-der, I'll be there, when the roll is called up
C
G/D
D7
G
yon - der, when the roll is called up yon - der, I'll be there.

2. On that bright and cloudless morning
when the dead in Christ shall rise,
and the glory of his resurrection share;
when his chosen ones shall gather
to their home beyond the skies,
and the roll is called up yonder, I'll be there.

3. Let us labour for the Master
from the dawn till setting sun,
let us talk of all his wondrous love and care;
then when all of life is over,
and our work on earth is done,
and the roll is called up yonder, I'll be there.

1618 When we walk with the Lord *Trust and obey*

Words: John Henry Sammis

Music: Daniel Brink Towner

TRUST AND OBEY 66 9 66 9 and Refrain

F C7 F C C7 F
Capo 3 D A7 D A A7 D
1. When we walk with the Lord in the light of his word what a
Bb F C F C7 F
G D A D A7 D
glo - ry he sheds on our way! While we do his good will, he a -
C C7 F Bb F C7 F
A A7 D G D A7 D
bides with us still, and with all who will trust and o - bey.
Chorus
C F D D7 Gm C7
A D B B7 Em A7
Trust and o - bey, for there's no o - ther way to be

2. Not a shadow can rise,
not a cloud in the skies,
but his smile quickly drives it away;
not a doubt nor a fear,
not a sigh nor a tear,
can abide while we trust and obey.

3. Not a burden we bear,
not a sorrow we share,
but our toil he doth richly repay;
not a grief nor a loss,
not a frown nor a cross,
but is blest if we trust and obey.

4. But we never can prove
the delights of his love
until all on the altar we lay;
for the favour he shows,
and the joy he bestows,
are for them who will trust and obey.

5. Then in fellowship sweet
we will sit at his feet,
or we'll walk by his side in the way;
what he says we will do,
where he sends we will go –
never fear, only trust and obey.

1619 Where do I go *My help*

Words and Music: Mark Beswick and Howard Francis

F Bb C F
Capo 3 D G A D
Where do I go when I'm feel-ing down, who do I call
- fer my foot to be moved, the one who keeps
Bb C Dm7
G A Bm7
when friends aren't a-round? I look to the lift -
me will watch o - ver you. Trust in the Lord,
Bb Gm Dm
G Em Bm
- er of my head, Je - sus, my Sa -
be - lieve, have faith, lift up your voice
Bb C
G A
1.
- viour, Lord and Friend. He will not suf -
to him and say:

2.
F D
Gm/F Em/D
I will lift up mine eyes to the hills from
C7 A7
F D
Dm7 Bm7
C A
whence com - eth my strength, my help com - eth from the
Gm/B♭ Em/G
Dm/A Bm/F♯
Gm Em
C A
F D
Lord, who made hea - ven and earth.

1620 Where the Spirit of the Lord is *Freedom*

Words and Music: Darrell Evans

(♩ = 120)
G
C
G
Where the Spi-rit of the Lord is, there is free - dom,
C²
G
where the Spi-rit of the Lord is,
C²
there is free - dom,
there is

G
C2
peace, there is love,
G
C2
there is joy.
D
Em7
C2
It is for free - dom you've set us free,
D
Em7
it is for free -
C2
- dom you've set us free,
I'm

G
C2
free, I'm free.
1.
G
Where the
2.
So we will
G
C2
walk in your free - dom, walk in your li - ber - ty,
G
we will walk in your free - dom, walk in your li - ber -
C2
G
ty, we will dance in your free - dom,

C2
dance in your li - ber - ty, we will
G
C2
dance in your free - dom, dance in your li - ber - ty.
G
Where the Spi-rit of the Lord is, there is free-dom,
C2
G
where the Spi-rit of the Lord is,
1.
C2
there is free-dom. Where the

2.
C2
D
Em7
It is for free-
-dom you've set us free,
C2
D
Em7
it is for free - dom you've set us free,
C2
G
I'm free!

But seek first his kingdom
and his righteousness,
and all these things
will be given to you as well.

Matthew 6:33

1621 Where would I be *Lord, you are good*

Words and Music: Steve Merkel

F F/E♭ B♭/D B♭m/D♭
D D/C G/B Gm/B♭
Where would I be if you had not been by my side?
F/C G/B Gm7 C7sus4
D/A E/G♯ Em7 A7sus4
How could I rise to meet the morn-ing of the day?
F F/E♭ B♭/D B♭m/D♭
D D/C G/B Gm/B♭
Your ten-der mer - cy al - ways call - ing from be - hind; at
F/C G/B Gm7 C7
D/A E/G♯ Em7 A7
times I could not see you, e - ven though you were close by.

F
D
Chorus
F/E♭
D/C
B♭/D
G/B
And Lord, you are good,
B♭m/D♭
Gm/B♭
F/C
D/A
Gm7
Em7
C7sus4
A7sus4
you are good, and your mer - cy for - e - ver en-dures;
F
D
F/E♭
D/C
B♭/D
G/B
O Lord, you are good,
B♭m/D♭
Gm/B♭
F/C
D/A
Gm7
Em7
C7sus4
A7sus4
you are good, and your mer - cy for - e - ver en-dures.
Bridge
F
D
B♭/F
G/D
F
D
Fine
Gm7
Em7
F/A
D/F♯
Help me to see your lov - ing kind-

B♭ F/A Gm7 F/A
G D/F♯ Em7 D/F♯
- ness; help me to see you as you are;
Csus4 C Gm7 F/A
Asus4 A Em7 D/F♯
help me to see your lov - ing kind -
B♭ F/A Gm7 F/A
G D/F♯ Em7 D/F♯
- ness; help me to see you as you
Csus C Csus4 C
Asus A Asus4 A
D.S. al Fine
are, as you real - ly, real - ly are.

1622 Who can cheer the heart *All that thrills*

Words and Music: Thoro Harris

ALL THAT THRILLS 87 87 and Refrain

A D A A7 D D6 Dm6 E7 Bm7 E E7 A
1. Who can cheer the heart like Je - sus, by his pre - sence all - di-vine?
D A A7 D D6 Dm6 E7 Bm7 E E7 A
True and ten - der, pure and pre - cious, O how blest to call him mine!
Chorus
C#7 F#m C#7 D B B7 E A E7
All that thrills my soul is Je - sus; he is more than life to me;
A D A A7 D Bm7 Bdim E7 D E E7 A
and the fair - est of ten thou - sand, in my bles - sed Lord I see.

2. Love of Christ so freely given,
grace of God beyond degree,
mercy higher than the heaven,
deeper than the deepest sea.

3. What a wonderful redemption!
Never can a mortal know
how my sin, though red like crimson,
can be whiter than the snow.

4. Every need his hand supplying,
every good in him I see;
on his strength divine relying,
he is all in all to me.

5. By the crystal-flowing river
with the ransomed I will sing,
and for ever and for ever
praise and glorify the King.

1623 Who is like the Lord?

Stand up and give him the praise

Words and Music: Lynn DeShazo

Am Dm Em F G Am G Am
Chorus
Am Dm Em7
Who is like the Lord? There is no one.
Am Dm Em7
Who is like the Lord? He is strong and migh - ty.
Am Dm Em7
Who is like the Lord? He is wor - thy;
1.
F G Am G Am
stand up and give him the praise.

2.
Am G Am Verse Dm
Praise the Lord, praise the
Am E
Lord; our God is wor - thy of glo -
Am G/B C C♯m7(♭5) Dm
- ry; from the ris - ing of the sun
Am Last time to Coda F
to its go-ing down, the name of the Lord is to be
E Bridge G Am G Am
praised. Stand up and praise him and

G Am E7(♯9) G Am G Am
give him the glo - ry; stand up and praise him and
G Am E7(♯9) G Am G Am
give him the glo - ry; stand up and praise him and
G Am E7(♯9) F
give him the glo - ry; our God is wor - thy of praise.
CODA
E D E F
name of the Lord is to be
E D E G Am G Am
praised. Who is like the Lord?

For the revelation awaits an appointed time;
it speaks of the end
and will not prove false.
Though it linger, wait for it;
it will certainly come and will not delay.

Habakkuk 2:3

1624 Who is like you, O Lord *The diamond turns*

Words and Music: Lynn DeShazo

Free tempo (♩ = 50)
Am⁹
Dah dah dah,
dah dah dah,
Fmaj⁷
Dm⁷
Em⁷
dah dah,
dah dah dah;
Am⁹
dah dah dah,
dah dah
Fmaj⁷
Dm⁷
Em⁷
dah,
dah dah dah,

(v.2)
Strict tempo
Fmaj9
Am
Verse
F
dah.
1. Who is like you, O
2. Who is there like you,
C
Am
F
Lord, a-mong gods? Who can but wor-ship as you
O ra-di-ant one, e-ver ex-ceed-ing all
C
Dm7
Am7
shine? Who could e-ver know in
we know? Mer-ci-ful and just,

G/B C E♭ F
just a sin - gle gaze all the glo - ry of your
full of grace and love e - ver shin - ing from your
C E♭ Dm7
face; all the glo - ry of your
throne, e - ver shin - ing from your
G Chorus Am F
face? The dia - mond turns, the an - gels
throne.
C G/B Am F
bow, ho - ly, ho - ly, ho - ly is the
C G/B Am F
Lord; the glo - ry burns, the saints cry

C G/B Am F
out, holy, holy, holy is the
C G/B Am F G
Lord; holy, holy, holy is
1. Am9
the Lord. Dah dah dah
2. Am9
the Lord.
Fmaj7 G Am
Who can stand, O Lord, before your eyes of fire or
fall up - on our knees and join the an - cient cry,

1.
Dm7 Em7 Am G Am
speak a-gainst the wis-dom you've re-flec-ted in your bride? We
ho-ly, ho-ly, ho-ly is the Lord
2.
Fmaj7 Em7 Dm7 Em7
most high. Ho-ly, ho-ly, ho-ly is the
Fmaj7 Em7 Dm7 Em7
Lord. Ho-ly, ho-ly, ho-ly.
Fmaj7 Am9
The dia-mond turns.

1625 Who is moving on the waters *He is Yahweh*

Words and Music: Dean Salyn

With strength
D
Gsus2
1. Who is mov-ing on the wa - ters,
2. Who is he that makes me hap - py,
D
A
who is hold-ing up the moon,
who is he that gives me peace,
D
Gsus2
who is peel-ing back the dark - ness
who is he that brings me com - fort,
Bm7
Asus4
A
with the burn-ing light of noon?
and turns the bit - ter in - to sweet?

D/F#
Gsus2
Who is stand-ing on the moun - tains,
Who is he that turns my pas - sion,
D
A/C#
who is on the earth be - low,
who is ris - ing up in me,
Bm7
A
Gsus2
who is big-ger than the hea - vens,
who is fill-ing up my hun - ger
D/F#
Gsus2
A
D/F#
and the lov - er of my soul?
with ev - 'ry - thing I need?

Gsus2 Chorus
Bm7
A
D/F#
Cre - a - tor God, he is Yah-weh. The great 'I Am,' he is Yah-weh.
Rose of Sha-ron, he is Yah-weh. The right - eous Son, he is Yah-weh.
Gsus2
Bm7
1, 3.
A
D/F#
The Lord of all, he is Yah-weh.
The Three - in - One, he is Yah-weh.
Last time
Asus4
A
D
Fine
2.
A
Gsus2
D.C.
4.
A
Gsus2
You are ho - ly and e - ter -
All the an - gels give you glo -
A
D
A/C#
- nal, and for e - ver you will reign.
- ry, as they stand be - fore your throne.

1.
Bm7
A
Gsus2
Ev - 'ry knee will bow be - fore
A
Bm7
D/F#
you, ev - 'ry tongue will con - fess your name.
2.
Gsus2
A
And here on earth we ga - ther
G/B
A/C#
D/F#
D.S.
to de - clare your name a - lone.

1626 Who is there like you

Words and Music: Paul Oakley

With a gentle rhythm
Capo 3
F2 D2 Bb G F2 D2
Verse
Who is there like you, and who else would
Bb G Dm7 Bm7 Gm7 Em7
give their life for me, e - ven suf-fer-ing in my
C7sus4 A7sus4 F2 D2 Bb G
place? And who could re-pay you?
Dm7 Bm7 Bb G Dm7 Bm7
All of cre - a - tion looks to you, and you pro-vide
Gm7 Em7 C7sus4 A7sus4
Chorus
for all you have made. So I'm lift-ing up my

F Gm7 F/A
D Em7 D/F#
hands, lift-ing up my voice, lift-ing up your name, and in your grace I
B♭ Gm7 C7sus4
G Em7 A7sus4
rest, for your love has come to me and set me
F2 C7sus4 F
D2 A7sus4 D
free. And I'm trust-ing in your word, trust-ing in your
Gm7 F/A B♭
Em7 D/F# G
cross, trust-ing in your blood and all your faith-ful - ness. For your
Gm7 C7sus4 F
Em7 A7sus4 D
pow'r at work in me is chang - ing me.
Last time
Gm7 B♭ C7sus4 F2
Em7 G A7sus4 D2

1627 Who is this who rises like the dawn? *Always*

Words and Music: Daniel Goodman

(♩ = 84)
Verse
C F G C F C Csus4
Who is this who ris - es like the dawn? Fair as the moon, bright as the sun, my Lord.
C Csus4 C
Ma - ny wa - ters can - not quench your love,
F G C F
strong-er than death, sweet-er than wine al-ways.
C Csus4 C F G
Chorus
Al -

C F G C
ways your light shines in all of the earth.
F G C F
1.
Al - ways I love you and you will al-ways re-main.
2.
G G
you will al-ways re-main the strength of my
C Csus4 C Csus4 D.C.
Last time
heart. you will al - ways re-main
G C Csus4 C Csus4 C
the strength of my heart.

1628 Who made the stars *Hallelujah*

Words and Music: Matthew W.J. Chapman and Jonathan Scarlet

F Fadd#4 F F6 F Fadd#4 F F6
D Dadd#4 D D6 D Dadd#4 D D6
the wa-ters be-neath sing your praise.
Chorus
C G/C F/C C F/C C F/C G/C C
A E/A D/A A D/A A D/A E/A A
Hal - le - lu - jah, hal - le - lu - jah.
C G/C F/C C F/C C F/C G/C C
A E/A D/A A D/A A D/A E/A A
Hal - le - lu - jah, hal - le - lu - jah.
1.
F G/F F C/F F C/F F C Csus2
D E/D D A/D D A/D D A Asus2
Hal - le - lu - jah, hal - le - lu - jah.
Last time
Csus4 C Csus4 C Csus2 C F C
Asus4 A Asus4 A Asus2 A D A
Fine
lu - jah.

2.
F Gsus4 G A♭maj7
D Esus4 E Fmaj7
lu - jah. Lord of
B♭sus2 A♭maj7 B♭sus2 A♭maj7
Gsus2 Fmaj7 Gsus2 Fmaj7
mer - cy, you can hear me sing - ing,
B♭sus2 A♭maj7 B♭sus2 F Fadd♯4
Gsus2 Fmaj7 Gsus2 D Dadd♯4
Sov - 'reign I a - dore thee,
F F6 Fmaj7 F F9 F
D D6 Dmaj7 D D9 D
D.S.al Fine
I a-dore thee.

O God, you are my God,
earnestly I seek you;
my soul thirsts for you,
my body longs for you,
in a dry and weary land
where there is no water.

I have seen you in the sanctuary
and beheld your power and your glory.
Because your love is better than life,
my lips will glorify you.
I will praise you as long as I live,
and in your name I will lift up my hands.

Psalm 63:1-4

1629 Whom have I in heaven but you?

God is the strength of my heart

Words and Music: Eugene Greco

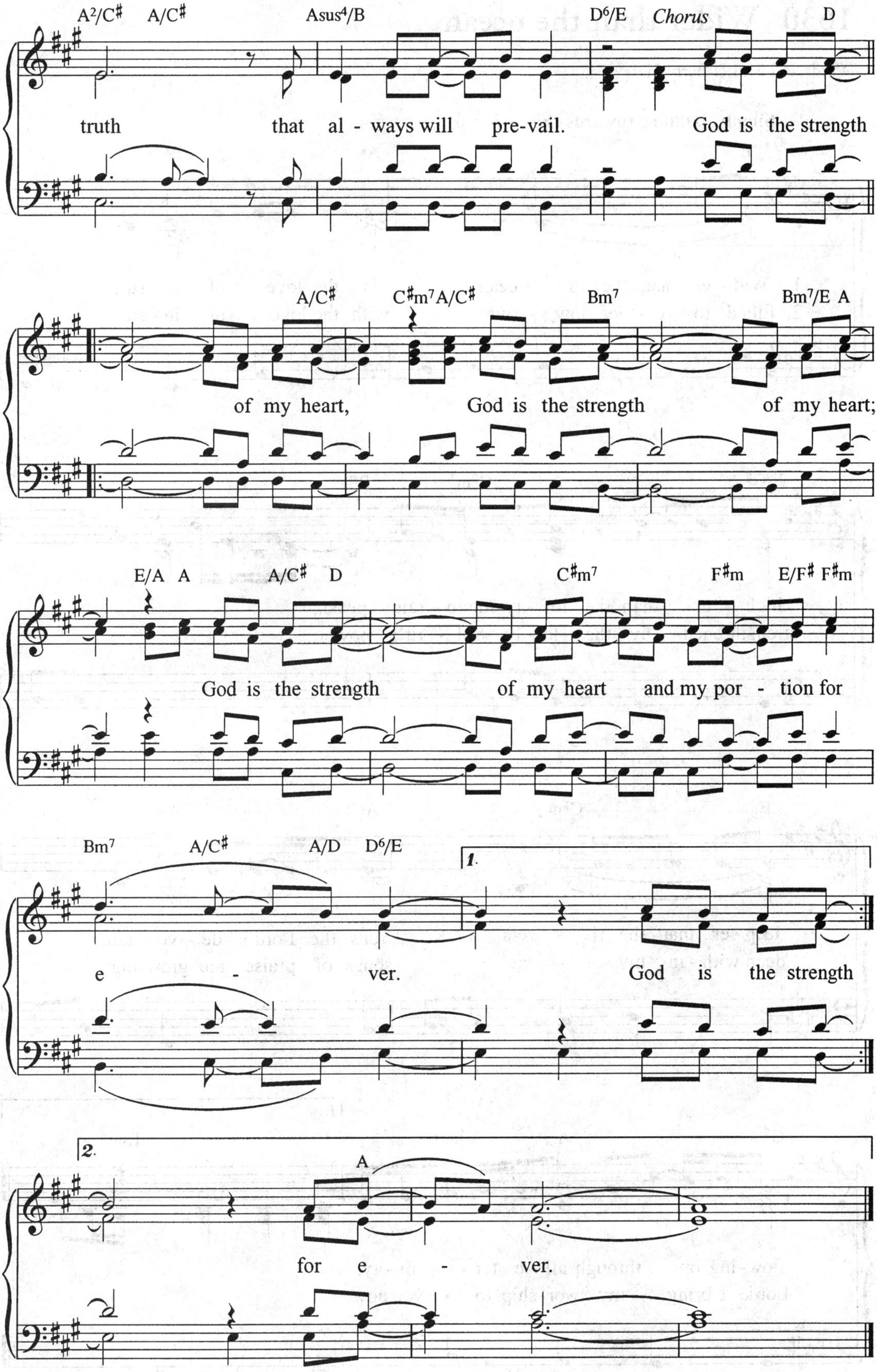
A2/C# A/C# Asus4/B D6/E Chorus D
truth that al - ways will pre-vail. God is the strength
A/C# C#m7 A/C# Bm7 Bm7/E A
of my heart, God is the strength of my heart;
E/A A A/C# D C#m7 F#m E/F# F#m
God is the strength of my heart and my por - tion for
Bm7 A/C# A/D D6/E
1.
e - ver. God is the strength
2.
A
for e - ver.

1630 Wider than the ocean

Words and Music: Barry Hart

2.
E Esus4 E B B/A
Root - ed and es - tab - lished in this
E/G# A Bsus4 B E/G# A2 E/B C#m7
love of Christ, I will sing, for the King and my thank - ful heart will
B/D# B D/A Chorus G D/F#
cry: Glo - ry to the Fa - ther through -
C2/E D G D/F#
out all ge - ne - ra - tions, worth - y to be hon - oured with - out
C2/E D G D/F#
end! To the one who far sur - pas - ses

C/E D G/B Em
ev - 'ry ex - pec - ta - tion we cry glo - ry, glo - ry,
C D Em D G/B Em
glo - ry to you! A - men. We cry glo - ry, glo - ry,
To continue
C D G D/F♯
glo - ry to you! A - men.
Last time
C/E D E/B
D.C.
G
men.

I can do everything through
him who gives me strength.

Philippians 4:13

1631 With a true heart

Be my all

Words and Music: Steve McGregor

B E F#m7 B/D#
de - si - res just to know you more: this time,
To next verse
C#m7 B A B E2
this place we come to wor - ship you.
Last time
F#/E E
2. In all we you.

2. In all we do,
   all our ways acknowledge your purpose.
   We reach for you,
   need you, Lord, to guide and direct us.

3. Changes in time,
   winds that blow may cause some distraction.
   We keep our minds
   stayed on you, whose love is unfailing.

1632 With every breath

Child of God

Words and Music: Kathryn Scott

A D/A A E/G♯ A²/F♯ D E
you're all I need, my soul's suf-fic - ien-cy,
A²/F♯ E/G♯ A D/A A E/G♯
my strength when I am weak, the love
A²/F♯ D E A²/F♯
that car - ries me, your arms en-fold
Esus⁴ E D² E
me till I am on - ly a child of God.
A²
1.
2.
2. With ev - 'ry

1633 With God all things are possible

Words and Music: John L. Bell and Graham Maule

1634 Wonderful, so wonderful *Beautiful one*

Words and Music: Tim Hughes

Chorus
G A G
Beau-ti-ful one, I love you, beau-ti-ful one, I a-
A G A D
To Coda 1.
Fine
dore, beau-ti-ful one, my soul must sing.
2. 3.
D.S.
Bridge
G
Beau-ti-ful
You o-pened my eyes to your won-
A G A
-ders a-new, you cap-tured my heart with this love, 'cause no-
1.
G A D
-thing on earth is as beau-ti-ful as you.

2.
G
A
D
- thing on earth is as beau - ti - ful as you.
D.S. al Coda
CODA
3
G
Beau - ti - ful
My soul, my soul must sing,
A
G/B
A/C♯
my soul, my soul must sing, my soul,
G
A
D
D.S. al Fine
3
my soul must sing, beau - ti - ful one.
Beau - ti - ful

1635 Worship the Lord

Words and Music: Louise Fellingham

Bm G A
- jes - ty, his splen - dour and pow'r. Pro -
Bm G D/G
claim sal - va - tion, his good - ness and mer-
D/A A Bm
- cy; for great is the Lord and most
G Em7 D
wor - thy, wor - thy of praise.

2. We are his people, belonging to our Father,
set apart for truth, we are chosen by God.
With confidence we come, we are free and we're forgiven.
Blessed are the ones who put their hope in God.

3. Please come upon us now, we want to see your face, Lord.
Soften our hearts, take us deeper into you.
Spirit, fill our minds with the knowledge of your wisdom.
Come and touch our mouths, help us tell of all you've done.

1636 Worthy

Words and Music: David Wellington

B/D♯ C♯m B A2 A
stones to speak your name,
F♯m7 Bsus4 B A
your migh - ty name! And in your will my
B/D♯ E A
hands shall move; and in your grace my
B/D♯ E A B/D♯ C♯m B
feet will go; this liv-ing stone will see your king - dom come,
A2 A F♯m7 Bsus4 B
D.C. al Fine
your king - dom come!

1637 Worthy, you are worthy

Worthy

Words and Music: Matt Redman

With a 'half-time' feel

1. Wor-thy, you are wor-thy, much more wor-thy than I've known,
2. Glo-ry, I give glo-ry to the one who saved my soul. You

I can-not i-ma-gine just how glo-ri-ous you are.
found me and you freed me from the shame that was my own.

I can-not be-gin to tell how deep a love you bring,
I can-not be-gin to tell how mer-ci-ful you've been,

Lord, my ears have heard of you, but now my eyes have seen.
Lord, my ears have heard of you, but now my eyes have seen.

2nd time to Chorus 2
E♭2 F2 E♭2 B♭ Cm7
C2 D2 C2 G Am7
Chorus 1
You're wor-thy, you're wor-thy, you're
1, 3.
B♭/D E♭2 B♭ Cm7 B♭/D E♭2
G/B C2 G Am7 G/B C2
wor-thy, you're wor-thy to be praised, for e-ver and a day. You're
2.
Last time
B♭/D E♭2 B♭/D E♭2
G/B C2 G/B C2
D.C.
Fine
e-ver and a day. e-ver and a day.
E♭2 B♭ Cm7
C2 G Am7
Chorus 2
You're wor - thy, you're wor - thy, you're
glo - ry, your glo - ry, your

B♭/D E♭2 B♭ Cm7
G/B C2 G Am7
wor - thy, you're wor - thy to be praised, for
glo - ry, your glo - ry reach - es high, so
B♭/D E♭2 B♭ Cm7
G/B C2 G Am7
e - ver and a day. You're wor - thy, you're wor - thy, you're
high a - bove the heav'ns. Your glo - ry, your glo - ry, your
B♭/D E♭2 B♭ Cm7
G/B C2 G Am7
wor - thy, you're wor - thy to be praised, for
glo - ry, your glo - ry reach - es high, so
1.
2.
B♭/D E♭2 B♭/D E♭2
G/B C2 G/B C2
D.S. al Fine
e - ver and a day. Your high a - bove the heav'ns.

1638 You are

Words and Music: Clint Brown

C
G/B
Fmaj9
G7sus4
C
G/B
You are the love of my life;
Am7(add4)
C2/G
F2
you are the hope that I cling to; you mean
F/G
C
more than this world to me; I would-n't trade you for
G/B
Am7(add4)
sil - ver or gold; I would-n't trade you for

Last time to Coda
C2/G F2 G7sus4 G7
rich-es un-told; you are more than this world to me.
1.
C G7sus4 G7
2, 3.
C
3rd time to v. 2
Fmaj7 Em7 Am7
1. I would-n't take one step with - out you;
Dm7 F/G C Dm7 C2/E
I could ne-ver go on;
Fmaj7 Em7 Am7
I would-n't live one day with - out you;
Dm7 C2/E F G7sus4
I don't have the strength to make it on my own.

Fmaj7 Em7 Am7
2. Until the world stops turning,
Dm7 F/G C Dm7 C2/E
until the stars fade from the sky,
Fmaj7 Em7 Am7
until the sun stops rising, I'll
Dm7 C2/E F G7sus4
need you in my life, and here's the reason why
CODA
C D.S. C
you are.

1639 You are all that matters *All that matters*

Words and Music: Eoghan Heaslip

Dm7 Bm7 C/E A/C# B♭2 G2
you and a - dore you. I come just as I am
- ion, would you form me? Ful - fil your pur - pose and your plan;
1, 3.
F D Dm7 Bm7 C/E A/C#
to wor - ship with my whole heart, Je -
I'm sur-ren - dered to your
2.
B♭ G C A C/E A/C#
D.S. CODA
- sus, Je - sus. ways. 1. I give All
F D C/E A/C# Dm7 Bm7
that, all that, all that mat - ters, all that, all that mat -
1. 2.
B♭ G C A B♭ G C A F D
- ters, you are all - ters, you are.

1640 You are beautiful

Words and Music: Daniel Goodman

1.
2.
- dore.
joy.
earth.
name.
D
C
G
All
Hal - le -
G
A
D
lu - - jah,
hal - le-
Last time to Coda
1.
C
G
D.C.
lu - - jah.
2.
Em
G
D
Make me more like you, O Lord.
Make me
2.
D.S. al Coda
CODA
C
G
D
Hal - le-

1641 You are exalted, Lord *Above all else*

Words and Music: Kirk Dearman and Deby Dearman

(♩= 100)
G F/G C/G D/G G C/D
You are ex - al - ted, Lord, a - bove all else,
G F/G C/G D/G G C/D
we place you at the high-est place a - bove all else;
G F/G C/G D/G G C/D
right now where we stand and ev - 'ry - where we go,
G F/G C/E Dsus4 D
we place you at the high-est place so the world will know.
G F/G C/G D G C/D
You are a migh-ty war - rior dressed in ar - mour of light,

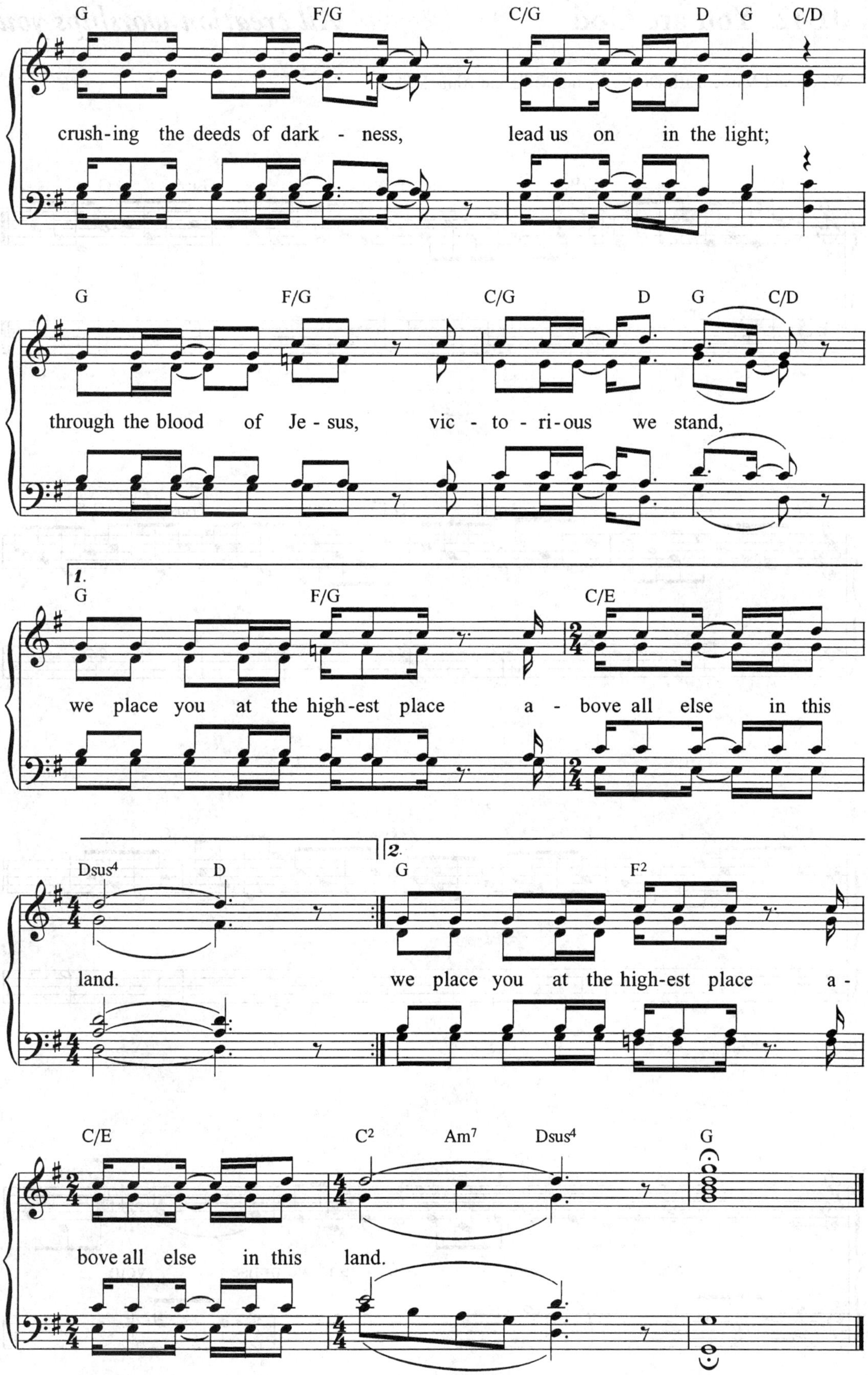
G F/G C/G D G C/D
crush-ing the deeds of dark - ness, lead us on in the light;
G F/G C/G D G C/D
through the blood of Je - sus, vic - to - ri - ous we stand,
1.
G F/G C/E
we place you at the high-est place a - bove all else in this
Dsus4 D
land.
2.
G F2
we place you at the high-est place a -
C/E C2 Am7 Dsus4 G
bove all else in this land.

1642 You are God *All creation worships you*

Words and Music: Kirk Dearman, Jim Mills and Anne Mills

Gsus4 G C C/B
you are God, we ac-
F/A Gsus4 G F Chorus G
claim you. You are e-
C F/A C/G F G Am G
ter - nal Fa - ther; all cre - a - tion wor - ships
D/F# F G Am G
you; all cre - a - tion wor - ships
D/F# F G Am G
you; all cre - a - tion wor - ships

F
G7
C
you; a - men.
C/B
F/A
Gsus4
G
C
C/B
F/A
Gsus4
G7
C

I will extol the Lord at all times;
his praise will always be on my lips.
My soul will boast in the Lord;
let the afflicted hear and rejoice.
Glorify the Lord with me:
let us exalt his name together.

Psalm 34:1-3

1643 You are God in heaven

Let my words be few

Words and Music: Beth Redman and Matt Redman

Steadily
G
Gaug
1. You are God in hea - ven, and here
2. The simp-lest of all love - songs I want
Em7
C2
G
am I on earth; so I'll let
to bring to you; so I'll let
Gaug
Em7
C2
my words be few: Je -
my words be few: Je -
Am7
G/B
C2
D7
G
- sus, I am so in love with you.
- sus, I am so in love with you.
Chorus
F2
And I'll stand in awe of you,

Em7 A2 C2 G
yes, I'll stand in awe
F2 Em7 C2
of you. And I'll
Am7 Em7 C C2 Am7 G/B
let my words be few: Je - sus, I am so
C2 D7sus4 G
in love with you.
1. C2
2. G/F Em7 C2 G2

1644 You are my anchor

Words and Music: Stuart Townend

With a steady rock feel
A
1. You are my an - chor, my light and my sal -
Lord, make straight the path be -
E/G#
F#m7
va - tion. You are my re - fuge,
fore me. Do not for - sake me,
Esus4
E
A/C#
my heart will not fear. Though my foes
my hope is in you. As I walk
D
A/C#
A
A/C#
sur - round me on ev - 'ry hand, they will stum -
through life, I am con - fi - dent I will see
D
A/C#
E
A/C#
- ble and fall while in grace I stand. In my day
your good - ness with e - ve - ry step, and my heart

D F#m7 G D/F#
of trou - ble, you hide me and set me a-bove
di - rects me to seek you in all that I do,
Esus4 E A Chorus D Esus4 E
to sing this song of love:
so I will wait for you.
One thing I will ask of you, this will I pray:
A D Esus4 E F#m B/D#
to dwell in your house, O Lord, e - ve - ry day; to gaze up - on
E/D A/C# D A/C# Bm7 D/E A
Fine
your love - ly face, and rest in the Fa - ther's em - brace.
E/G# F#m E D/E A E/G# F#m E D/E
2. Teach me your way,

1645 You are my God

Words and Music: Kent Henry

(♩ = 78)
F/C
Capo 3 D/A Chorus
F Gm7 F/A B♭ B♭/C
D Em7 D/F♯ G G/A
You are my God, yeah! and I will e-ver praise you, you are my
F Gm7 F/A B♭ B♭/C
D Em7 D/F♯ G G/A
God, yeah! I will e - ver seek your face; you are my
F Gm7 F/A B♭ B♭/C
D Em7 D/F♯ G G/A
God, yeah! and I will e - ver praise you, and
3rd time to verse 2
1.
Gm7 F/A B♭ B♭/C F B♭/C
Em7 D/F♯ G G/A D G/A
glo - ri - fy your ho - ly name. You are my

Last time
F D B♭/F G/D F D B♭/F G/D F D
2.
F D B♭/F G/D F D B♭/F G/D Dm7 Bm7 B♭maj9 Gmaj9
1. For my de-sire is to
F D Gm7 Em7 Dm7 Bm7 B♭maj9 Gmaj9
live so much clo - ser; my de-sire is to learn of you;
C A Dm7 Bm7 B♭maj9 Gmaj9 F D Gm7 Em7
ho-ly fire, I am touched by your pre - sence, Lord,
B♭ G Csus4 Asus4 C A
Chorus D.S.
flame of the Lord, come now and move. You are my

F D
B♭/F G/D
F D
B♭/F G/D
2. Ho - ly Spi-
Dm7 Bm7
B♭maj9 Gmaj9
F D
Gm7 Em7
- rit, well in you so much pow - er, Spi -
Dm7 Bm7
B♭maj9 Gmaj9
C A
- rit, now it's break-ing through, I can hear
Dm7 Bm7
B♭maj9 Gmaj9
F D
Gm7 Em7
it, it's the strong voice of hea - ven say - ing,
B♭ G
Csus4 Asus4
C A
D.S.
'look now what I can do in you.' You are my

1646 You are my God

Words and Music: Macon Delavan

(♩ = 120)
C
B♭
C
You are my God, you are my King, you are my
B♭
C
Gm7
mas - ter, my ev - 'ry - thing; you are my Lord,
C
A♭maj7
B♭
that's why I sing to you, 'Hal - le - lu -
C
A♭maj7
B♭
C
jah, hal - le - lu - jah!'

1647 You are my soul's desire *Soul's desire*

Words and Music: Robin Mark

Capo 3
B♭ G
Dm7 Bm7
1. You are my soul's de - sire; I was
in my mouth; I am
Gm Em
B♭/F G/D
wand-'ring, I was wand-'ring, wand-'ring all my
prais - ing, I am prais - ing, prais - ing on - ly
E♭ C
F D
B♭ G
days from my Fa - ther's house;
you for the things you've done;
F D
B♭ G
Dm Bm
from the heights to the depths love was
there's a flag in my hand and I am

Gm Em
B♭/F G/D
E♭ C
call-ing, love was call-ing, call-ing out to me, just to bring
wav-ing, I am wav-ing, wav-ing it for you, just to make
F D
B♭ G
me home;
you smile;
E♭/B♭ C/G
F/B♭ D/G
Lord of the earth, the sea, the sky,
ma - ny will see and hear and trust;
E♭/B♭ C/G
F/B♭ D/G
E♭ C
in glo - ry and pow - er how can it
for you are sal - va - tion; ma - ny will

F
D
E♭/G
C/E
be that I'm your child and you are my
turn and seek your face, from out of all
F/A
D/F♯
Chorus
B♭
G
F
D
Fa - ther?
na - tions.
So I, O I, I will
Gm
Em
E♭
C
B♭
G
ex-alt your name a-gain, Most High, ev-'ry way
F
D
B♭
G
I can; so I,
Dm7
Bm7
Gm
Em
O I, I will ex-alt your name

E♭ C B♭ G F D
a-gain, Most High, ev-'ry way I
1. 3.
B♭ G F D F D B♭ G
Fine
can. 2. You put songs
2.
F D E♭/B♭ C/G F/B♭ D/G
Ma-ny will see and hear and trust
E♭/B♭ C/G F/B♭ D/G E♭ C
in you, our sal - va - tion; ma-ny will turn
F D E♭/G C/E F/A D/F♯
D.S. al Fine
Chorus
and seek your face from out of all na - tions. So I,

1648 You are righteous

My hope

Words and Music: Darlene Zschech

Dsus4 D Bm A/C♯ Dsus4 D
You are right - eous,
Bm A/C♯ Dsus4 D Bm D/A
you love jus - tice, and
G D/F♯ Bm A
those who hon - our you will see your face.
A/G D/F♯ G Asus4 A
I will a - rise
D/F♯ G Asus4 A Bm
and lift my eyes to see your ma - jes - ty, your ho -

Esus4 E G G/A
Chorus
- li - ness, and all I am will bless you. My
D C/D
hope is in the name of the Lord,
G D/F# G
where my help comes from. You're my strength, my song.
Asus4 A D
My trust is in the name
C/D G
of the Lord. I will sing your praise,
D/F# G A D
you are faith - ful.

1649 You are the Lord

Glorious

Words and Music: Mick Goss and Eghan Heaslip

Steadily
G Verse Am7 Csus2 D G Am7
You are the Lord, the King of hea - ven and all the earth,
Be - fore your throne the el - ders fall, and an - gels sing:
Csus2 D G Am7 1. Csus2 D
you'll reign for e - ver. First and the last, you are
'Al - migh - ty God'. Bright morn - ing star,
G Am7 Csus2 D 2. Csus2 D
glo - ri - ous. you are
C D C D
glo - ri - ous, you are glo - ri - ous.
Chorus G D/F#
To you, the na - tions will come, ev - 'ry

Am7 C D G
tribe, ev-'ry tongue and wor - ship be-fore you, the
D/F♯ Am7
An-cient of Days, the Name a-bove all names, who is
1.
C D Em7 C D G Am7
wor-thy of all our praise. You are glo - ri-ous. Yeah, you
2.
Csus2 D G Am7 Csus2 D D.C. G Am7
are glo - ri-ous.
Csus2 D G Am7 Csus2 D G
Glo-ri - ous. Glo-ri - ous.

1650 You are the Lord, the famous one *Famous one*

Words and Music: Chris Tomlin and Jesse Reeves

With excitement
Chorus F
Capo 3 D
F/A
D/F♯
B♭2
G2
You are the Lord, the famous one,
Dm7
Bm7
C
A
famous one; great is your name in all
B♭
G
F
D
the earth. The hea - vens de-clare
F/A
D/F♯
B♭2
G2
you're glo - ri-ous, glo - ri-ous;

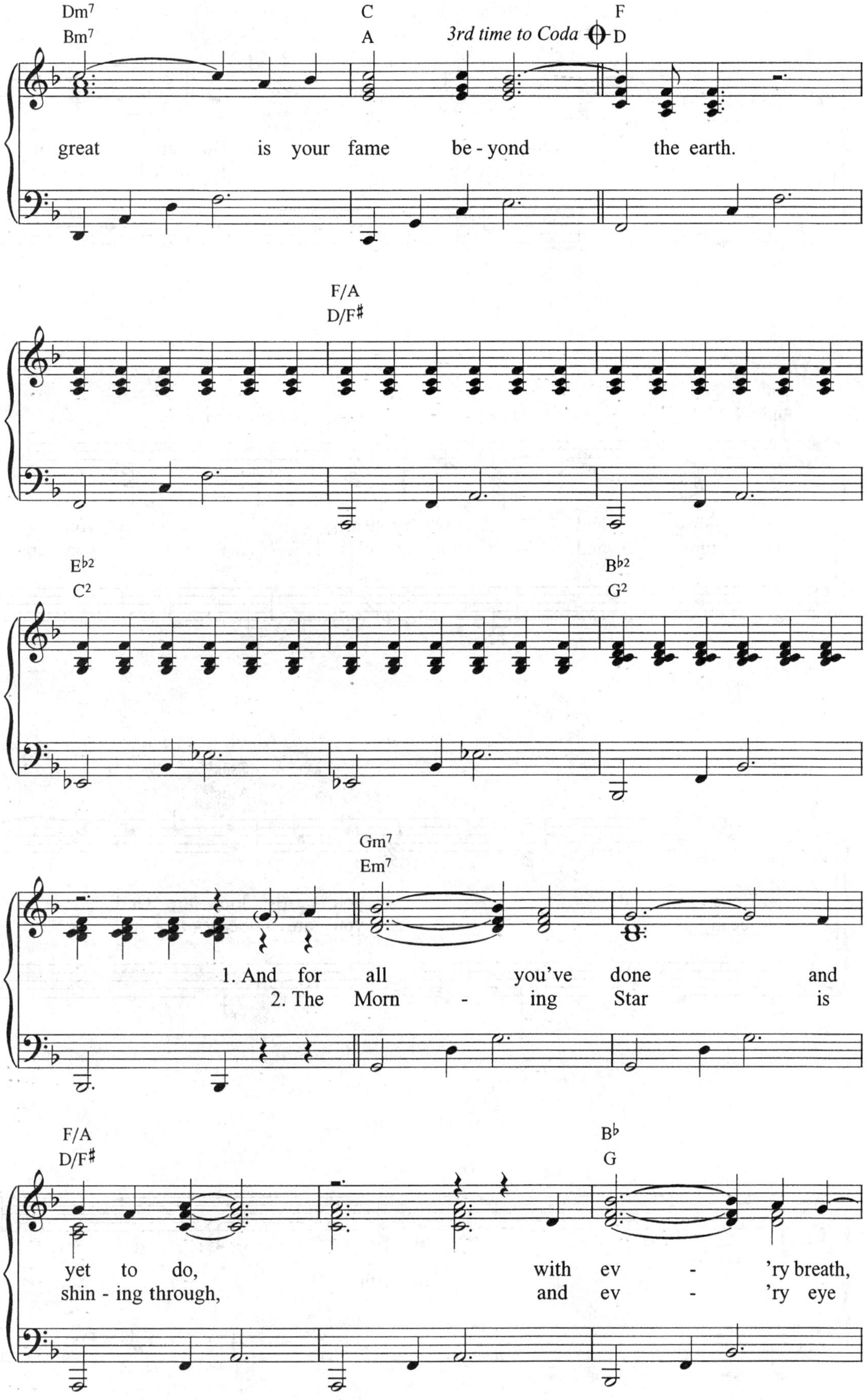
Dm7
Bm7
C
A
3rd time to Coda
F
D
great is your fame be - yond the earth.
F/A
D/F♯
E♭2
C2
B♭2
G2
Gm7
Em7
1. And for all you've done and
2. The Morn - ing Star is
F/A
D/F♯
B♭
G
yet to do, with ev - 'ry breath,
shin - ing through, and ev - 'ry eye

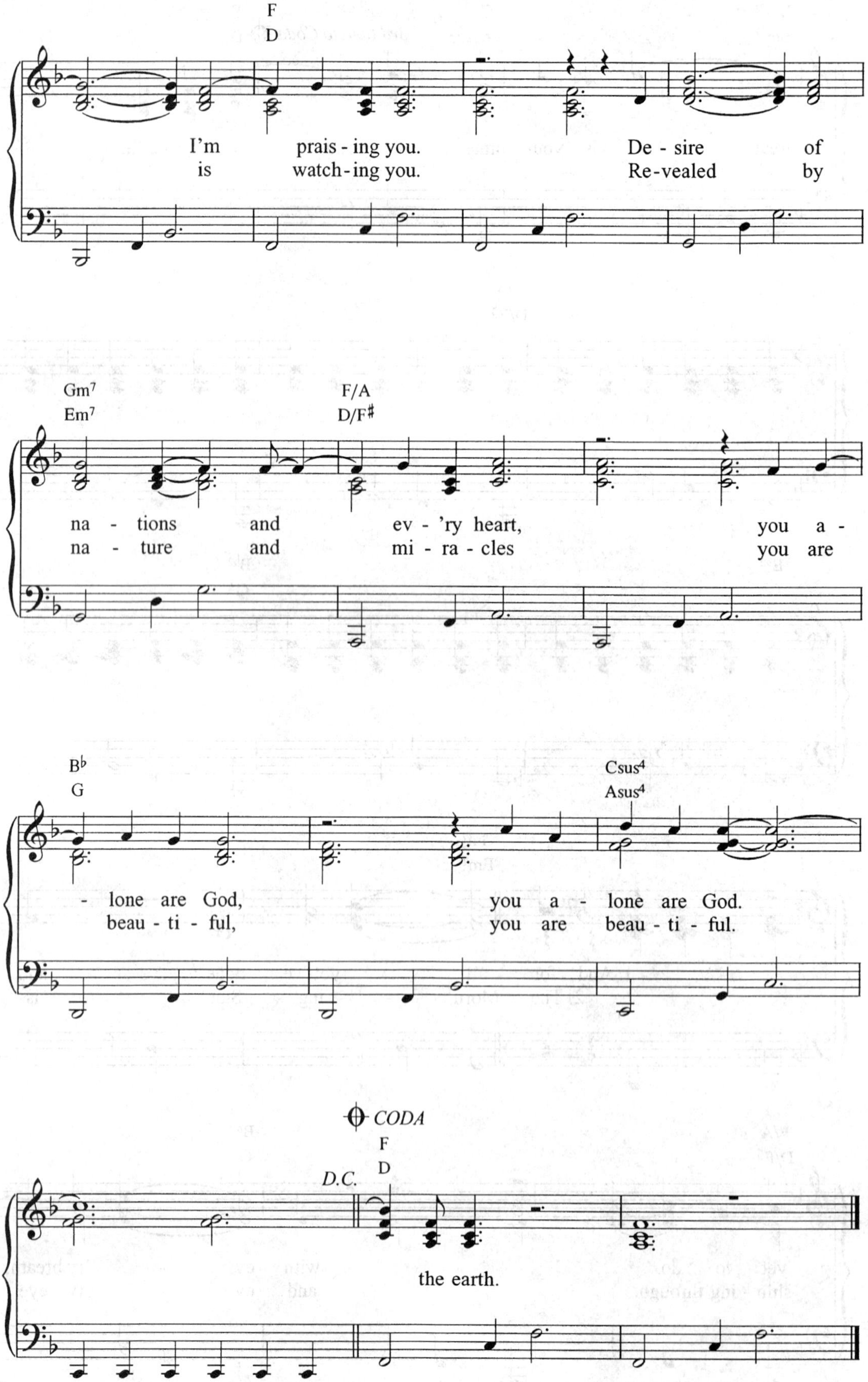
F
D
I'm praising you. Desire of
is watching you. Re-vealed by
Gm7
Em7
F/A
D/F♯
na-tions and ev-'ry heart, you a-
na-ture and mi-ra-cles you are
B♭
G
Csus4
Asus4
-lone are God, you a-lone are God.
beau-ti-ful, you are beau-ti-ful.
CODA
D.C.
F
D
the earth.

Through Jesus, therefore, let us continually
offer to God a sacrifice of praise
—the fruit of lips that confess his name.

Hebrews 13:15

1651 You are *with* You are Lord

'You are': Words and Music: Darlene Zschech
'You are Lord': Words and Music: Jennifer Va'a

Capo 3
F D
Dm Bm
B♭ G
1. You are my light and sal - va - tion, whom shall I fear?
2. Lord, it is you I de-sire, it's you that I seek;
(verse 2)
Gm7 Em7
C A
C/E A/C♯
Fsus4 F Dsus4 D
Dm Bm
You are the strength of all my days, of
to live with you in your house for e - ver, be-
B♭maj7 Gmaj7
C A
Dm Bm
whom shall I be a-fraid? Though war may rise a-gainst
hold - ing your beau - ty. And in the time of trou -

Gm9 C Dm B♭
Em9 A Bm G
Chorus
me, of this will I be sure. That
- ble, of this will I be sure.
F Dm B♭ G/B
D Bm G E/G♯
I will bless the Lord for e - ver, I'll bless your ho - ly name.
1. 2.
Csus4 C C F
Asus4 A A D
D.C.
Bridge
Yes, You ask me, who do I
Dm B♭ G/B
Bm G E/G♯
say that you are, and I say that you are the Christ,

1.
2.
Chorus
That
C
A
C
A
the Son of the Liv - ing God.
the Son of the Liv - ing God.
F
D
Dm
Bm
I will bless the Lord for e - ver, I'll
You ask me, who do I say that you are and I
B♭
G
G/B
E/G♯
C
A
bless your ho - ly name. Yes,
say that you are the Christ, the Son of the Liv - ing God.

Dm Bm
C/E A/C♯
F D
I will bless the Lord for e - ver, I'll
You ask me, who do I say that you are and I
B♭ G
G/B E/G♯
1.
C A
bless your ho - ly name. Yes,
say that you are the Christ, the Son of the Liv - ing God.
2.
C A
F D
the Son of the Liv - ing God.
the Son of the Liv - ing God.

1652 You are the peace

You alone

Words and Music: Don Harris

(♩ = 92)
Verse
A C♯m7 F♯m7 Dmaj7 E
You are the peace that guards my heart, my help in time of need;
D2/F♯ A C♯m7 F♯m7
you are the hope that leads me on, and
Dmaj7 C♯7sus4 C♯7/E♯ F♯m C♯m/E
brings me to my knees. For there I find you wait - ing, and
Dmaj7 A/C♯ Bm7 A/C♯
there I find re-lease; so, with all my heart I'll wor -
Dmaj7 E2/G♯ Chorus A2/C♯ Dmaj7
- ship, and un - to you I'll sing. For you a - lone

E/D C#m7 F#m7
de-serve all glo - ry, for you a-lone de-serve all praise;
F#m/E Dmaj7 E/D C#m7
Fa-ther, we wor - ship and a - dore you, Fa-ther, we long
F#7sus4 F#7 A/C# Dmaj7 E/D
to see your face. For you a-lone de-serve all glo-
C#m7 F#m7 Bm7
- ry, for you a-lone de-serve all praise; Fa-ther, we love
Dmaj7/E E D/E E A
you, and we wor-ship you this day.

1653 You are the perfect and righteous God

I come by the blood

Words and Music: Steve Cook and Vikki Cook

G A/G G A/G B♭ C
1. You are the per - fect and right - eous God whose pre - sence bears no
Gsus2 G A/G G A/G
sin. You bid me come to your ho - ly place; how
B♭ C Dsus4 D B♭ C Dsus4 D
can I en - ter in, when your pre - sence bears no sin? Through
Em7 C2 D
him who poured out his life for me, the a - ton - ing Lamb of
Asus4 A Em7 C2
God. Through him and his work a - lone I bold - ly

F F/E Dsus4 D C
Chorus
come. I come by the blood, I come by the cross
G/B Am G
where your mer - cy flows from hands pierced for me.
D/F# D C
For I dare not stand on my right - eous - ness,
Em7 Fmaj7 Em7
my ev - 'ry hope rests on what Christ has done
Dsus4 D G A/G G
and I come by the blood.

2. You are the high and exalted King,
the One the angels fear.
So far above me in ev'ry way Lord,
how can I draw near to the One the angels fear?
Through him who laid down his life for me
and ascended to your side,
through him, through Jesus alone I boldly come.

1654 You are the stone *No one like you, Lord*

Words and Music: Robin Mark

G
D/G
C/G
G
D/G
C/G
G
D/G
C/G
1. You are the stone that the buil-ders re-jec - ted,
2. When from the cross you to the depths des - cend - ed,
3. Then from the earth you to the heights as - cend - ed,
G
D/G
C/G
a rock of ref-uge where my pride is bro - ken,
the host of hell con-spired to make you cap - tive,
where you are seat-ed at your Fa-ther's right hand,
G
D/G
C/G
a sure foun-da-tion when the sand is sink - ing,
but ev-'ry chain of sin and death you've bro - ken,
for-e-ver plead-ing for the souls you've cap - tured,

G
where we are built up-on like liv-ing stones.
are tri-umphed o-ver by your migh-ty power. There is
for-e-ver watch-ing as you call us home.
Chorus
C G C
no one else like you, there is no one like you, Lord,
G C Em C
there is no one else like you, Son of Man
Last time to Coda
G D G C G D
and Son of God, Son of Man and Son of God,
1. 2.
G D/G C/G G Bridge
I want to run

Bm7 C G C/G
the race you've set be - fore me,
G Bm7 C
e-ven to share in the suff-'ring of the cross,
D Bm7
that I might gain the prize
C G C/G G
for which you called me, to be with

C D Em
you, Son of Man, and Son of God,
C D
to be with you, Son of Man, and Son of God.
G D/G C
D.S. al Coda
CODA
G C G D G
Son of Man and Son of God.

1655 You call us first

If there's one thing

Words and Music: Tim Hughes

Worshipfully
Dm7 C/E F Dm7 C/E
Capo 5 Am7 G/B C Am7 G/B
1. You call us first to love your name, to worship you.
2. Your honour, Lord, your name's renown we long to see.
B♭2 Dm7 C/E F
F2 Am7 G/B C
To please your heart, our one desire,
So let the glory of your name
Dm7 C/E B♭2 F C/E
Am7 G/B F2 C G/B
Chorus
O Lord.
be praised.
If there's one thing we are
Dm7 B♭ F/A B♭ C7sus4
Am7 F C/E F G7sus4
called to do, it's to love you, to adore you.

Last time to Coda
F C/E Dm7 Bb F/A
C G/B Am7 F C/E
We will bring our all and wor - ship you, bow be - fore you, as we
Bb C7sus4 Am7 Bb2
F G7sus4 Em7 F2
love you. I will ce - le-brate this love, Je - sus, you are ev - 'ry -
F C/E Dm7 Am7
C G/B Am7 Em7
thing to me. For what more, Lord, can I do?
Bb2 F C/E Dm7
F2 C G/B Am7
I will give this heart, this life to you.
CODA
Bb2 Bb C7sus4 F
F2 F G7sus4 C
D.S. al Coda
love you, Lord.

1656 You came from heaven's splendour

Jesus, almighty Saviour

Words and Music: James Wright

1. You came from hea - ven's splen-dour to earth's hu-ma - ni - ty, heal - ing the bro - ken - heart - ed, sett - ing them free. But for the joy that fol - lowed you gave up ev - 'ry - thing;

2. There in the tomb your bro - ken bo - dy in si - lence lay, but for three days, three nights it did not see de - cay. You had a great - er pur - pose, you had a great - er plan

C F/C C B♭ Csus4 C
A D/A A G Asus4 A
death on a cur - sed cross that we might have life.
that through the death of one man all might have life.
Chorus
F B♭/F F B♭/F F B♭/F F B♭/D
D G/D D G/D D G/D D G/B
Je - sus, al - migh - ty Sa - viour, you rose up from
Csus4 C F B♭/F F B♭/F F B♭
Asus4 A D G/D D G/D D G
the dead, vic - to - ri - ous, tri - um - phant just like you
Csus4 C F B♭/F F B♭/F F B♭/F F B♭/D
Asus4 A D G/D D G/D D G/D D G/B
said. In re - sur - rec - tion pow - er the grave you o -

Csus4 C F B♭/F F B♭/D C7/E F
Asus4 A D G/D D G/B A7/C♯ D
- ver - came and now you sit in hea-ven for
B♭ Csus4 C F F/A B♭
G Asus4 A D D/F♯ G
e - ver - more to reign.
Dm C/E F/A B♭2 F2
Bm A/C♯ D/F♯ G2 D2

My heart is steadfast, O God,
my heart is steadfast;
I will sing and make music.
Awake, my soul!
Awake, harp and lyre!
I will awaken the dawn.

Psalm 57:7-8

1657 You came into my life *While today is still today*

Words and Music: Tim Hughes

F G
I will ne - ver know why you took that cross,
F G
but you did, yes, you did.
C Chorus G
While to-day is still to-day I'll live just for your praise,
Am F G C
a liv-ing sac - ri-fice; hold-ing out to be
G Am F C/E
faith-ful un - to you, so in my life be glo-ri-fied,
F C
I pray.

1658 You came to earth *I surrender*

Words and Music: Andrew Grinnell

(♩ = 116)
G D Em C
1. You came to earth, dis - played your glo - ry, re -
one who breathed life in - to my be - ing is
give me Lord, when my pas - sion's fad - ed, for
G D Em C G D
vealed the king - dom of heav'n, and here you showed me the
call - ing me 'Come and die'. As I lose my - self I am
all I've seen in your word. In - crease the fire that
Em C Am D
love and mer - cy I need in my life. You
found in you, Lord, for you have my life. You
burns with - in me for more of your love. The
G D Em C
healed the sick, re - stored the bro - ken, you're the
turned the ta - bles, re - vealed your jus - tice, in your
Prince of Peace, my 'Ab - ba' Fa - ther, the

© Copyright 2000 Kevin Mayhew Ltd.

G D Em C
rea - son blind eyes now see. My
name the de - mons will flee. You have
Sa - viour and Light of the world. I
G D Em C
heart's res - pond - ing to your in - vi - ta - tion to come,
shown me ser - vice, taught me how to fol - low, now yours
give you praise, you are all I wor - ship, you're Lord
Am D G Am
Chorus
fol - low me.
I will be. I sur - ren - der my life to you, Je -
of my life.
Em D G Am Em D
- sus, I am want-ing to fol - low your call. You are

G Am Em D G Am
teach-ing me more of the ways that you want me to live.
Em D G Am Em D
I have heard how you called, 'Come and fol - low' you can
G Am Em D G Am
lead me wher-e - ver you will. And I'm liv-ing to see all you've pro -
1, 2.
Em D G Am Em D
- mised for me is ful - filled.
3.
G Am Em D G Am
2. The
3. For -

G D G Am
And I'm liv - ing to see all you've pro -
Em D G Am Em D
- mised for me is ful - filled. And I'm
G Am Em D G
liv - ing to see all you've pro - mised for me is ful - filled.

1659 You chose the cross *Lost in wonder*

Words and Music: Martyn Layzell

E A/C♯ Bm7 A/C♯
o - be - di - ent to death you o - ver -
'yet not my will but yours be done' you
E Chorus A E/G♯
- came.
said.
I'm lost in won - der, I'm lost in
F♯m7 D
love, I'm lost in praise for e - ver-more.
E A E/G♯
Be-cause of Je - sus' un - fail - ing
F♯m7 D
love, I am for - giv - en, I am re-stored.
1. 2.
E Esus4 E Esus4 E A
2. You

1660 You come close to the broken-hearted

Sing over me, Jesus

Words and Music: Joanne Gorrie and Sam Reynold

G
C
You come close to the broken-hearted, you draw near to the
Am7
C/D
D
crushed in spirit; sing your songs of healing over
G
me.
So
Chorus
sing over me, Jesus, touch me with your hand,

C
Am7
sing o-ver me, Je - sus, like on-ly you can, sing your songs of
C/D
D
G
Last time
To continue
Fine
heal - ing o-ver me.
C
Cm6
I am sa-tis-fied with no-thing less; to
Em7
A7
Am7
feel the close-ness of your breath, so sing your songs of
C/D
D
G
D.S. al Fine
heal - ing o-ver me. So

1661 You forgave my sins *I live to worship*

Words and Music: Mark Stevens/Abundant Life

1. You for-gave my sins, you washed me with
2. How can I re-pay all you've done

your blood, you gave me new life in your Son.
for me? God, here I am, I give my life.

I gave to you
Lord, I seek

my heart, you crowned me with your love,
your face, the fi - re burns in - side,

Bm
G
Asus4
now you are mine and I am yours.
I want you close, I want your love.
Chorus
A
G
D/F#
I live to wor - ship you, my Lord, and with this song
- ship you, my Lord, and tell the world
G
Bm
G
I ce - le - brate, I live to wor - ship you, my Lord,
of your great love, I live to wor - ship you, my Lord,
1, 3, 5.
D/F#
Asus4
A
I praise your name. I live to wor -
I stand a - mazed.

2.
Asus4
A
D.C.
Last time
Asus4
A
D
Fine
4.
Asus4
A
D
Em7
I live to wor - ship you, my Lord.
D/F#
G
Bm
I live to wor-
G
Asus4
A
D.S. al Fine
- ship you, my Lord.
I live to wor-

1662 You formed us from the dust *Created to worship*

Words and Music: Vicky Beeching

A B C#m7 F#m7
a - dor - ing you with all we have.
but as we praise you, we are free.
Chorus
A C#m7 B E
('Cause) we were cre - a - ted to wor-ship your
A C#m7 B E A C#m7
name, and we were cre - a - ted
B E A C#m7
1.
B
D.C. for v.2
to bring you our praise.
2, 3.
B E A C#m7 B E
So, we will wor - ship, so, we will

A C#m7 B E F#m7 E/G#
praise you, our cre - a - tor for
A A C#m7
1. (Fine)
all our days.
2.
A C#m7
For this is what we were made to do.
Repeat x2
A
So we lift up our
B
Chorus D.S. al Fine
praise to you. We were cre - a-

1663 You have been so good

Words and Music: Lenny LeBlanc and Mark Moses

You have been so good; you have been so good to me; in my faith-less hour you've been my strength; you are my tow - er from the e - ne -

G/C
G/B
C2
G/B
my;
you have been so good,
Dsus4
G
C/G
G
so good to me.
C
G
D
So good, you have been so
C2
C
G
good.
So good,
1.
D
Em7
you have been so good.

2.
Em7 G/B C G/B
good. You are my tow - er
Em7 G/C G/B
from the e - ne - my; you have been so
C2 G/B D7sus4 N.C.
good so good to me.
G/B C G2/B D7sus4 G

1664 You have given me new life *Over me*

Words and Music: Nathan Fellingham and David Fellingham

A2/C#
Bm7
F#m7
liv - ing in the glo - ry of the re - sur - rec - ted Son.
liv - ing in the joy of a heart that's pu - ri - fied.
E
A/C#
Bm7
I'm walk - ing in the light and
I'm walk - ing now with you, and
F#m7
E
D2
all that I now do is for you.
all I have is yours, take my life.
A/C#
Bm7
Esus4
E

Chorus
A D E
Pour - ing o - ver me, e - ver - last - ing love
Pour - ing o - ver me, a - bound - ing grace
D/F# A D
and mer - cy, o - ver me in a
so free, o - ver me your un -
1, 3.
E/G# Bm7
flood of pow'r.
2.
E
end -
Bm7
- ing love.
D.C.
Last time
E
end -
Bm7 A
- ing love.

1665 You hear, O Lord

Arise: a prayer for peace

Words and Music: Graham Kendrick

You hear, O Lord, the de-sire of

the af-flic-ted. You hear, O

Lord, you give them strength and lis-ten to their

cry. You hear, O Lord, de-fend-ing the fa-ther-

Cmaj7/E Cmaj7/D C2 Bb2
less and the op - pressed, that they may
Esus4 E
live in fear no more. A -
A2 D/A
rise, Lord! Lift up your hand,
Bm2 Bm7/A G G/F#
God of mer - cy, save the help - less,
E E/D A/C# A
show your kind - ness. A-rise, O Lord!

D
Bm7/D
A/E
Reach out to save, a - rise, O God.
1.
Asus4
E
A -
2.
A/E
Asus4/E
E
E/D
A/C♯
A - rise, O God,
Esus4
E
A
hear our prayer.
Bm/A
A

The sacrifices of God are a broken spirit;
a broken and contrite heart,
O God, you will not despise.

Psalm 51:17

1666 You hold the sea *All honour*

Words and Music: Russ Hughes

D Chorus C/D D C/D D
All hon-our, all pow-er, all glo-ry be-
1. 2.
G D G D
longs to you, Lord! longs to you, Lord! The
1.
Am7 Bm7 C D
an-gels cry 'ho-ly', the an-gels cry 'ho-ly is the Lord'.
2.
D C/D
The Lord'.
Last time
D C/D D G/D D
D.C.
Lord'.

1667 You know that I love you

King of majesty

Words and Music: Marty Sampson

With movement

You know that I love you, you know that
These words are from my heart, these words are

I want to know you so much more, more than I have be-fore.
not made up, I will live for you,

I am de-vo-ted to

you. King of ma - jes-ty,

I have one de-sire. Just to be

E F#m7 D E F#m7
with you, my Lord. Just to be with you, my Lord.
D A D E D A F#m7
Je - sus, you are the Sa - viour of my soul.
E D A F#m7 E D
3 3
And for e - ver and e - ver I'll give my prai - ses to
A D 1. E D D.C. 2. E D A D
you. Je - sus, you are the
E D A F#m7 E D A F#m7
3 3
Sa - viour of my soul. And for e - ver and e - ver I'll

E D A D E D
give my prai - ses to you.
A
A D E D A F♯m7
Je - sus, you are the Sa - viour of my soul.
E D A F♯m7 E D
3
3
And for e - ver and e - ver I'll give my prai - ses to
A F♯m7 E D A
you.

1668 You laid down your majesty

That's why I give my life

Words and Music: James Wright

1. You laid down your majesty to show us your love
love is a mys-te-ry to lay down your life

for hu-ma-ni-ty, to pay the price that I may go free,
for some-one like me, to give me hope and des-ti-ny,

O Lamb of God, my sac-ri-fice. And then you
O Lamb of God, my sac-ri-fice. Now I have

rose up-on the third day, con-quer-ing death,
peace deep in my heart, the kind that this world

G D C D Em7
hell and the grave that I may know the joy
could ne - ver im - part and I can live free
Asus4 A7 Am7 Csus2 G/D
of your for - give-ness, to know your love e - ver - last -
from con - dem - na - tion, know - ing your grace and your fav -
D C2 Chorus G D
- ing.
- our.
That's why I give my life to you,
C C2 Dsus4 D7 G D
that's why I bring my wor - ship to you,
C C2 Dsus4 D7 Em7
that's why I lift my hands up in gra - ti -

Am7 C2 Dsus4 D C
tude for all you have done. That's why I give my
G D C C2 Dsus4 D7
life to you, that's why I bring my
G D C C2 Dsus4 D7 Em7
wor-ship to you, that's why I lift my hands up in gra-ti-
Am7 C2 Dsus4
tude for all you have done.
1. 2.
D D.S. D G
2. Lord, your

1669 You led me to the cross

Jesus, keep me near the cross

Words and Music: Matt Redman

D♭ E♭/G A♭ E♭/G
C D/F♯ G D/F♯
Chorus
leads to the cross. Je - sus, keep me near the cross,
Fm Fm/E♭ B♭7/D D♭ A♭
Em Em/D A7/C♯ C G
I won't for-get the love you've shown. Sa - viour,
E♭/G Fm Fm/E♭ B♭7/D
D/F♯ Em Em/D A7/C♯
teach me of the cross, I won't for-get the love,
D♭ A♭ A♭sus4 A♭
C G Gsus4 G
I won't for - get the love you've shown.

2. And there's an empty tomb,
that tells me of your resurrection
and my life in you.
The stone lies rolled away,
nothing but those folded grave-clothes
where your body lay.
Now that I'm living as a risen child of God,
my every road leads to the cross.

1670 You lived

All the earth will sing

Words and Music: Paul Baloche

B♭2 F5 Csus4 Dm7 B♭2
G2 D5 Asus4 Bm7 G2
sing your prai - ses;
B♭2/G B♭2 Last time to Coda F5 Csus4
G2/E G2 D5 Asus4
all the earth will sing your prai - ses.
Dm7 B♭2 B♭2/G B♭2
Bm7 G2 G2/E G2
F5
D5
You took,
C/F Dm7
A/D Bm7
you take our sins a - way, O God;

F5 D5
C/F A/D
Dm7 Bm7
you give, you gave your life a-way for us;
Bb2 G2
you came down, you saved us
Dm7 Bm7
Bb2 G2
through the cross; our hearts are
CODA
Csus Asus
D.C. al Coda
F5 D5
Csus Asus
changed be-cause of your great love.
Dm7 Bm7
Bb2 G2
Bb2/G G2/E
Bb2 G2
F5 D5
All the earth will sing your prai-ses.

Shout with joy to God, all the earth!
Sing the glory of his name;
make his praise glorious!
Say to God. "How awesome are your deeds!
So great is your power
that your enemies cringe before you.
All the earth bows down to you;
they sing praise to you,
they sing praise to your name."

Psalm 66:1-4

1671 You make me lie down in green pastures

Words and Music: Kathy Zuziak

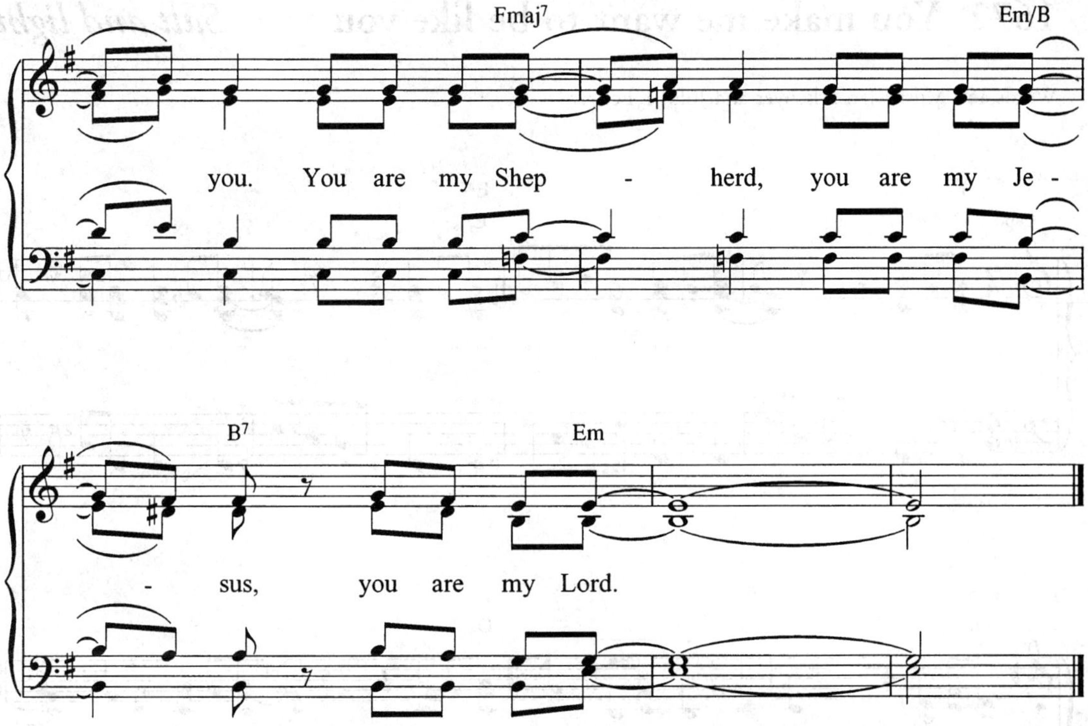
Fmaj7
Em/B
you. You are my Shep - herd, you are my Je -
B7
Em
- sus, you are my Lord.

1672 You make me want to be like you *Salt and light*

Words and Music: Jan L'Ecuyer and John L'Ecuyer

F
D
- sus;
show me the mean-
E♭2
C2
- ing of your grace; I want to give the world a taste
Dm
Bm
E♭2
C2
F
D
of the love of Je - sus.
F
D
C
A
Dm
Bm
Chorus
Make me salt, make me light; let your ho -
B♭
G
F
D
C
A
- ly fire ig - nite; re-veal your glo - ry in my life.

Dm
Bm
B♭
G
F
D
I am not
C
A
Dm
Bm
B♭
G
a-shamed to lift up your ho - ly name;
F
D
C
A
Dm
Bm
make me salt, make me light.
B♭
G
1st time D.C.
2nd time continue
Last time to Coda
F
D
E♭
C
Set me as a ci - ty on a hill,

F
D
E♭
C
B♭
G
a lamp on a stand; mould me in
C
A
Dm
Bm
E♭2
C2
your i - mage, the work of your hand.
D.S. al Coda
CODA
F
D
E♭2
C2
Dm
Bm
B♭
G
F
D

1673 You, O Lord, are a holy God *We humble ourselves*

Words and Music: Paul Baloche, Rita Baloche and Malcolm DuPlessis

D F♯m D
but we, your peo - ple have turned
A E F♯m D
from you, re - sist - ing your pow - er and grace;
A E F♯m D
tak - ing our lives in - to
A E F♯m G2
our hands, we have stum - bled and lost our way.
D Chorus F♯m E D
So we hum - ble our - selves be - fore you, and con -

F#m E D Bm
fess our un-faith-ful-ness t'ward you; for-give our sins, re-
A/C# F#m F#m7/E
move our shame, re-store the church that bears
B/D# A/E
your name, that re-vi-val may come to this land
D/E F#m D
once a-gain.
1. A E
F#m D A Bm
2. A E Chorus D.S.
Lord, we
Last time A

Sing to God, sing praise to his name,
extol him who rides on the clouds —
his name is the Lord —
and rejoice before him.

Psalm 68:4

1674 Your beauty is astounding

Words and Music: Lara Osbourne

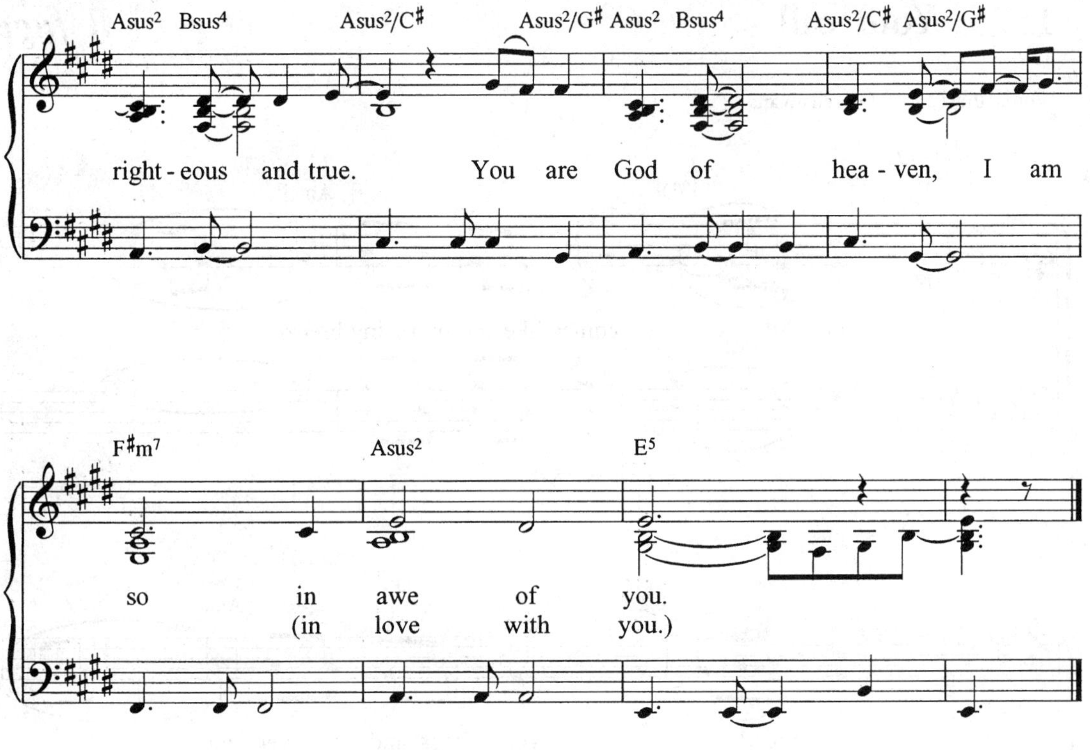
Asus2 Bsus4 Asus2/C# Asus2/G# Asus2 Bsus4 Asus2/C# Asus2/G#
right - eous and true. You are God of hea - ven, I am
F#m7 Asus2 E5
so in awe of you.
(in love with you.)

1675 Your call

Refuge

Words and Music: Darrell Evans

Amaj7 E/G# Amaj7
shel-ter, and there I'd like to stay.
B C#m E/G# A B C#m E/G# A
Chorus
Ref - uge, you're my ref - uge; when the
B C#m E/G# A
world is sha-ken and no-thing stands, I will hold on to your hand,
B C#m E/G# Amaj7 E
ref - uge.

1676 You're calling me *Unashamed love*

Words and Music: Lamont Hiebert

G/B
C
G/B
wor-thy,
so I o-pen up my heart and let my
C2
Em7
spi-rit wor-ship yours;
o-pen up my mouth and let a song
C2
G/B
of praise come forth;
wor - thy,
C
G/B
C
you are wor-thy.
Chorus
G
C2
Of a child - like faith,
of my hon - est praise,

Em7 C2 G
of my un-a-shamed love; of a ho-ly life,
C2 Em7 C2
of my sac-ri-fice, of my un-a-shamed love.
1.
G/B C2 Em7 C2
You're
2.
G C2
Of a child-like faith, of my hon-est praise,
Em7 C2 G
of my un-a-shamed love; of a ho-ly life,

C2
Em7
of my sac - ri - fice, of my un - a - shamed love.
C2
G/B
C
Wor - thy, you are
G/B
C
Repeat ad lib.
G
wor - thy.

1677 You're marvellous *King of love*

Words and Music: Tanya Riches

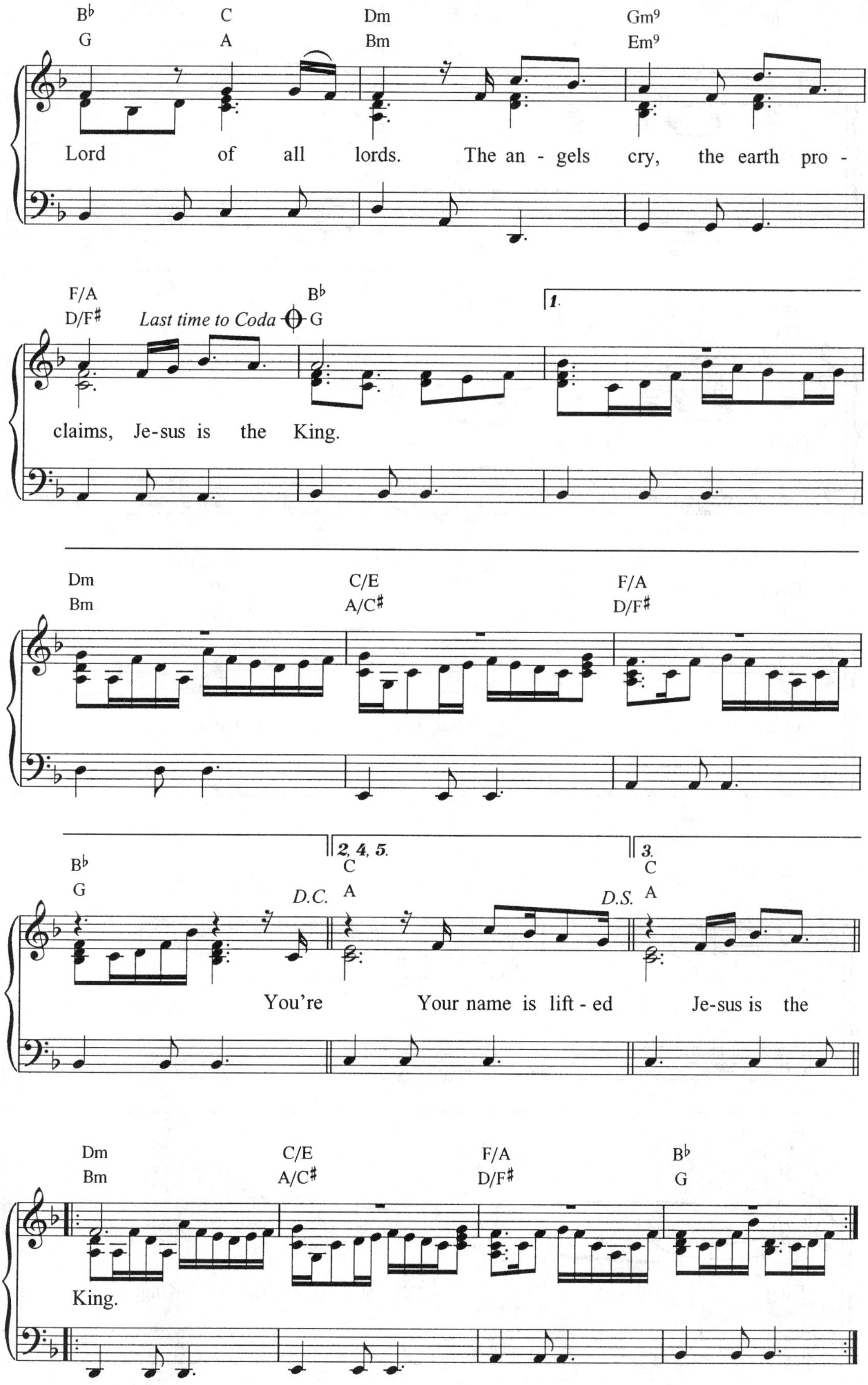
B♭ G C A Dm Bm Gm9 Em9
Lord of all lords. The an - gels cry, the earth pro -
F/A D/F♯ Last time to Coda B♭ G
1.
claims, Je-sus is the King.
Dm Bm C/E A/C♯ F/A D/F♯
B♭ G D.C.
2, 4, 5. C A D.S.
3. C A
You're Your name is lift - ed Je-sus is the
Dm Bm C/E A/C♯ F/A D/F♯ B♭ G
King.

B♭ G
C A
Gm9 Em9
C A
Faith, hope, love.
Dm Bm
C/E A/C♯
F D
1, 2, 3.
F/A D/F♯
B♭ G
Faith, hope, love.
4.
F/A D/F♯
B♭ G
D.S.
CODA
B♭ G
love. Your name is lift - ed King.
C A
Gm9 Em9
F/A D/F♯
Je - sus is the King. Je - sus is the
1.
B♭ G
C A
2.
B♭ G
King. Je - sus is the King.

1678 You're my shepherd

Words and Music: Greg Shepherd

D D/F♯ G G/A D D/F♯ G
I praise you.
G/A Em D/F♯ G
You re - store my soul,
Asus4 A Em D/F♯ G
you have made
Asus4 A
me whole.
Chorus
D D/F♯ G G/A D D/F♯ G
You are good to me, you have set me free;

G/A Bm Bm/A
love that lasts for e -
Gmaj7 G/A D D/F♯ G
- ver. Sa - viour and my friend,
G/A D D/F♯ G G/A
grace that ne - ver ends;
Bm Bm/A Gmaj7
I will be with you, Lord,
A D D/F♯ G A D
all e - ter - ni - ty.

1679 You're the one who made the heavens

You are the one

Words and Music: Paul Baloche and Lincoln Brewster

Csus4
Asus4
F/A
D/F♯
B♭2
G2
Csus
Asus
me; all my days have been or - dained, all your
F/A
D/F♯
B♭2
G2
Csus4
Asus4
thoughts t'ward me are ho - ly, full of love and
B♭2
G2
Gm11
Em11
Chorus
F5
D5
grace. You are the one, you are ho -
C/E
A/C♯
Gm11
Em11
C
A
- ly; you are the one, you are ho - ly;

1.
Bb2
G2
F/A
D/F#
Csus4
Asus4
you are the one, you are the one e - ver last - ing;
Bb2
G2
F/A
D/F#
Bb2
G2
Csus4
Asus4
you are the one. You're the
2.
Csus4
Asus4
Bb2
G2
D.S.
- ing;
3.
Csus4
Asus4
- ing;
Bb2
G2
F/A
D/F#
Bb2
G2
F
D
you are the one.

1680 You're the solid rock

The solid rock

Words and Music: Don Harris

C/G Am/G G Leader Am7 G2/B C2 All
ten - der mer - cies for his own. I praise you now, O ri - sen Lamb, I
C/E Am9 D G Leader
praise you now, O ri - sen Lamb, the so - lid rock on which I stand. You're the
C D Em All Am7 D G
so - lid rock on which I stand; the so - lid rock on which I stand.
C D G Fine D Verse All C
Day af - ter day I will

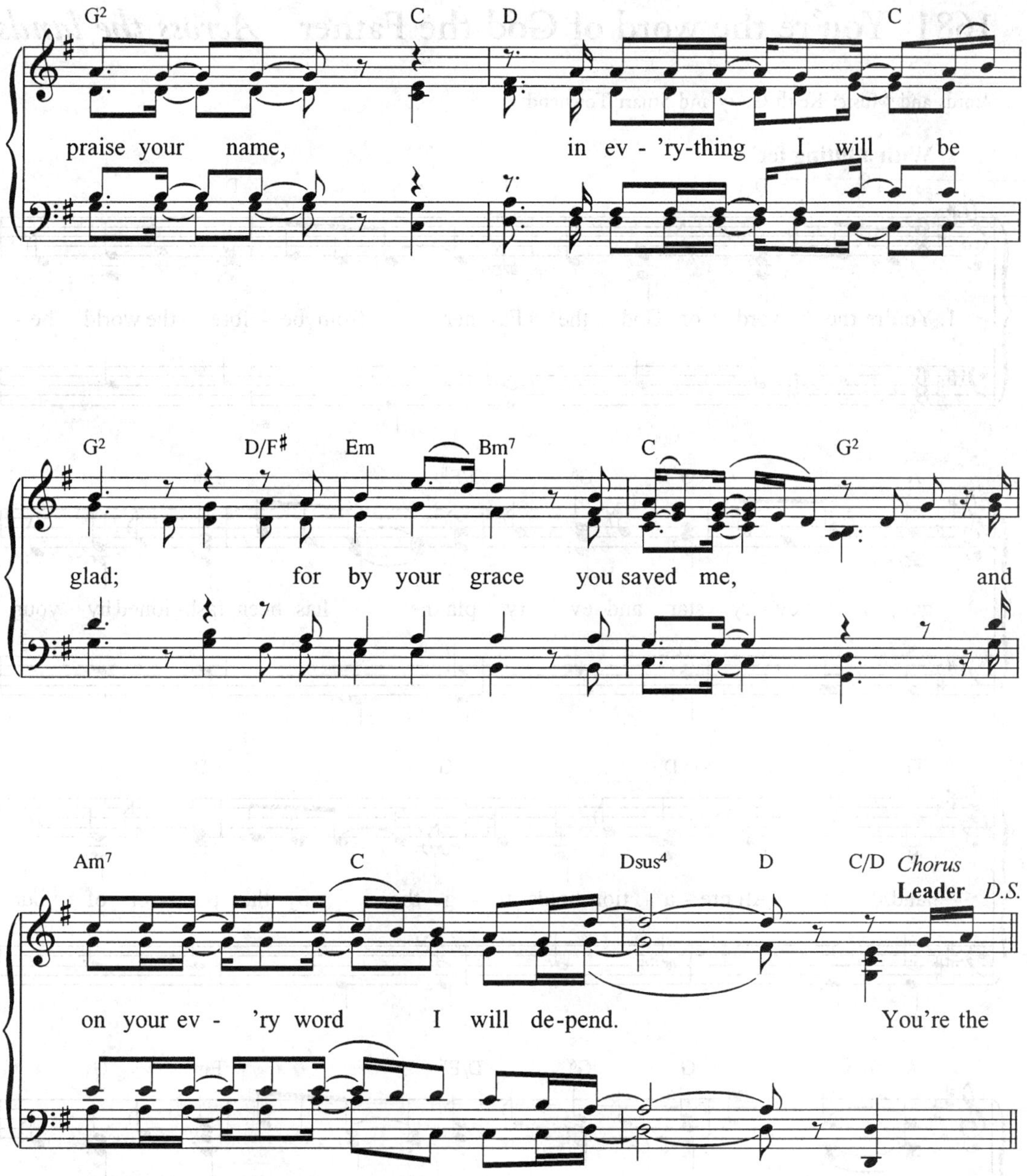
G2 C D C
praise your name, in ev - 'ry-thing I will be
G2 D/F# Em Bm7 C G2
glad; for by your grace you saved me, and
Am7 C Dsus4 D C/D Chorus
Leader D.S.
on your ev - 'ry word I will de-pend. You're the

1681 You're the word of God the Father *Across the lands*

Words and Music: Keith Getty and Stuart Townend

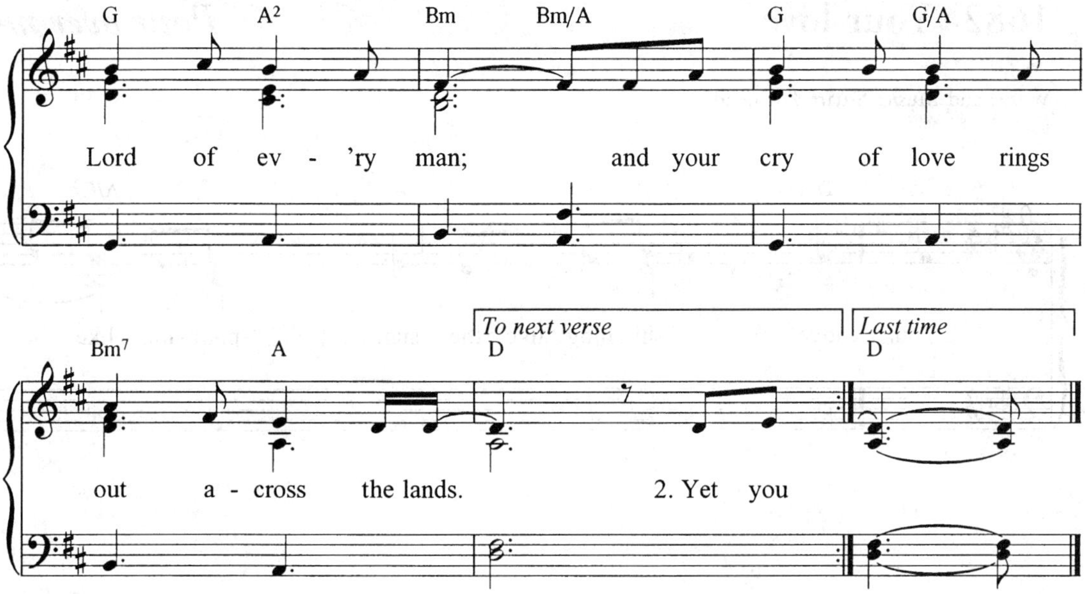

2. Yet you left the gaze of angels,
came to seek and save the lost,
and exchanged the joy of heaven
for the anguish of a cross.
With a prayer you fed the hungry,
with a word you stilled the sea;
yet how silently you suffered
that the guilty may go free.

3. With a shout you rose victorious,
wresting victory from the grave,
and ascended into heaven
leading captives in your wake.
Now you stand before the Father
interceding for your own.
From each tribe and tongue and nation
you are leading sinners home.

1682 Your love

Pour over me

Words and Music: Stuart Townend

2. Your grace frees me from the past,
it purges every sin,
it purifies my heart
and heals me from within,
I receive your grace.

3. I come and lay my burden down
gladly at your feet.
I'm op'ning up my heart,
come make this joy complete,
I receive your grace.

1683 Your love is deep

Words and Music: Susanna Bussey, Dan Collins and Jami Smith

D2
Your love is
D2
G2
deep,
your love is
high,
your love is
Bm
G2
Asus4
long,
your love is
wide;
your love is
D2
G2
deep,
your love is
high,
your love is

Bm G2 Last time to Coda Asus4
long, your love is wide; your love is
D2 G2
deep-er than my view of grace, high-er than this world-ly place;
Bm G2 Asus4
long-er than this road I tra-vel, wid-er than the gap you filled;
D2 G2
deep-er than my view of grace, high-er than this world-ly place;
Bm G2 Asus4
long-er than this road I tra-vel, wid-er than the gap you filled.

1.
2.
G2 Bridge
Your love is
Who shall se - pa-rate
D2
G2
us,
who shall se-pa-rate
D2 A
G2
us from your love;
no - thing can se - pa-rate
D2
G2
us,
no - thing can se-pa-rate
D2 A
D.S. al Coda
us from your love;
'cause your love is

CODA
D2 G2
deep, your love is high, your love is
Bm G2 Asus4 D2
long, your love is wide; your love is deep.

1684 Your love is everlasting

Better than life

Words and Music: Cindy Cruse-Ratcliffe and Israel Houghton

B♭2
F/A
lov - ing kind - ness, lov - ing kind - ness is bet - ter than
lov - ing kind - ness, lov - ing kind - ness is bet - ter than
C5
F5
C5
B♭2
life; your
life;
C5
grace is all - suf - fi - cient, it's an all - suf - fi - cient grace; your
all your ways are just, O Lord, you're just in all your ways, and
pow - er and your glo - ry are for - e - ver on dis - play and your
I will lift my hands, O Lord, with gra - ti - tude and praise, for your

B♭2 F/A
lov - ing kind - ness, lov - ing kind - ness is bet-ter than
lov - ing kind - ness, lov - ing kind - ness is bet-ter than
C5 F5 C5 Chorus G F
life. Oh, it's bet-
life.
C G F C
- ter, oh, bet-ter than life. Oh,
G F Am D7 F7
so much bet - ter; Je - sus, your lov - ing kind-

B♭2
Last time to Coda
1.
C5
F5
- ness
is bet-ter than
life.
C5
B♭2
C5
F5
C5
B♭2
2.
C
Dm
C/E
F
F/G
life.
Bridge
C
Dm
3
C/E
Je - sus,
your lov - ing
kind - ness

Am7
Dm7
1.
3
is bet - ter than life it - self, bet - ter than
F
G
2.
life it - self; self, bet-ter than
D.S. al Coda
CODA
C5 F5 C5 C5 F5
life. Oh, life, life,
C5 B♭2 C
bet - ter than life.

Lift up your heads, O you gates;
be lifted up, you ancient doors,
that the King of glory may come in.
Who is this King of glory?
The Lord strong and mighty,
the Lord mighty in battle.
Lift up your heads, O you gates;
lift them up, you ancient doors,
that the King of glory may come in.
Who is he, this King of glory?
The LORD Almighty —
he is the King of glory.

Psalm 24:7-10

1685 Your love, O Lord

Highest

Words and Music: Reuben Morgan

C/E
A/C♯
E♭
C
B♭
G
sing; glo - ry to God in the high-
Gsus4
Esus4
G
E
- - est.
1.
F/C
D/A
D.C.
Last time
C
A
Fine
2. F
D
C/E
A/C♯
F
D
Let us a - dore, won - der - ful Sa -
C/E
A/C♯
E♭
C
B♭
G
- viour, crown him for - e - ver our
Gsus4
Esus4
G
E
2nd time D.S.
King.

1686 Your love, your love is extravagant

Words and Music: Darrell Evans

D/F# G2 Bm A
I find I'm mov-ing to the rhy-thms of your grace, your fra - grance
D/F# G2 Bm A
is in-to - xi-cat - ing in our sec - ret place;
D/F# G2 Bm A
your love, (your love) is ex -
D/F# G2 Bm A
tra-va-gant.

A Chorus
Em7(add4)
Spread wide in the arms of Christ
D/G
G2
A
is the love that co-vers sin;
A
Em7(add4)
Last time to Coda
no great-er love have I e - ver known,
1.
D/G
G2
A
D/G
G2
you con-si-dered me a friend, cap-ture my heart a-gain,

D/F♯ G2 Bm A
cap - ture my heart a - gain.
D/F♯ G2 Bm A
2.
D/G G2 A
D.S. al Coda
you con - si - dered me a friend.
CODA
D/G G2 A D/G G2 D
you con - si - dered me a friend,
cap - ture my heart a - gain.

1687 Your love, your mercy

Words and Music: Graham Kendrick

D A Bm G D A
is love, un-chang - ing love. And God,
G D/F♯ Bm7 A G D/F♯ Em7 A
you're good, for - e - ver good.
G D/F♯
And here is love
Em7
that God should give
A
1st time D.C. (v.3)
2nd time D.C. (v.1)
CODA
Bm A
his Son.
G D/F♯ Em7 A D
Reach-ing out to all hu-ma - ni - ty

1688 Your mercy taught us *Dancing generation*

Words and Music: Matt Redman

G7sus4
C
can-not stay si - lent. And we'll be a danc-ing ge-ne-ra - tion,
Dm
F
danc-ing be-cause of your great mer - cy, Lord, your
C
great mer - cy, Lord. And we'll be a shout-ing
Dm
ge - ne-ra - tion, shout-ing be-cause of your great glo - ry, Lord,
F
C
your great glo - ry, Lord.
1.
D.C.
2.
D.S.
Last time
And we'll

1689 Your name is highly exalted *Name above all names*

Words and Music: Tim Hughes

1. Your name is high-ly ex-al-ted, Je-sus, for
2. Rul-ers will one day be si-lent, lost in the

e - ver be glo - ri - fied, for
won - der and awe of your name, the

e - ver be glo - ri - fied.
won - der and awe of your name.

Your name has pow-er to con-quer, your fame re-
E - ter - nal, none is your e - qual. We cry:

sounds through-out hea - ven and earth, re-
'No o - ther God but you,

B♭
G
Chorus
sounds through - out hea - ven and earth. Name a - bove
no o - ther God but you.'
F
D
Dm
Bm
all names, you are glo - ri - ous,
a day when ev - 'ry knee will bow
G7/B
E7/G♯
won - der - ful and true, pow - er - ful
be - fore your ho - li - ness, ev - 'ry tongue
B♭
G
Last time to Coda
1, 3, 5.
2, 4, 6.
are you. There will be name a - bove
con - fess,
F
D
1.
Last time
D.C.
Fine
all names.

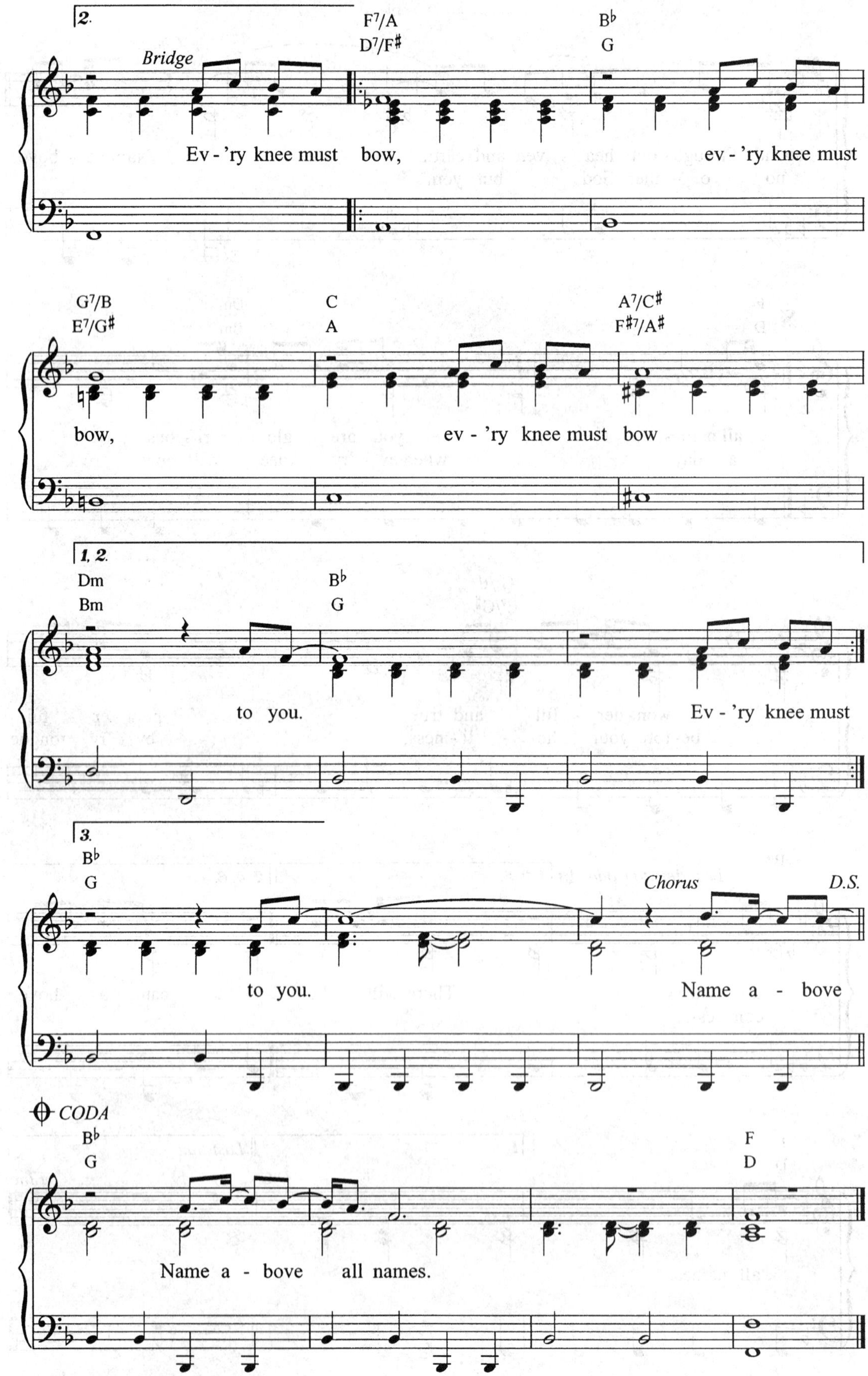
2.
Bridge
F7/A
D7/F#
B♭
G
Ev - 'ry knee must bow, ev - 'ry knee must
G7/B
E7/G#
C
A
A7/C#
F#7/A#
bow, ev - 'ry knee must bow
1, 2.
Dm
Bm
B♭
G
to you. Ev - 'ry knee must
3.
B♭
G
Chorus
D.S.
to you. Name a - bove
CODA
B♭
G
F
D
Name a - bove all names.

To you, O Lord, I lift up my soul;
in you I trust, O my God.
Do not let me be put to shame,
nor let my enemies triumph over me.

Psalm 25:1-2

1690 Your name is holy *Holy praise*

Words and Music: Susie Beattie

E Bm7 A E D
We bring ho - ly praise to the Fa-ther of our na - tion.
A2 E Bm7 F♯m7 A
Your go - vern - ment is great, your
E Bm7 A2 E Bm7
rule en - dures all time, your faith - ful - ness re - mains
F♯m7 A E Bm7 A2
Last time to Coda
stead-fast and di - vine; you are great-ly to be praised.
1. 2.
E D A2 E D

A2
B2
How sweet your grace, how great your com - pas -
A2/C#
B2/D#
sion, how rich in mer - cy, how great your love.
E2
B2
Though you came down, though you were temp -
A2/C#
Dmaj7
B/D#
ted, though you were slain you were with-out sin.
CODA
B
D.S. al Coda
E
D
A2
E

The LORD is my light and my salvation —
whom shall I fear?
The LORD is the stronghold of my life —
of whom shall I be afraid?

Psalm 27:1

1691 Your name is love

Words and Music: Greg Shepherd

Simply
Capo 3
F D Bb G
1. Your name is love, the love that went to the cross. Your name is
truth, the truth that sets me free. Your name is
Lord, I glad-ly bow the knee. You are a
F D Bb G
peace, you've ta-ken my sins a-way, and how I
hope, hope for e-ter-ni-ty, and how I
friend, a friend of sin-ners like me, and how I
C A Bb G
love all that you are, your name is
love all that you are, your name is
love all that you are, your name is
1.
F D Bb G Bb/C G/A
Je-sus. 2. Your name is
2, 3.
F D
Je-sus.

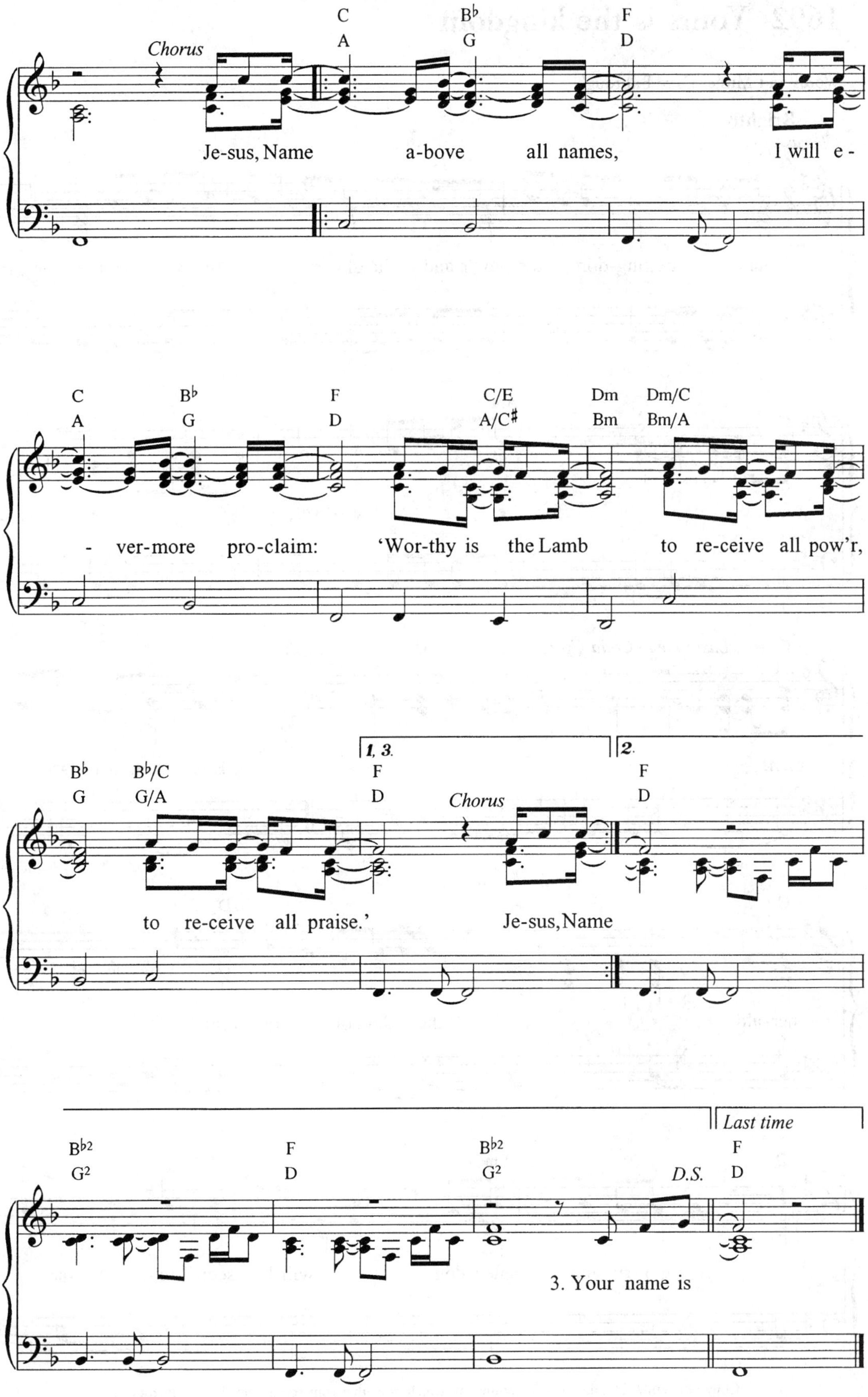
Chorus
C A
B♭ G
F D
Je-sus, Name a-bove all names, I will e-
C A
B♭ G
F D
C/E A/C♯
Dm Bm
Dm/C Bm/A
- ver-more pro-claim: 'Wor-thy is the Lamb to re-ceive all pow'r,
1, 3.
2.
B♭ G
B♭/C G/A
F D
Chorus
F D
to re-ceive all praise.' Je-sus, Name
Last time
B♭2 G2
F D
B♭2 G2
D.S.
F D
3. Your name is

1692 Yours is the kingdom

Words and Music: Dave Bilbrough

2. The time is drawing nearer,
I believe it's coming soon,
when we will rise to greet you
as a bride to meet the groom.
And oh, what a day. . .

1693 Your voice has stilled *Beauty of your peace*

Words and Music: Tim Hughes
Chorus based on a prayer by John Greenleaf Whittier

Dm7 C/E G/B C
lead us to the place where you'll re - store our souls, and
lead us to the place where you'll re - store our souls, and
Dm7 C/E G Chorus F
all our earth - ly striv - ings come to cease.
all our earth - ly striv - ings come to cease.
Take from our souls the
G/B C F G/B C
strain and stress, and let our or - dered lives con - fess the
F G C F G C
beau - ty of your peace, the beau - ty of your peace.

1694 Your voice is the voice *Awesome God*

Words and Music: Vicky Beeching

1. Your voice is the voice that com-mand-ed the u-ni-verse to be. Your voice is the voice that is speak-ing words of love to me. How can it be?

2. Your arms are the arms that hung shin-ing stars in deep-est space. Your arms are the arms that sur-round me in a warm em-brace. A-maz-ing grace.

Chorus

Awe-some God, ho-ly God, I wor-ship you in won-

C G C
- der. Awe-some God, ho - ly God, as
1, 3, 4.
Em C Am7
you draw near I'm hum - bled by your ma - jes - ty,
C D Last time to Coda
and the my - ste - ry of your great love for me.
Em C/E Em7
1st time D.C. v.2
2nd time D.C. v.1
2.
CODA
D C D.S. Em
- bled.

1695 Your whisper to my soul

Words and Music: Brian Houston

Your whis-per to my soul
You took me as I am,

when I was like a child,
you knew what I had done,

lift - ed off the yoke,
still you took my shame

plant-ed fields of hope
and you called my name,

in this heart of mine.
I was o - ver - come.

When you broke the bonds

of how I used to be,

you rolled a - way the stone,

you set the cap - tive free.

D Chorus
A
I wan - na thank you, you're the God of mer - cy;
Bm
G
I wan - na thank you, Lord, for giv - ing me peace.
D
A
I wan - na thank you, you're the God who loved me;
Bm
G
I wan - na thank you, you're the God who res - cued me.
A
Em7
G
(God who res - cued me.)
Last time to Coda
D
A
Em7
1.
G
D.C.

2.
Em
G Bridge
F#m
You co-vered all my sin, re-
G D A G
stored to me my youth a-gain. And I am sa-tis-fied,
F#m G Em7
for you have healed me and re-deemed me,
G A7
crowned my head with end-less beau-ty,
CODA
D.S. al Coda G D
end-less beau-ty.

but those who hope in the Lord
will renew their strength.
They will soar on wings like eagles;
they will run and not grow weary,
they will walk and not be faint.

Isaiah 40:31

1696 You said to seek

More than life

Words and Music: Jared Anderson

Gsus4
Gsus4/F
Gsus4
dwell in your house, to gaze up - on your beau-
Gsus4/F
Gsus4
Gsus4/F
- ty, to be a friend of God, Lord,
Gsus4
F2
Chorus
C2
all this is to me more than life,
Dm7
C/E
F2
more than breath, more than I
Last time to Coda
C
G
Am7
could e - ver hope or i - ma-

1.
F2
2.
F2
Chorus
D.S.
- gine.
- gine. More than life,
3.
F2
C
Dm7
- gine. More than life.
C/E
F2
C
G
Am7
F2
To

Gsus4
Gsus4/F
Gsus4
dwell in your house, to gaze up - on your beau -
Gsus4/F
Gsus4
Gsus4/F
- ty, to be a friend of God, Lord,
Gsus4
F2
Chorus
D.S. al Coda
all this is to me more than life,
CODA
F2
C
- gine.

1697 You shaped the heavens *Maker of all things*

Words and Music: Tim Hughes

Strongly
C2 G2 D C2
1. You shaped the hea - vens and the earth, re-vealed your splen -
2. Cre - a - tor God, in you all things now hold to - ge -
G2 D C2 G2 D
- dour. You spoke your life in - to our hearts,
- ther, work - ing your won - ders day by day,
C2 G2 D C2
so we be - long to you.
you'll reign for e - ver.
Chorus
D G
You are the mak - er of all things,

C2 D G C2
first and the last; cre - a - tion sings praise
D G C2
to you, God. You're
D G C2 D
reign - ing in glo - ry, An - cient of Days; your
1, 3.
Fine
C2 D G C2
peo - ple sing praise to you, God.

2.
D/F#
G
And earth joins with hea - ven, de -
C2
D/F#
clar - ing your glo - ry; pro - claim - ing the
1.
Em7
C2
works of your hands. Yes,
2.
Em7
C2
Chorus
D.S.al Fine
works of your hands. You are the

The righteous cry out, and the Lord hears them;
he delivers them from all their troubles.
The Lord is close to the broken-hearted
and saves those who are crushed in spirit.

Psalm 34: 17-18

1698 You shine

Why should I fear man?

Words and Music: Brian Doerksen

(♩ = 130)
Chorus
E
B/D♯
A2
You
shine
bright-er than the bright-
Bsus4
E
B/D♯
- est star;
your
love,
A2
Bsus4
A
pur - er than the pur - est heart;
you
E/G♯
A
E/G♯
shine,
fil - ling us with cou - rage and strength

To repeat
To continue
Bsus4
Last time to Coda
to fol - low you. fol - low you.
E2
Verse E
Why should I fear man,
F#m7
when you made the hea - vens?
A
E
Why should I be a-fraid when you put the stars in place?
Bsus4
E
Why should I lose heart when I

F#m7
A
know how great you are? Why should I give up
E
Bsus4
when your plans are full of love?
C#m
Bridge
F#m7
In this world we will have trou - ble,
E/G#
A2
Bsus4
B
D.C.
but you have o - ver-come the world.
CODA
E2
B
A2
E
Fol - low you.

1699 You spread out the skies *Wonderful Maker*

Words and Music: Matt Redman and Chris Tomlin

C
Em7
1. You spread out the skies o - ver emp-ty space, said 'Let there be light'; to a
C
D
G/B
dark and form-less world your light was born.
C
2. You spread out your arms o - ver emp - ty hearts,
3. eye has ful - ly seen how beau - ti - ful the cross and
Em7
said 'Let there be light'; to a dark and hope - less world your Son was
we have on - ly heard the faint - est whis - pers of how great you

C D Am7 G/B
born. You made the world and saw that it was
are.
C2 Am7 G/B C
good. You sent your on - ly Son, for you are good.
D/F# Chorus C2
What a won-der-ful Mak - er, what a won-der-ful Sa -
Em7 C2
- viour. How ma - jes - tic your whis - pers,
D/F# G G/B
and how hum - ble your love. With a strength like no o -

C2
Em7
-ther, and a heart of a Fa - ther,
C2
D/F♯
how ma-jes-tic your whis - pers, what a won-der-ful God.
1.
2, 3.
G
Am7
G/B
C
(2nd time: Instrumental)
3. No
What a won-der-ful God,
Am7
G/B
C
Am7
G/B
what a won - der-ful God.
1.
2.
C
D
D.S. al Fine
Am7
G/B
C
Fine
What a won-der-ful Mak-

1700 You've had mercy on me

Shadows

Words and Music: Marc James

Swung, with a lilt
G C Am7 C
1. You've had mer - cy on me,
2. You gave a new song to me,
G C Am7 C
ac - cord - ing to your love.
and you won me with your blood,
(v.2)
G C Am7 C
You've made a blind eye see,
and I'll ne - ver re - pay this love you give to me.
G C Am7 C
now I'm look - ing a - bove.
I want to show it to all the world.

D4 C G/B D4
Friend of the weak, you lift-ed me up from down on my knees,
C G/B D4
cry-ing for your love, you came to me.
Chorus
G C
Now I'm sing-ing of your love,
D4 C/E D4 G C
in the sha-dow of your wings;
D4 C/E D4 G C
I'm hid-ing in your love,

To verse
D4 C/E D C G/B D4
D.C.
in the sha-dow of your wings.
To Chorus
Last time
G/B D4 D.S. G/B D4 G
Now I'm sing-ing of your love,

I will sing of the Lord's great love for ever;
with my mouth I will make your
faithfulness known through all generations.
I will declare that your love stands firm for ever,
that you established your faithfulness in heaven itself.

Psalm 89:1-2

Indexes

Index of Songwriters, Authors, Composers and Arrangers

Arrangers are indented and in italics

Scriptural Index

JOHN

ACTS

ROMANS

1 CORINTHIANS

2 CORINTHIANS

GALATIANS

EPHESIANS

PHILIPPIANS

COLOSSIANS

1 THESSALONIANS

1 TIMOTHY

2 TIMOTHY

TITUS

HEBREWS

Key Word Index

The key word categories appear alphabetically and are cross-referenced to make it as easy as possible for worship leaders to find songs and hymns suitable for various themes and occasions.

ADORATION AND PRAISE – GODHEAD

ADORATION AND PRAISE – JESUS CHRIST

ADORATION AND PRAISE – THE FATHER

ADORATION AND PRAISE – TRINITY

ADVENT

See Jesus – Advent and Birth

ASCENSION

See Jesus – Ascension

ASSURANCE

ATONEMENT

See Jesus – Atonement, Suffering and Death

CALL TO WORSHIP

CELEBRATION

CHILDREN AND FAMILY WORSHIP

CHURCH – FELLOWSHIP AND UNITY

CHURCH – IN PRAYER

CHURCH – NATURE

CLOSING OF SERVICE

COMFORT AND ENCOURAGEMENT

See Faith and Hope

COMMITMENT AND CONSECRATION

JESUS – ASCENSION

JESUS – ATONEMENT, SUFFERING AND DEATH

JESUS – INCARNATION

See **Jesus – Advent and Birth and Jesus – Life**

JESUS – KINGSHIP AND KINGDOM

JESUS – LAMB OF GOD

JESUS – LIFE

JESUS – LORDSHIP

See **Jesus – Kingship and Kingdom**

JESUS – NAME AND GLORY

JESUS – RESURRECTION

JESUS – SACRIFICE

JESUS – SAVIOUR

JESUS – SECOND COMING

JESUS – THE WAY

JOY

JUSTICE

LORD'S SUPPER

See **Communion**

LOVE – GOD'S LOVE

LOVE – OUR LOVE FOR OTHERS

MISSION

NATURE

Index of First Lines and Titles

This index gives the first line of each hymn. If a hymn is known by an alternative title, this is also given, but indented and in italics.

Also available

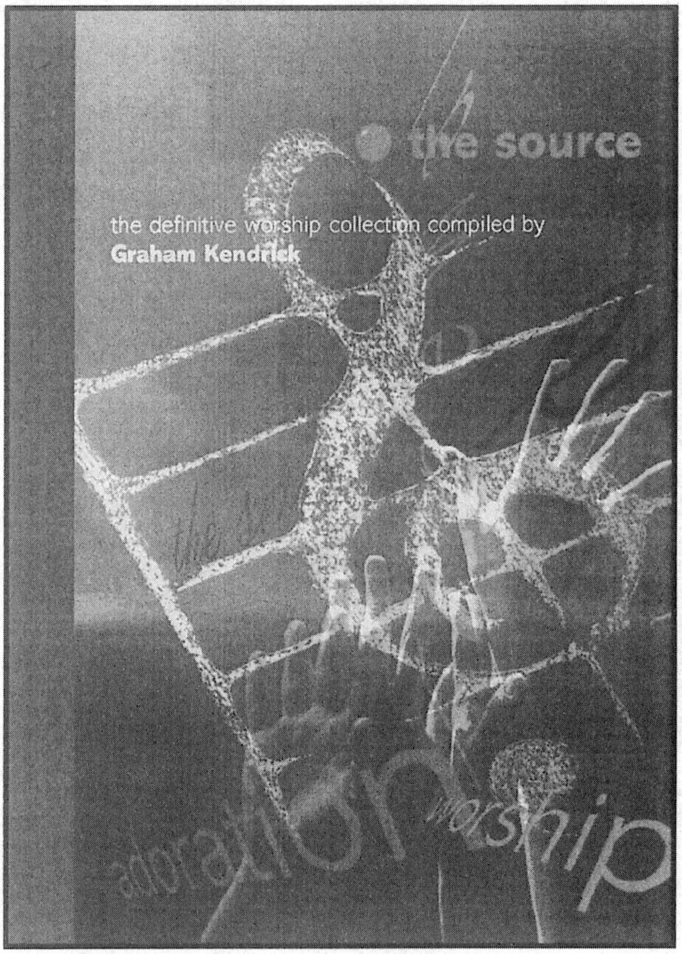

● the source

Full Music
1470104 1 84003 120 4

Guitarists' Edition
1470110 1 84003 287 1

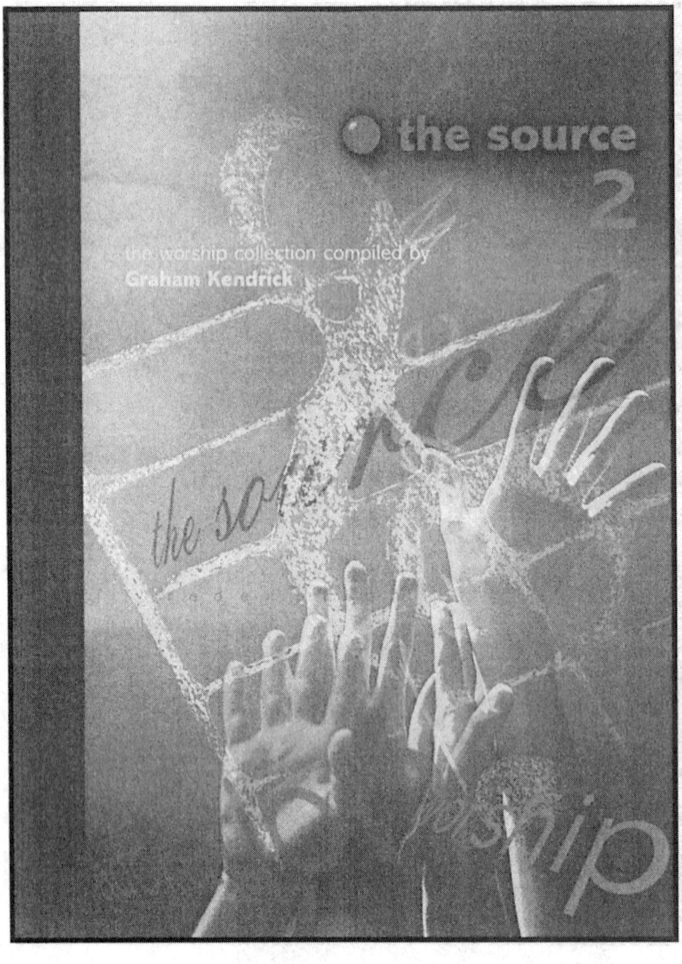

● the source 2

Full Music
1470105 1 84003 724 5

Guitarists' Edition
1470112 1 84003 725 3

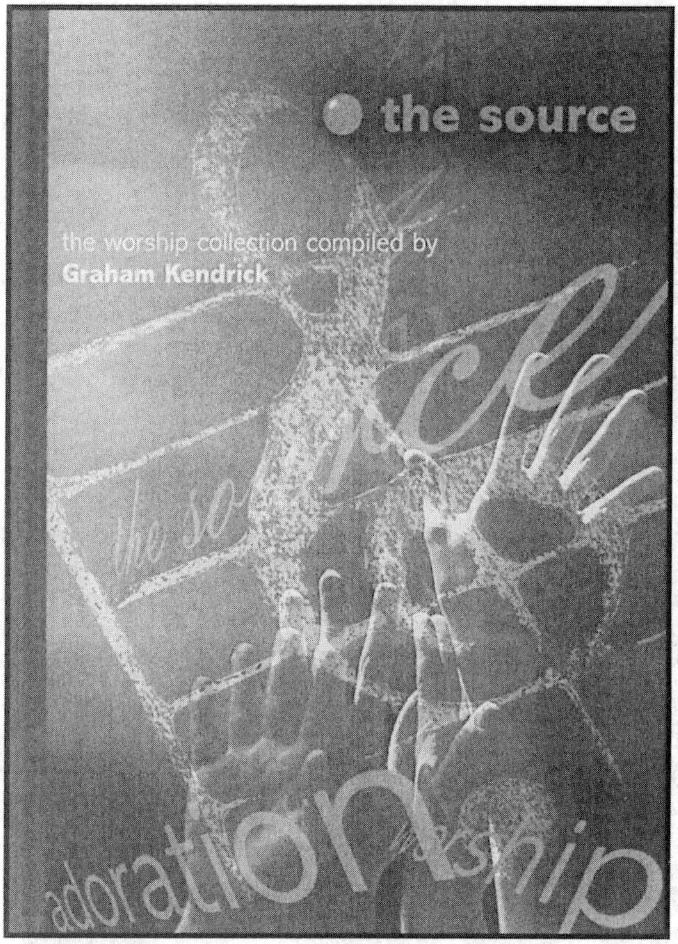

● the source combined words

(includes the words to source 1, 2 and 3)

1470103
1 84417 331 3

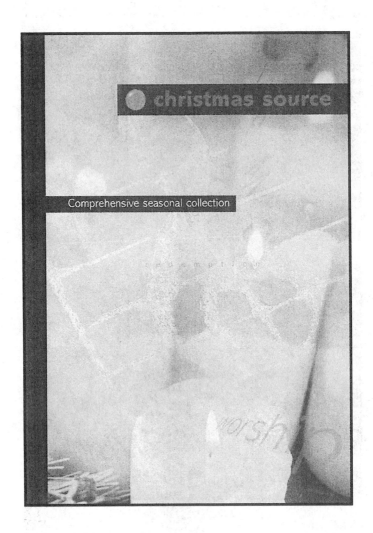

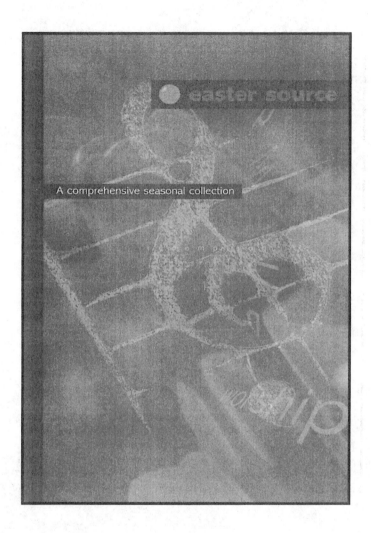

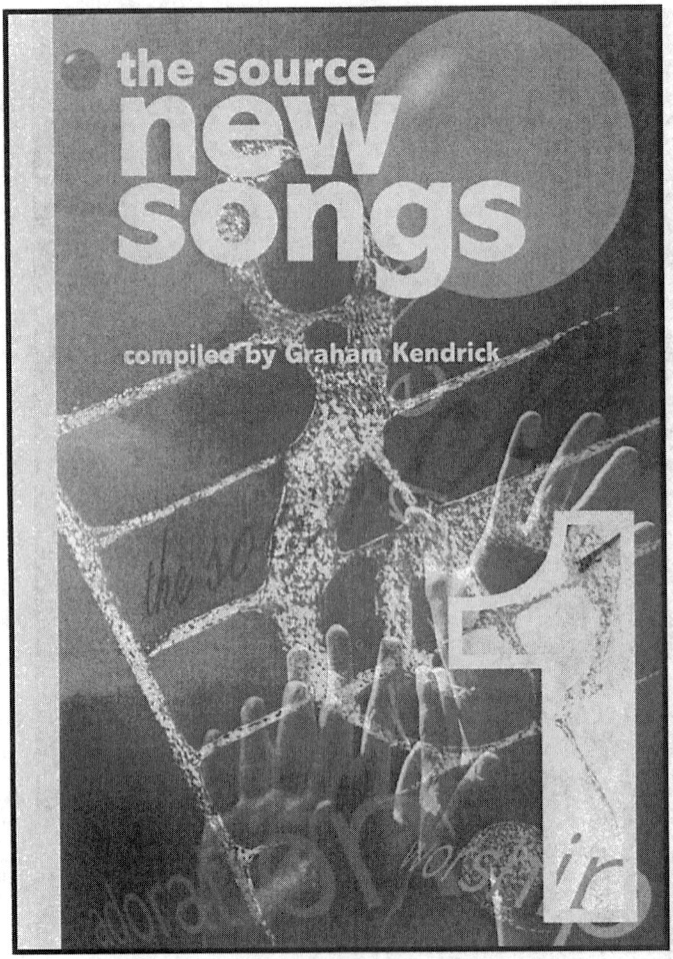

● the source new songs 1

● the source new songs 1 includes over 80 songs released since the publication of the first volume of *The Source*. It provides the full piano score with chords and lyrics for each song, with separate sections for guitarists (just the lyrics with the chords set above) and acetate masters.
● arrangements for worship groups cater for C, B♭ and E♭ instruments.

Music Book
1470106 1 84003 380 0

Arrangements for Worship Groups
1470319 1 84003 476 9

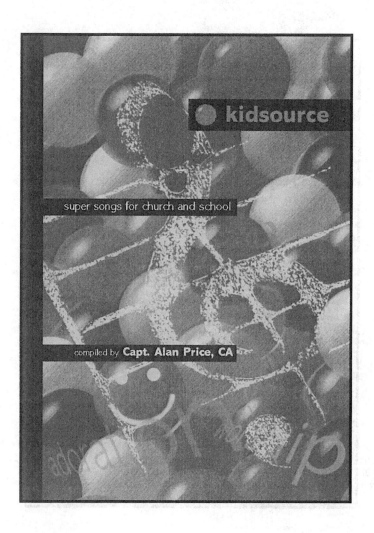

kidsource 2
super songs for church and school
compiled by Capt. Alan Price, CA

kidsource 2

1470155
1 84003 845 4

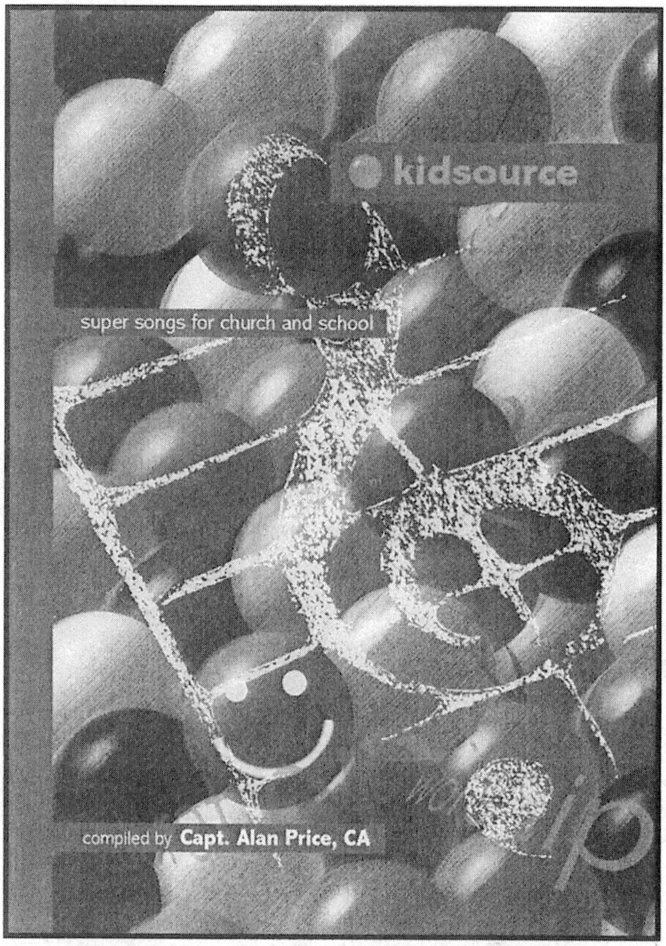
kidsource
super songs for church and school
compiled by Capt. Alan Price, CA

● kidsource Combined Words

1470152
1 84003 844 6

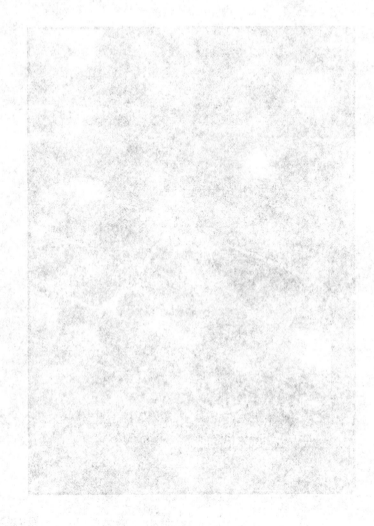